Laser Light Scattering

Benjamin Chu

Chemistry Department
State University of New York
Stony Brook, New York

1974

ACADEMIC PRESS

New York   San Francisco   London

A Subsidiary of Harcourt Brace Jovanovich, Publishers

PHYSICS

ACADEMIC PRESS, INC.
111 Fifth Avenue, New York, New York 10003

United Kingdom Edition published by
ACADEMIC PRESS, INC. (LONDON) LTD.
24/28 Oval Road, London NW1

Library of Congress Cataloging in Publication Data

Chu, Benjamin.
    Laser light scattering.

    (Quantum electronics—principles and applications)
    Includes bibliographies.
    1.   Laser beams—Scattering.   I.   Title.
QC446.2.C48   535.5'8   74-1630
ISBN 0-12-174550-3

PRINTED IN THE UNITED STATES OF AMERICA

Contents

v

Chapter IV   Light Mixing Spectroscopy

Chapter V   Interferometry

Chapter VI   Photon-Counting Fluctuations

Chapter VII   Experimental Methods

Chapter VIII   Macromolecules

Chapter IX **Reaction Kinetics—Concentration Correlation Spectroscopy**

Chapter X **Anemometry**

Chapter XI **Critical Opalescence**

Preface

This book is intended to serve as an introduction to the interdisciplinary area of laser light scattering. The treatment is not designed to review all the recent developments in this rapidly expanding field, for the subject matter is highly diversified. Rather it is based on a biased selection of topics which very much favor my own interests. The decision not to treat in detail the quantal approach was made in order to discuss theoretical concepts at a realistic level, readily understood by a (physical) chemistry graduate student. In this respect, pertinent references have been listed even in the first two review chapters (Chapters 2 and 3) for those who may need them. I have attempted to develop the topics following a sequence similar to my own experience and to smooth out the difficulties which I encountered when I first entered this field a few years ago.

The subject matter concentrates almost exclusively on quasielastic laser scattering. I assume as background some knowledge in the physical sciences equivalent to a chemistry graduate student whose training in physics is relatively limited, as he is likely to be unfamiliar with topics in electrodynamics, optics, electronics, hydrodynamics, and quantum mechanics. Therefore, Chapters 2 and 3, which constitute a brief review of classical electricity and magnetism and the general scattering theory, may appear to be a bit tedious to physicists and can certainly be omitted by a number of readers. However, normally experimentalists in fields other than physics are not familiar with *all* these physical theories.

Chapter 4 deals with basic theoretical concepts related to light mixing spectroscopy. The quantal approach has not been emphasized for the reason I have already stated, even though the equivalence of quantal and classical treatments in the present context has been discussed briefly. Chapter 5 on the Fabry–Perot interferometry may be skipped altogether. It is

included with the anticipation that optical mixing spectroscopy and interferometry will become truly complimentary techniques. Eventually, stable
single-frequency CW lasers and piezoelectric scanned Fabry–Perot etalons
with servomechanisms that automatically compensate the laser frequency
drift, and the tilt, nonlinearity, and cavity extension of the etalons, will
become routine, so that the entire time domain ranging from seconds to
10^{-12} sec will be readily accessible. Photon counting fluctuations, discussed
in Chapter 6, will become increasingly more important because digital
photon counting and correlation are much more efficient than analog devices and are certain to play a prominent role in laser light scattering.
Chapter 7 on experimental methods should be very useful to the novice
experimentalist. I have intentionally skipped discussions on the standard
conventional light scattering instrumentation and established precau-
tionary procedures in solution clarificat.on by ultrafiltration and ultra-
centrifugation. Instead, emphasis has been on considerations to set up a
light scattering spectrometer using digital photon counting and correlation
techniques.

The applications of laser light scattering to biology, chemistry, engineering, and physics will surely be expanded. I am certain that otherwise
unavailable new information can be obtained for macromolecular systems
(Chapter 8) using this technique. Anemometry (Chapter 10) is being
revolutionized. However, its utility in reaction kinetics (Chapter 9) is
less certain, even though specific successes have been realized (Section
9.4), and its potential capability is tempting indeed. Chapter 11 dealing
with critical opalescence is more compact and is intended primarily for
the expert. Research in critical phenomena should be particularly fruitful
in asymmetry and tricritical point studies with both being difficult but
challenging experiments.

Acknowledgments

I am grateful to the late Professor Peter J. W. Debye who introduced me to the study of light scattering, to the John Simon Guggenheim foundation which provided me an opportunity to have more free time to think and to learn, to Professors Bruno H. Zimm and George B. Benedek in whose departments at the University of California, San Diego, and the Massachusetts Institute of Technology, respectively, the project was launched. Professor S. H. Chen and Dr. W. Tscharnuter were helpful in making thoughtful criticisms and in pointing out a number of minor errors in the manuscript. I wish to express my appreciation to many of my professional colleagues who have supplied me with preprints, reprints, original tracings of figures, and occasional helpful comments during the preparation of this book. In particular, I have the pleasure of thanking Professors G. B. Benedek, S. H. Chen, H. Z. Cummins, and R. Pecora and Drs. P. Berge, S. Fujime, J. Lastovka, and E. R. Pike for sending me complete sets of their reprints and preprints. I also wish to gratefully acknowledge the support of my work by the National Science Foundation, the United States Army Research Office—Durham, the Petroleum Research Fund of the American Chemical Society, and the State University of New York. Finally, the most important support and encouragement throughout this endeavor has come from my wife Louisa, to whom this volume is dedicated.

Note added in proof†:   We have so far emphasized the technique of optical heterodyning in laser Doppler velocimeters. For high-speed fluid flows, the shifted frequency is very large, and hence the use of scanning Fabry–Perot interferometry becomes a natural alternative. However, either approach is restricted to measuring mean flow and rms fluctuation velocities due to low duty cycle of the instruments. Laser Doppler velocimeters that permit direct measurements of instantaneous velocities have been reported (Paul and Jackson, 1971; Avidor, 1974). The technique uses a static slightly defocused spherical Fabry–Perot (DSFP) interferometer together with a cleverly designed mask that relates the Doppler shifted frequency to the photomultiplier tube output. Thus the PM tube displays the instantaneous flow velocity. A second PM tube can be introduced to monitor the total fringe intensity. By dividing the two signals, Avidor (1974) was able to retrieve the instantaneous velocity. The reader should consult the article by Avidor for the mask construction and the details of this ingenious LDV.

References

Avidor, J. M. (1974). *Appl. Opt.* **13**, 280.
Paul, D. M., and Jackson, D. A. (1971). *J. Phys. E.* **4**, 170.

† See p. 289.

Laser Light Scattering

Chapter I
INTRODUCTION

The study of electromagnetic scattering is a field tinted with considerable interdisciplinary complexion. Chemists have utilized light scattering and small-angle x-ray scattering to study the size and shape of macromolecules in solution as well as a whole range of materials including colloidal suspensions, glasses, and solid polymers. Meteorologists have used microwaves to observe the scattering by rain, snow, hail, and other objects in the atmosphere, while astrophysicists have been interested in the scattering of starlight by interplanetary and interstellar dust. The same basic scattering principles apparently govern all such different phenomena whenever the wavelength of the electromagnetic radiation is of the same magnitude as that of the scatterer. Before the onset of lasers, most light-scattering studies have been concerned with the integrated scattered intensity.

J. B. Richter reported observations of the phenomenon of light scattering by colloidal gold as far back as 1802. The scientific study of light scattering may be said to have commenced with the work of Tyndall on aerosols in 1869. It was in 1871 that Lord Rayleigh first explained the observed color and polarization of the sunlight scattered in the atmosphere even though he originally considered light as mechanical vibrations and based his treatment on the old elastic theory of light. Later, Rayleigh (1881, 1889) deduced the same results from Maxwell's electromagnetic wave theory and found that for noninteracting, nonabsorbing, and optically isotropic particles having sizes very small compared with the wavelength of the incident light the amount of scattering should be proportional to the reciprocal fourth power of the wavelength, now known as the Rayleigh law. Rayleigh's approach has since been elaborated to cover absorbing and anisotropic particles having sizes comparable to the wavelength of the incident radia-

1

tion. Following the classical text by Van de Hulst (1957), Kerker (1969) has written a comprehensive book on "The Scattering of Light and Other Electromagnetic Radiation." There are also standard chapters in books (Flory, 1953; Tanford, 1961) and a monograph (Stacey, 1956) on applications of light scattering to macromolecules. Other specific topics have been presented by Kerker (1963) and Rowell and Stein (1967).

In condensed media or whenever the scatterers are close to one another, a detailed computation of the induced electromagnetic field surrounding a particle becomes very complex because intermolecular interactions have to be taken into account. Einstein (1910) was able to bypass the difficulties inherent in Rayleigh's analysis as applied to a collection of interacting particles. He assumed that local density fluctuations in neighboring volume elements could be independent of one another and carried out a quantitative calculation of the mean-square amplitude of those fluctuations from a statistical mechanics approach. Although Einstein's theory was able to explain the scattering from pure liquids and to predict the enormous increase in the scattering as the liquid–gas critical point was approached, the so-called *critical opalescence*, it failed to account for the angular dissymmetry of the strong scattered intensity in critically opalescent systems. Nevertheless, his theory remains valid for $K = 0$ $[K = ks = (2\pi/\lambda)\,(2\sin\frac{1}{2}\theta)]$ even in the critical region. Later Ornstein and Zernike (1914, 1915, 1916, 1926) tried to account for the scattering behavior at $K \neq 0$ by stressing the effects of correlation between fluctuations of neighboring volume elements. Again, there have been extensive reviews (Chu, 1967) on the fluctuation theory.

In laser light scattering (Chu, 1968), we study not only the changes in the number (intensity) and the direction (momentum) of each type of photon in the incident and the emerging light beams but also the corresponding frequency (energy) changes. Whereas angular dissymmetry and polarization of the scattered intensity can determine static properties such as the isothermal compressibility of a liquid and sizes and shapes of macromolecules in solution, polarized and depolarized optical spectra as well as their angular variations can be related to dynamical and structural properties of molecules. Brillouin (1914) realized that the local density fluctuations in a liquid could be considered as thermally excited sound waves (Debye, 1912). By retaining the time behavior of the thermal phonons, Brillouin (1922) reported the first consideration of the *spectrum* of light scattered from a condensed medium. In Russia, Mandel'shtam (1926) had independently deduced the spectrum of light scattered by thermal phonons and obtained the frequency shift. Gross (1930) made the first experimental observation of the Brillouin–Mandel'shtam components, and noticed the presence of an unshifted "central" component which was then explained by Landau and Placzek (1934) using nonpropagating local temperature fluctuations. Although the Landau–Placzek theory has been known for quite some time, accurate measurements on the frequency spectrum have been extremely difficult to obtain for the lack of intense monochromatic light sources and sufficiently high-resolution spectrometers. Thus, there are few noteworthy papers during the prelaser days (Fabelinskii, 1965).

In 1964, the first observations of the Brillouin–Mandel'shtam lines were reported using lasers coupled with ultrahigh-resolution Fabry–Perot etalons (Chiao et al., 1964; Chiao and Stoicheff, 1964) and grating spectrometers (Benedek et al., 1964). However, even the highest resolving power Fabry–Perot etalons fall short of providing sufficient resolution to measure the narrowing of the central component in critically opalescent systems. Thus, optical mixing spectrometers (Ford and Benedek, 1965; Cummins et al., 1964) have been devised to measure very narrow linewidths. During the past few years, several types of laser-related spectroscopic techniques which permit high-resolution measurements of changes in photon energy have been improved. The time has come for us to utilize these new powerful tools as initial difficulties in both instrumentation and theory have been resolved.

The scattering process which will be discussed in this book can be described classically and will be based on selected topics covered in a review article on laser light scattering (Chu, 1970). Quantum-mechanical phenomena, such as the Raman effect, are excluded. There now exist many other review articles, all of which cover one or more aspects of topics related to laser light scattering, and several (those marked with *) include extensive references to the literature:

1.* Multiphoton Spectroscopy (Peticolas, 1967), Inelastic Light Scattering (Peticolas, 1972);
2. Optical Mixing Spectroscopy, with Applications to Problems in Physics, Chemistry, Biology, and Engineering (Benedek, 1969);
3.* Light Beating Spectroscopy (Cummins and Swinney, 1970);
4. A New Probe for Reaction Kinetics—The Spectrum of Scattered Light (Yeh and Keeler, 1969b);
5.* Quasi-Elastic Light Scattering from Macromolecules (Pecora, 1972).
6. Liquids: Dynamics of Liquid Structure (Mountain, 1970);
7.* Spectral Distribution of Scattered Light in a Simple Fluid (Mountain, 1966);
8.* Study of Fluids by Light Scattering (McIntyre and Sengers, 1968);
9. Brillouin Spectroscopy with Lasers (Stoicheff, 1968);
10.* Brillouin Light Scattering from Crystals in the Hydrodynamic Region (Griffin, 1968);
11. Correlation Functions for Molecular Motion (Gordon, 1968);
12. Light Scattering with Laser Sources (Porto, 1969);

Furthermore, the Physical Society of Japan (1969) has published a volume including thirty selected reprints and a list of references with titles consisting of ninety-five articles on Rayleigh and Brillouin scattering and one-hundred thirty-one articles on Raman scattering. Unfortunately, this volume is available for use mainly by domestic (Japanese) members. In view of the extensive number of review articles, we shall give only pertinent references which are intended as guides to the interested reader or are listed because of their historical significance.

In radiation-scattering studies, many types of radiation, each of which has different advantages, are available. However, in all such experiments there are usually two kinds of measurement that may be made. These are (a) the intensity as a function of the momentum and the energy transferred in the scattering process; and (b) the intensity as a function of the momentum transfer but integrated over all possible energy transfers. Figure 1.1 shows typical regions of momentum- and energy-transfer space covered by different types of radiation (Egelstaff, 1967). Using visible light, it clearly illustrates that optical scattering experiments follow the energy axis and involve only small momentum transfers. Extension of optical measurements to cover larger momentum transfers will be limited even if the incident radiation is extended to the ultraviolet wavelengths. On the other hand, optical mixing spectroscopy enables us to observe extremely small energy changes which are many orders of magnitude smaller than those detectable by other spectroscopic methods.

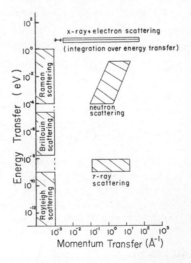

Fig. 1.1. Momentum- and energy-transfer space diagram showing regions covered by different types of radiation (Chu, 1970).

Table 1.1
Scattering phenomena[a]

Process	Detection[b] techniques	Principal application
Rayleigh	Spectrum analysis (Benedek, 1969, Cummins and Swinney, 1969) Signal correlation (Pusey and Goldburg, 1968; Chen and Polonsky-Ostrowsky, 1969) Interferometry (Chiao and Stoicheff, 1964)	Phase transitions (Swinney and Cummins, 1968; Chu *et al.*, 1968) Dynamics of macromolecules in solution (Pecora, 1972; Dubin *et al.*, 1967; Cummins *et al.*, 1969) Reaction kinetics (Yeh and Keeler, 1969a) Liquid crystals (Lister and Stinson, 1970)
Brillouin	Photobeating (Lastovka and Benedek, 1966) Interferometry (Chiao and Stoicheff, 1964) Spectrograph (Benedek *et al.*, 1964)	Fluid dynamics (Pike *et al.*, 1968) Phase transitions (Chen and Polonsky, 1968; Gammon *et al.*, 1967) Gases (Greytak and Benedek, 1966) Liquids (Eastman *et al.*, 1969). Solids (Benedek and Fritsch, 1966; Gammon and Cummins, 1966; Peticolas *et al.*, 1967) Solutions (Miller *et al.*, 1970)
Rayleigh wing (Raman anisotropy)	Interferometry	Orientational fluctuations, shear waves (Shapiro and Broida, 1967; Stegeman and Stoicheff, 1968; Ben-Reuven and Gershon, 1969)
Surface waves	Interferometry (Katyl and Ingard, 1967) Photobeating (Katyl and Ingard, 1968)	Ripplons

[a] Chu, 1970.
[b] Laser excitation: continuous-wave gas lasers.

The shaded area along the energy-transfer axis between Rayleigh and Brillouin scattering corresponds to energy changes which should be within reach by extending existing optical interferometric and beating techniques. Scattering of x rays and electrons usually involves the integration of intensity over all possible energy changes, as in (b). Then, by means of near-ultraviolet radiation for light scattering and extension of x-ray scattering to very small angles, the gap in the momentum transfer for integrated intensities can be filled (Chu, 1967) as shown by the two opposing arrows in Fig. 1.1. A striking feature of Fig. 1.1, as has been pointed out by Egelstaff (1967), is the extent of the blank spaces which are not accessible by present-day techniques, even though the shaded areas are being expanded rapidly, especially in neutron scattering. Thus, it becomes important to explore the complementary nature of various radiation-scattering processes.

A deeper understanding of the dynamical properties of systems often requires theoretical and experimental examinations of the scattering phenomena over wide ranges of momentum and energy changes and the combination of these results with measurements using other techniques such as ultrasonics, dielectric relaxation, and magnetic resonance. Brillouin scattering is often associated with optical interferometers. Studies of the spectral width of the central (Rayleigh) component have become very popular ever since the optical beat-frequency techniques were devised. Overlapping of detection techniques should become a logical extension of developments in the techniques of laser light scattering. Whenever the linewidth of the central (Rayleigh) component is very broad, optical interferometers become appropriate. Table 1.1 summarizes the common scattering phenomena related to laser light scattering (Chu, 1970) and should provide us with a broader perspective. Representative references of historical interest are listed to serve as convenient starting points for specific topics. Although the Raman effect definitely should be included as part of laser light scattering and is better developed when compared with Rayleigh and Brillouin scattering (Peticolas, 1972), we will discuss the scattering processes related mainly to light-beating spectroscopy and optical interferometry.

References

Benedek, G. B. (1969). "Polarization Matiere et Rayonnement, Livre de Jubile en l'honneur de Professeur A. Kastler," pp. 49–84. Presses Universitaires de France, Paris.

Benedek, G. B., and Fritsch, K. (1966). *Phys. Rev.* **149**, 647.

Benedek, G. B., Lastovka, J. B., Fritsch, K., and Greytak, T. (1964). *J. Opt. Soc. Amer.* **54**, 1284.

Ben-Reuven, A., and Gershon, N. D. (1969). *J. Chem. Phys.* **51**, 893.

Brillouin, L. (1914). *Compt. Rend.* **158**, 1331.

Brillouin, L. (1922). *Ann. Phys.* (Paris) **17**, 88.

Chen, S. H., and Polonsky, N. (1968). *Phys. Rev. Lett.* **20**, 909.

Chen, S. H., and Polonsky-Ostrowsky, N. (1969). *Opt. Commun.* **1**, 64.

Chu, B. (1967) "Molecular Forces based on the Baker Lectures of Peter J. W Debye." Wiley, New York.

Chu, B. (1968). *J. Chem. Educ.* **45**, 224.

Chu, B. (1970). *Ann. Rev. Phys. Chem.* **21**, 145.

Chu, B., Schoenes, F. J., and Kao, W. P. (1968). *J. Amer. Chem. Soc.* **90**, 3042.

Chiao, R. Y., and Stoicheff, B. P. (1964). *J. Opt. Soc. Amer.* **54**, 1286.

Chiao, R. Y., Townes, C. H., and Stoicheff, B. P. (1964). *Phys Rev. Lett.* **12**, 592.

Cummins, H. Z., Carlson, F. D., Herbert, T. J., and Woods, G. (1969). *Biophys. J.* **9**, 518.

Cummins, H. Z., Knable, N., and Yeh, Y., (1964). *Phys. Rev. Lett.* **12**, 150.

Cummins, H. Z. and Swinney, H. L. (1970). *In Progr. Opt.* **8**, 133.

Debye, P. (1912). *Ann. Phys. (Leipzig)* **39**, 789.

Dubin, S. B., Lunacek, J. H., and Benedek, G. B. (1967). *Proc. Nat. Acad. Sci.* **57**, 1164.

Eastman, D. P., Hollinger, A., Kenemuth, J., and Rank, D. II. (1969). *J. Chem. Phys.* **50**, 1567.

Egelstaff, P. A. (1967). *Discuss. Faraday Soc.* **43**, 149.

Einstein, A. (1910). *Ann. Phys. (Leipzig)* **33**, 1275.

Fabelinskii, I. I. (1965). "Molecular Scattering of Light." Nauka, Moscow [transl. (1968). Plenum, New York].

Flory, P. J. (1953). "Principles of Polymer Chemistry." Cornell Univ. Press, Ithaca, New York.

Ford, Jr., N. C., and Benedek, G. B. (1965). *Phys. Rev. Lett.* **15**, 649.

Gammon, R. W., and Cummins, H. Z., (1966). *Phys. Rev. Lett.* **17**, 193.

Gammon, R. W., Swinney, H. L., and Cummins, H. Z. (1967). *Phys. Rev. Lett.* **19**, 1467.

Gordon, R. G. (1968). *Advan. Magn. Resonance* **3**, 1.

Greytak, T. J., and Benedek, G. B. (1966). *Phys. Rev. Lett.* **17**, 179.

Griffin, A. (1968). *Rev. Mod. Phys.* **40**, 167.

Gross, E. F. (1930). *Nature* **126**, 201; **126**, 400; **126**, 603; *Z. Physik* **63**, 685; *Naturwiss.* **18**, 718.

Katyl, R. H., and Ingard, U. (1967). *Phys. Rev. Lett.* **19**, 64.

Katyl, R. H., and Ingard, U. (1968). *Phys. Rev. Lett.* **20**, 248.

Kerker, M., ed. (1963). "Proceedings of the Interdisciplinary Conference on Electromagnetic Scattering." Pergamon, New York.

Kerker, M. (1969). "The Scattering of Light and Other Electromagnetic Radiation." Academic Press, New York and London.

Landau, L., and Placzek, G. (1934). *Phys. Z. Sowjetunion* **5**, 172.

Lastovka, J. B., and Benedek, G. B. (1966). *In* "Physics of Quantum Electronics, Conference Proceedings, San Juan, 1965" (P. L. Kelley, B. Lax, and P. E. Tannenwald, eds.), pp. 231–240. McGraw-Hill, New York.

Lister, J. D., and Stinson, T. W. (1970). *J. Appl. Phys.* **41**, 996.

Mandel'shtam, L. I. (1926). *Zh. Russ. Fiz. Khim. Obshchest.* **58**, 381.

McIntyre, D., and Sengers, J. V. (1968). *In* "Physics of Simple Liquids" (H. N. V. Temperley, J. S. Rowlinson, and G. S. Rushbrooke, eds.), pp. 449–505. North-Holland, Amsterdam.

Miller, G. A., SanFilippo, F. I., and Carpentor, D. L. (1970). *Macromolecules* **3**, 125.
Mountain, R. D. (1966). *Rev. Mod. Phys.* **38**, 205.
Mountain, R. D. (1970). Critical Reviews in Solid State Sciences, **1**, 5.
Ornstein, L. S. and Zernike F. (1914). *Proc. Acad. Sci. Amsterdam* **17**, 793.
Ornstein, L. S. and Zernike F. (1915). *Proc. Acad. Sci. Amsterdam* **18**, 1520.
Ornstein, L. S., and Zernike, F. (1916). *Proc. Acad. Sci. Amsterdam* **19**, 1312; **19**, 1321.
Ornstein, L. S., and Zernike, F. (1926). *Physik. Z.* **27**, 761.
Pecora, R. (1972). *Ann. Rev. Biophys. Bioeng.* **1**, 257.
Peticolas, W. L. (1967). *Ann. Rev. Phys. Chem.* **18**, 233.
Peticolas, W. L. (1972). *Ann. Rev. Phys. Chem.* **23**, 93.
Peticolas, W. L., Stegeman, G. I. A., and Stoicheff, B. P. (1967). *Phys. Rev. Lett.* **18**, 1130.
Phys. Soc. Japan (1969). Light scattering by lasers, *In* "Series of Selected Papers in Physics," Vol. 41. Phys. Soc. Japan, Tokyo.
Pike, E. R., Jackson, D. A., Bourke, P. J., and Page, D. I. (1968). *J. Phys. E* **1**, 727.
Porto, S. P. S. (1969). *In* "Proc. Int. Conf. Light Scattering Spectra of Solids" (G. B. Wright, ed.), pp. 1–24. Springer-Verlag, Berlin and New York.
Pusey, P. N., and Goldberg, W. I. (1968). *Appl. Phys. Lett.* **13**, 321.
Rayleigh, J. W. S. (1881). *Philos. Mag.* **12**, 813.
Rayleigh, J. W. S. (1899). *Philos. Mag.* **47**, 375.
Rowell, R. L., and Stein, R. S., eds. (1967). "Proc. Interdisciplinary Conference on Electromagnetic Scattering II." Gordon and Breach, New York.
Shapiro, S. L., and Broida, H. P. (1967). *Phys. Rev.* **154**, 129.
Stacey, K. A. (1956). "Light-Scattering in Physical Chemistry." Academic Press, New York and London.
Stegeman, G. I. A., and Stoicheff, B. P. (1968). *Phys. Rev. Lett.* **21**, 202.
Stoicheff, B. P. (1968). *In* "Molecular Spectroscopy" (P. Hepple, ed.), pp. 261–273. Elsevier, Amsterdam.
Swinney, H. L., and Cummins, H. Z. (1968). *Phys. Rev.* **171**, 152.
Tanford, C. (1961). "Physical Chemistry of Macromolecules." Wiley, New York.
Van de Hulst, H. C. (1957). "Light Scattering by Small Particles." Wiley, New York.
Yeh, Y., and Keeler, R. N. (1969a). *J. Chem. Phys.* **51**, 1120.
Yeh, Y., and Keeler, R. N. (1969b). *Quart. Rev. Biophys.* **2**, 315.

Chapter II

BRIEF REVIEW OF CLASSICAL ELECTRICITY AND MAGNETISM

Classical electricity and magnetism is a standard topic for physicists who can skip this brief review entirely. This short chapter is intended primarily for physical chemistry graduate students who have little formal background in electricity and magnetism, while biologists are likely to find the outline too sketchy. No derivations are given because it would be pointless for us to discuss in a few pages a topic which often requires book-length discussions, and many excellent textbooks indeed exist. Furthermore, the material covered in such a condensed version tends to look very complicated unless the reader has already been exposed to it. The primary purpose of this chapter is to provide a guide for those who are vaguely familiar with the subject matter so that they can consult the pertinent references for details.

2.1. Maxwell's Equations

Maxwell's equations form the basis of all classical electromagnetic phenomena and are valid for time-dependent fields. In the presence of matter,

$$\nabla \cdot \mathbf{D} = \rho \qquad (2.1.1)$$

$$\nabla \times \mathbf{E} = -\partial \mathbf{B}/\partial t \qquad (2.1.2)$$

$$\nabla \cdot \mathbf{B} = 0 \qquad (2.1.3)$$

$$\nabla \times \mathbf{H} = \mathbf{J} + \partial \mathbf{D}/\partial t \qquad (2.1.4)$$

where the four field vectors are: the electric field $\mathbf{E}$, the dielectric displacement $\mathbf{D}$, the magnetic field $\mathbf{H}$, and the magnetic induction $\mathbf{B}$. The vector fields are three-dimensional linear fields which obey the principle of superposition. ρ is the true free-charge density at the field point where the divergence is taken and $\mathbf{J}$ is the current density due to free charge only. We may consider the Maxwell equations as axioms of electrodynamics, just as the Newtonian axioms of mechanics, which put order to the totality of experience in classical electricity and magnetism into a simplified and idealized form.

To proceed, the field equations must be supplemented by constitutive relations which connect $\mathbf{D}$ and $\mathbf{J}$ with $\mathbf{E}$, and $\mathbf{H}$ with $\mathbf{B}$.

$$\mathbf{J} = \sigma_c \mathbf{E} \tag{2.1.5}$$

$$\mathbf{D} = \epsilon \mathbf{E} \tag{2.1.6}$$

$$\mathbf{B} = \mu \mathbf{H} \tag{2.1.7}$$

σ_c, ϵ, and μ denote the specific conductance, the electric inductive capacity, and the magnetic inductive capacity, respectively. For an isotropic medium, the factors σ_c, ϵ, and μ are scalars; otherwise they become components of a symmetric tensor. We define the dielectric displacement $\mathbf{D}$ such that

$$\mathbf{D} = \epsilon_0 \mathbf{E} + \mathbf{P} \tag{2.1.8}$$

where the polarization field $\mathbf{P}$ is that field whose flux comes from the polarization charge density and ϵ_0 is the electric inductive capacity in free space. In an isotropic medium,

$$\mathbf{P} = \epsilon_0 \chi_e \mathbf{E} \tag{2.1.9}$$

with χ_e being the electric susceptibility. Equation (2.1.9) assumes that the medium polarizes isotropically, or that the polarization properties of the medium are independent of the direction of polarization, and is valid for gases, liquids, amorphous solids, and cubic crystals. From Eq. (2.1.8), we get

$$\mathbf{D} = \kappa_e \epsilon_0 \mathbf{E} \tag{2.1.10}$$

where κ_e $(= \epsilon/\epsilon_0 = 1 + \chi_e)$ is the specific inductive capacity, often called the dielectric constant.

Similarly, we have $\mathbf{M} = \chi_m \mathbf{H}$, where $\mathbf{M}$ is the magnetic polarization and χ_m $[= \kappa_m - 1 = (\mu/\mu_0) - 1]$ is the magnetic susceptibility with κ_m as the specific magnetic inductive capacity, sometimes referred to as the relative magnetic permeability. In our case, $M = 0$.

In a dielectric medium, we further assume that the free-current density $\mathbf{J}$ and the free-charge density ρ are both zero. Then, the total fields which include the incident and the scattered fields must satisfy a simplified form of the Maxwell equations. From Eqs. (2.1.1)–(2.1.4), we obtain

$$\nabla \cdot \mathbf{D} = 0 \qquad\qquad (2.1.11)$$

$$\nabla \times \mathbf{E} = -\partial \mathbf{B}/\partial t \qquad\qquad (2.1.2)$$

$$\nabla \cdot \mathbf{B} = 0 \qquad\qquad (2.1.3)$$

$$\nabla \times \mathbf{H} = \partial \mathbf{D}/\partial t \qquad\qquad (2.1.12)$$

The above four equations are the four basic relations which form the background of our light scattering theory.

Historically, laser light scattering was applied to studies of liquids and second-order phase transitions of one- and two-component systems near the critical point. A general expression for the scattered field in a dielectric medium from the fluctuating part of the electric susceptibility can be derived from the Maxwell equations by making use of the Hertz potential $\mathbf{\Pi}$. (Jackson, 1962) and by taking

$$\chi_e(t) = \langle \chi_e \rangle + \Delta\chi_e(t) \qquad\qquad (2.1.13)$$

where $\Delta\chi_e$ and $\langle\chi_e\rangle$ represent the fluctuating components of the electric susceptibility at time t and the time-spatial average (Lastovka, 1967).

2.2. Vector and Scalar Potentials

Maxwell's equations are a set of four coupled first-order partial differential equations describing the sources and relating the various components of electromagnetic fields. In practice, they can be solved as they are only in simple situations. It is often convenient to obtain a smaller number of second-order equations while satisfying some of Maxwell's equations automatically.

By application of the general vector condition $\nabla \cdot \nabla \times \mathbf{V} = 0$, and Eq. (2.1.3), we can define

$$\mathbf{B} = \nabla \times \mathbf{A} \qquad\qquad (2.2.1)$$

where $\mathbf{A}$ is a vector potential. Then Eq. (2.1.2) becomes

$$\nabla \times (\mathbf{E} + \partial\mathbf{A}/\partial t) = 0 \qquad\qquad (2.2.2)$$

Thus, we can write the quantity with vanishing curl as the gradient of a scalar potential:

$$\mathbf{E} = -\nabla\phi - \partial\mathbf{A}/\partial t \qquad\qquad (2.2.3)$$

Equations (2.2.1) and (2.2.3) automatically satisfy the two homogeneous Maxwell's equations [Eqs. (2.1.2) and (2.1.3)]. The behavior of $\mathbf{A}$ and ϕ will be determined by the other two inhomogeneous equations [Eqs. (2.1.1) and (2.1.4)]. In terms of vector and scalar potentials, Eqs. (2.1.1) and (2.1.4) can be reduced to two coupled equations. The uncoupling can be achieved by considering the arbitrariness involved in the definition of the potentials. The electric and the magnetic fields remain unchanged by transformations of the type

$$\mathbf{A}^* = \mathbf{A} - \boldsymbol{\nabla}\psi \tag{2.2.4}$$

$$\phi^* = \phi + \partial\psi/\partial t \tag{2.2.5}$$

where ψ is any scalar function of the coordinates and time. We can then take out the arbitrariness by choosing a set of potentials (A and ϕ) such that the Lorentz condition

$$\boldsymbol{\nabla}\cdot\mathbf{A} + \mu\epsilon(\partial\phi/\partial t) = 0 \tag{2.2.6}$$

is satisfied. By substituting Eq. (2.2.6) into the coupled equations

$$\nabla^2\phi + (\partial/\partial t)(\boldsymbol{\nabla}\cdot\mathbf{A}) = -\rho/\epsilon \tag{2.2.7}$$

and

$$\nabla^2\mathbf{A} - \mu\epsilon(\partial^2\mathbf{A}/\partial t^2) - \boldsymbol{\nabla}[\boldsymbol{\nabla}\cdot\mathbf{A} + \mu\epsilon(\partial\phi/\partial t)] = -\mu\mathbf{J} \tag{2.2.8}$$

we obtain a symmetrical set of two inhomogeneous wave equations, one for ϕ and one for $\mathbf{A}$:

$$\nabla^2\phi - \mu\epsilon(\partial^2\phi/\partial t^2) = \rho/\epsilon \tag{2.2.9}$$

and

$$\nabla^2\mathbf{A} - \mu\epsilon(\partial^2\mathbf{A}/\partial t^2) = -\mu\mathbf{J} \tag{2.2.10}$$

where $\mu\epsilon = 1/c_m{}^2$ with c_m being the velocity of light in the medium.

2.3. The Hertz Potential

The Lorentz condition which relates the scalar and the vector potentials tells us that charges and currents cannot be specified independently. In our case, it is advantageous to use a *single* potential so chosen that the Lorentz condition is automatically satisfied.

Let us set a vector $\mathbf{\Pi}$, known as the Hertz potential, by the equations:

$$\phi = -\boldsymbol{\nabla}\cdot\mathbf{\Pi} \tag{2.3.1}$$

and

$$\mathbf{A} = 1/c_m{}^2(\partial\mathbf{\Pi}/\partial t) \tag{2.3.2}$$

so that the Lorentz condition of Eq. (2.2.6) is automatically satisfied. The vector $\mathbf{\Pi}$ satisfies the homogeneous wave equations (2.1.2) and (2.1.3) in source-free space:

$$\nabla \times \mathbf{E} + \frac{\partial}{\partial t} \mathbf{B} = \nabla \times \left(\nabla(\nabla \cdot \mathbf{\Pi}) - \frac{1}{c_{\mathrm{m}}^2} \frac{\partial^2 \mathbf{\Pi}}{\partial t^2} \right) + \frac{1}{c_{\mathrm{m}}^2} \nabla \times \left(\frac{\partial^2 \mathbf{\Pi}}{\partial t^2} \right) = 0$$

$$\nabla \cdot \mathbf{B} = \nabla \cdot \nabla \times \left(\frac{1}{c_{\mathrm{m}}^2} \frac{\partial \mathbf{\Pi}}{\partial t} \right) = 0$$

since, by the general vector rules, the curl of a gradient of any scalar and the divergence of a curl of any vector are zero.

In a fluctuating medium, Eqs. (2.2.9) and (2.2.10) have the forms

$$\nabla^2 \phi - \frac{1}{c_{\mathrm{m}}^2} \left(\frac{\partial^2 \phi}{\partial t^2} \right) = \frac{1}{\epsilon_0} (\nabla \cdot \mathbf{P}^*) \tag{2.2.9a}$$

and

$$\nabla^2 \mathbf{A} - \frac{1}{c_{\mathrm{m}}^2} \left(\frac{\partial^2 \mathbf{A}}{\partial t^2} \right) = - \frac{1}{\epsilon_0 c_{\mathrm{m}}^2} \left(\frac{\partial \mathbf{P}^*}{\partial t} \right) \tag{2.2.10a}$$

where $\mathbf{P}^* \left[= \epsilon_0 \Delta \chi_{\mathrm{e}} \mathbf{E} / (1 + \langle \chi_{\mathrm{e}} \rangle) \right]$ is the polarization field due to fluctuations of the local electric susceptibility and μ has been replaced by μ_0. By introducing

$$\rho_{\mathrm{eff}} = - (\epsilon/\epsilon_0)(\nabla \cdot \mathbf{P}^*) \tag{2.3.3}$$

and

$$\mathbf{J}_{\mathrm{eff}} = (c_0/c_{\mathrm{m}})^2 (\partial \mathbf{P}^*/\partial t) \tag{2.3.4}$$

we have retrieved Eqs. (2.2.9) and (2.2.10):

$$\nabla^2 \phi - 1/c_{\mathrm{m}}^2 (\partial^2 \phi/\partial t^2) = - \rho_{\mathrm{eff}}/\epsilon \tag{2.2.9b}$$

$$\nabla^2 \mathbf{A} - 1/c_{\mathrm{m}}^2 (\partial^2 \mathbf{A}/\partial t^2) = - \mu_0 \mathbf{J}_{\mathrm{eff}} \tag{2.2.10b}$$

The quantity $\epsilon \left[= (1 + \langle \chi_{\mathrm{e}} \rangle) \epsilon_0 \right]$ is the electric inductive capacity in a dielectric medium while c_0 is the velocity of light in free space. In our case, $\mu = \mu_0$. From Eqs. (2.3.3) and (2.3.4), we see that the equation of continuity

$$\nabla \cdot \mathbf{J}_{\mathrm{eff}} + \frac{\partial \rho_{\mathrm{eff}}}{\partial t} = \nabla \cdot \left(\frac{c_0}{c_{\mathrm{m}}} \right)^2 \left(\frac{\partial \mathbf{P}^*}{\partial t} \right) - \frac{\epsilon}{\epsilon_0} \frac{\partial}{\partial t} (\nabla \cdot \mathbf{P}^*) = 0$$

is satisfied. The Hertz vector obeys the inhomogeneous wave equations with $\mathbf{P}^*$ as the source. We have

$$\nabla^2 \mathbf{\Pi} - \frac{1}{c_{\mathrm{m}}^2} \frac{\partial^2 \mathbf{\Pi}}{\partial t^2} = - \frac{\mathbf{P}^*}{\epsilon_0} \tag{2.3.5}$$

Equations (2.2.9b), (2.2.10b), and (2.3.5) all have the general form

$$\nabla^2 \Psi - \frac{1}{c_m^2}\left(\frac{\partial^2 \Psi}{\partial t^2}\right) = -4\pi g(x_\alpha, t) \qquad (2.3.6)$$

where $g(x_\alpha, t)$ is an "effective" source distribution. The solution to this equation can best be represented by Green's function. A detailed derivation of this problem has been presented by Jackson (1962). The result is:

$$\Psi(x_\alpha, t) = \int G(x_\alpha, t; x_\alpha', t')g(x_\alpha', t')\, dx_\alpha'\, dt' \qquad (2.3.7)$$

where $G(x_\alpha, t; x_\alpha', t')$ $[= (1/r)\delta(t' - t + r/c_m)]$ is the retarded Green's function observed at field point x_α and at time t due to a source disturbance at x_α' and at an *earlier* time t' $[=t - r/c_m$ with r being the distance between the source and the field points]. From Eq. (2.3.5), we thus obtain the Hertz potential as

$$\mathbf{\Pi}(x_\alpha, t) = \frac{1}{4\pi\epsilon_0}\int \frac{\mathbf{P}^*(x_\alpha', t')\delta[t' - t + (r/c_m)]}{r}\, dx_\alpha'\, dt' \qquad (2.3.8)$$

The fields **E** and **B** can be derived from **Π** by defining

$$\mathbf{C} = \nabla \times \mathbf{\Pi} \qquad (2.3.9)$$

Then we get

$$\mathbf{B} = \frac{1}{c_m^2}\frac{\partial \mathbf{C}}{\partial t} = \frac{1}{c_m^2}\frac{\partial(\nabla \times \mathbf{\Pi})}{\partial t} \qquad (2.3.10)$$

and

$$\mathbf{E} = \nabla \times \mathbf{C} = \nabla \times (\nabla \times \mathbf{\Pi}) = \nabla(\nabla \cdot \mathbf{\Pi}) - \nabla^2\mathbf{\Pi}$$

$$= \nabla(\nabla \cdot \mathbf{\Pi}) - [-(\mathbf{P}^*/\epsilon_0) + (1/c_m^2)(\partial^2\mathbf{\Pi}/\partial t^2)]$$

$$= \nabla(\nabla \cdot \mathbf{\Pi}) - (1/c_m^2)(\partial^2\mathbf{\Pi}/\partial t^2) \qquad (2.3.11)$$

since by definition, $\mathbf{E} = \nabla \times \mathbf{C}$ only if $\mathbf{P}^* = 0$ at the point of observation, i.e., the observation (field) point is outside the illuminated region.

References

Jackson, J. C. (1962). "Classical Electrodynamics." Wiley, New York.
Lastovka, J. C. (1967). "Light Mixing Spectroscopy and the Spectrum of Light Scattered by Thermal Fluctuations in Liquids." Ph.D. thesis. MIT, Cambridge, Massachusetts.

An additional textbook, such as the one by Panofsky and Phillips (Panofsky, W. K. H., and Phillips, M. (1955). "Classical Electricity and Magnetism." Addison-Wesley, Reading, Massachusetts) should be a good reference for those not familiar with the topic. Derivations of the hydrodynamic equations have been presented by Landau and Lifshitz (Landau, L. D., and Lifshitz, E. M. (1959). "Fluid Mechanics." Addison-Wesley, Reading, Massachusetts) and by Benedek (Benedek, G. B. (1968). Thermal Fluctuations and the Scattering of Light *in* "Statistical Physics, Phase Transitions and Superfluidity" (M. Cretien, E. P. Gross, and S. Deser, eds.). Gordon and Breach, New York).

Chapter III
SCATTERING THEORY

The approach to the scattering theory which is presented in this chapter and sections of Chapter IV derives mainly from an excellent and monumental Ph.D. thesis of J. B. Lastovka (1967). We are particularly indebted to him for permission to use many of the original unpublished tracings from his thesis.

3.1. General Expression for the Scattered Electric Field

3.1.1. Scattered Electric Field from a Fluctuating Dielectric Medium

When a beam of linearly polarized light is passed through a dielectric medium, the incident electric field induces an oscillating dipole of the same frequency at each point along its path. Each oscillating dipole radiates energy in all directions. So, the net field at any point in space is the vector sum of the induced dipole fields. In our calculations, we treat the dielectric medium as a continuum even for dimensions small compared to the wavelength of light and take the electric susceptibility to be a scalar.

The scattered electric field $\mathbf{E}_s(x_\alpha, t)$ can be computed by either summing the induced dipole fields reaching the point x_α in such a way so as to include the relative phase between waves originating from spatially separated points in the scattering volume v, or by demanding that the total fields $\mathbf{E}$ ($= \mathbf{E}_{\text{INC}} + \mathbf{E}_s$ with $\mathbf{E}_{\text{INC}}$ the incident electric field which represents the amplitude of the linearly polarized incident light) satisfy the modified Maxwell equations (2.1.2), (2.1.3), (2.1.11), and (2.1.12) throughout all space as we have discussed in Chapter II. The second approach avoids the dipolar sum associated with the time–spatial average susceptibility $\langle \chi_e \rangle$ which is independent of the space coordinates in scattering volume v if the system is at equilibrium. The effect corresponds to changing c_0 in free space to c_m in the scattering medium with $c_m = c_0/n$, with n the refractive index of the scattering medium.

By substituting (2.3.8) into (2.3.11), we get

$$\mathbf{E}_{(s)}(x_\alpha, t) = \nabla \times (\nabla \times \mathbf{\Pi})$$

$$= \frac{1}{4\pi\epsilon_0} \nabla$$

$$\times \left(\nabla \times \int_v \int_{t'=-\infty}^{\infty} \frac{\mathbf{P}^*(x_\alpha', t')\delta[t' - t + (r/c_m)]}{r} dx_\alpha' \, dt' \right)$$

$$(3.1.1)$$

in which we recall

$$\mathbf{P}^*(x_\alpha', t') = \epsilon_0 \Delta\chi_e(x_\alpha', t') \mathbf{E}_{\text{INC}}(x_\alpha', t')/(1 + \langle \chi_e \rangle)$$

The symbol $\mathbf{E}_{(s)}$ denotes that the radiation field is one of the terms in the scattered electric field $\mathbf{E}_s$. The coordinates of the scattering volume element dx_α' located at x_α' are shown in Fig. 3.1.1. Refractive effects at the interface of the scattering cell have been avoided by taking Q in the scattering medium. Equation (3.1.1) represents a summing of effective induced dipoles over the volume integral $\int dx_\alpha'$ with a phase factor which measures the interference between the wavelets emitted by different volume elements in the scattering volume v and is sometimes referred to as the interference or the phase integral. In an idealized homogeneous medium where $\Delta\chi_e = 0$, there is no light scattering except in the direction of the incident beam.

We shall proceed to simplify Eq. (3.1.1) by assuming the far-field approximation and the equivalence of $\mathbf{E}$ and $\mathbf{E}_{\text{INC}}$ since the scattered intensity is usually only a very small fraction of the incident intensity. With the far-field approximation, r' is the microscopic distance from the origin 0 to the scattering center and r is the distance traveled by the scattered wave from the scattering center located at x_α' to the point of observation Q located at x_α. $\mathbf{r}$ and $\mathbf{R}$ are almost parallel because of the microscopic nature of $\mathbf{r}'$. Thus,

$$r = R - \mathbf{r}' \cdot \mathbf{R}/R = R - \mathbf{r}' \cdot \hat{\mathbf{R}} \qquad (3.1.2)$$

where $\hat{\mathbf{R}}$ is a unit vector in the direction $\mathbf{R}$. Furthermore, we may take the zeroth-order approximation in the denominator of the integrand: $r \simeq R$.

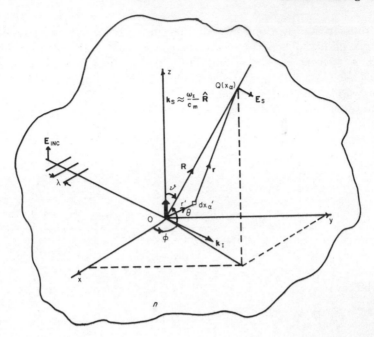

Fig. 3.1.1. Relative position of the observer $Q(x_\alpha)$ and the scattering volume $v(x_\alpha')$. (Index of refraction $= n$.)

With $\epsilon = \epsilon_0(1 + \langle \chi_e \rangle)$, we have approximated Eq. (3.1.1) in the form

$$\mathbf{E}_{(s)}(\mathbf{R}, t) = \frac{1}{4\pi R} \left(\frac{\epsilon_0}{\epsilon} \right) \mathbf{\nabla} \times \left\{ \mathbf{\nabla} \times \int_v \int_{t'=-\infty}^{\infty} \Delta\chi_e(x_\alpha', t') \mathbf{E}_{\mathrm{INC}}(x_\alpha', t') \right.$$

$$\left. \times \delta \left[t' - t + \frac{1}{c_m} (R - \mathbf{r}' \cdot \hat{\mathbf{R}}) \right] dx_\alpha' \, dt' \right\} \quad (3.1.3)$$

Equation (3.1.3) represents a far-field approximation of the general solution for the scattered electric field in terms of the fluctuating part of the electric susceptibility.

3.1.2 Scattered Electric Field from a Propagating Sound Wave

Let us consider the scattering from a plane-wave fluctuation in which

$$\Delta\chi_e(\mathbf{R}, t) = \Delta\chi_e^0 \exp[i(\mathbf{q} \cdot \mathbf{R} - \bar{\omega}t)] \quad (3.1.4)$$

and

$$\mathbf{E}_{\text{INC}}(\mathbf{R},\, t) = \mathbf{E}_{\text{I}}{}^0 \exp[i(\mathbf{k}_{\text{I}} \cdot \mathbf{R} - \omega_{\text{I}} t)] \qquad (3.1.5)$$

$\Delta\chi_e$ and $\mathbf{E}_{\text{INC}}$ are simple sinusoidal traveling waves of frequencies $\bar{\omega}$ and ω_{I} in the directions $\hat{\mathbf{q}}$ and $\hat{\mathbf{k}}_{\text{I}}$ with phase velocities v_s ($= \bar{\omega}/|\mathbf{q}|$) and c_m ($= \omega_{\text{I}}/|\mathbf{k}_{\text{I}}|$), respectively. The symbol $\wedge$ denotes a unit vector. The periodic fluctuations are represented by complex exponentials for convenience. Only the real part has physical significance. Both $\Delta\chi_e{}^0$ and $\mathbf{E}_{\text{I}}{}^0$ are real. Then, we have for real $\mathbf{E}_{(s)}(\mathbf{R},\, t)$:

$$\mathbf{E}_{(s)}(\mathbf{R},\, t) = \frac{1}{4\pi R} \left(\frac{\epsilon_0}{\epsilon}\right) \nabla_R \times (\nabla_R \times \Delta\chi_e{}^0 \mathbf{E}_{\text{I}}{}^0)$$

$$\cdot \int_v \int_{t'=-\infty}^{\infty} \cos(\mathbf{k}_{\text{I}} \cdot \mathbf{r}' - \omega_{\text{I}} t') \cos(\mathbf{q} \cdot \mathbf{r}' - \bar{\omega} t')$$

$$\times \delta\left[t' - t + \frac{1}{c_m}(R - \mathbf{r}' \cdot \hat{\mathbf{R}})\right] dx_\alpha'\, dt' \qquad (3.1.6)$$

By performing the time integration, Eq. (3.1.6) becomes

$$\mathbf{E}_{(s)}(\mathbf{R},\, t) = \frac{1}{4\pi R} \left(\frac{\epsilon_0}{\epsilon}\right) \nabla_R \times (\nabla_R \times \Delta\chi_e{}^0 \mathbf{E}_{\text{I}}{}^0)$$

$$\times \int_v \cos\left\{\mathbf{k}_{\text{I}} \cdot \mathbf{r}' - \omega_{\text{I}}\left[t - \frac{1}{c_m}(R - \mathbf{r}' \cdot \hat{\mathbf{R}})\right]\right\}$$

$$\times \cos\left\{\mathbf{q} \cdot \mathbf{r}' - \bar{\omega}\left[t - \frac{1}{c_m}(R - \mathbf{r}' \cdot \hat{\mathbf{R}})\right]\right\} dx_\alpha' \qquad (3.1.7)$$

where we have set $t' = t - (1/c_m)(R - \mathbf{r}' \cdot \hat{\mathbf{R}})$. The terms without $\mathbf{r}'$ can be taken out of the integral. In addition, if we let

$$x = (\mathbf{k}_{\text{I}} + \mathbf{q}) \cdot \mathbf{r}' - (\omega_{\text{I}} + \bar{\omega})t + \frac{\omega_{\text{I}} + \bar{\omega}}{c_m} R - \frac{\omega_{\text{I}} + \bar{\omega}}{c_m} \mathbf{r}' \cdot \hat{\mathbf{R}}$$

$$y = (\mathbf{k}_{\text{I}} - \mathbf{q}) \cdot \mathbf{r}' - (\omega_{\text{I}} - \bar{\omega})t + \frac{\omega_{\text{I}} - \bar{\omega}}{c_m} R - \frac{\omega_{\text{I}} - \bar{\omega}}{c_m} \mathbf{r}' \cdot \hat{\mathbf{R}}$$

and with the relation

$$2 \cos \tfrac{1}{2}(x + y) \cos \tfrac{1}{2}(x - y) = \cos x + \cos y$$

we then have for $\mathbf{E}_{(s)}$ in its complex form as

$$
\mathbf{E}_{(s)}(\mathbf{R}, t) = \frac{1}{4\pi R}\left(\frac{\epsilon_0}{\epsilon}\right) \boldsymbol{\nabla}_R \times (\boldsymbol{\nabla}_R \times \Delta\chi_e^0 \mathbf{E}_I^0)
$$

$$
\times \left\{ \tfrac{1}{2} \exp\left[i\left(\frac{\omega_I + \bar{\omega}}{c_m}\right)R - i(\omega_I + \bar{\omega})t\right] \right.
$$

$$
\times \int_v \exp\left[i\left(\mathbf{k}_I + \mathbf{q} - \frac{\omega_I + \bar{\omega}}{c_m}\hat{\mathbf{R}}\right)\cdot\mathbf{r}'\right]d\mathbf{r}'
$$

$$
+ \tfrac{1}{2}\exp\left[i\left(\frac{\omega_I - \bar{\omega}}{c_m}\right)R - i(\omega_I - \bar{\omega})t\right]
$$

$$
\left. \times \int_v \exp\left[i\left(\mathbf{k}_I - \mathbf{q} - \frac{\omega_I - \bar{\omega}}{c_m}\hat{\mathbf{R}}\right)\cdot\mathbf{r}'\right]d\mathbf{r}'\right\} \quad (3.1.8)
$$

where $dx_\alpha' = d\mathbf{r}'$. Equation (3.1.8) tells us that the fluctuating part of the electric susceptibility impresses its time dependence on the electric field by modulating the amplitude of the scattered field from every point in the scattering volume v. The modulation gives rise to two dipole wavelets of frequencies $\omega^+ (= \omega_I + \bar{\omega})$ and $\omega^- (= \omega_I - \bar{\omega})$. We define

$$
\mathbf{k}_s^+ = (2\pi/\lambda^+)\hat{\mathbf{R}} = (\omega^+/c_m)\hat{\mathbf{R}} = [(\omega_I + \bar{\omega})/c_m]\hat{\mathbf{R}} \quad (3.1.9)
$$

and

$$
\mathbf{k}_s^- = (2\pi/\lambda^-)\hat{\mathbf{R}} = (\omega^-/c_m)\hat{\mathbf{R}} = [(\omega_I - \bar{\omega})/c_m]\hat{\mathbf{R}} \quad (3.1.10)
$$

In terms of $\mathbf{k}_s^+$ and $\mathbf{k}_s^-$, Eq. (3.1.8) has the form

$$
\mathbf{E}_{(s)}(\mathbf{R}, t) = \frac{1}{4\pi R}\left(\frac{\epsilon_0}{\epsilon}\right)\boldsymbol{\nabla}_R \times (\boldsymbol{\nabla}_R \times \Delta\chi_e^0 \mathbf{E}_I^0)
$$

$$
\times \left\{ \tfrac{1}{2}\exp[i(k_s^+ R - \omega^+ t)]\int_v \exp[i(\mathbf{k}_I + \mathbf{q} - \mathbf{k}_s^+)\cdot\mathbf{r}']\,d\mathbf{r}' \right.
$$

$$
\left. + \tfrac{1}{2}\exp[i(k_s^- R - \omega^- t)]\int_v \exp[i(\mathbf{k}_I - \mathbf{q} - \mathbf{k}_s^-)\cdot\mathbf{r}']\,d\mathbf{r}'\right\}
$$

$$
(3.1.11)
$$

The phase integrals

$$J^+(k_s{}^+, \mathbf{q}) = \int_v \exp[i(\mathbf{k_I} + \mathbf{q} - \mathbf{k_s}^+) \cdot \mathbf{r'}]\, d\mathbf{r'} \qquad (3.1.12)$$

and

$$J^-(k_s{}^-, -\mathbf{q}) = \int_v \exp[i(\mathbf{k_I} - \mathbf{q} - \mathbf{k_s}^-) \cdot \mathbf{r'}]\, d\mathbf{r'} \qquad (3.1.13)$$

measure the interference between the elementary dipole wavelets emitted from spatially separated points in v. We shall invoke the Bragg relation which we plan to prove later:

$$\mathbf{q}^+ = \mathbf{k_s}^+ - \mathbf{k_I} \qquad (3.1.14)$$

$$\mathbf{q}^- = \mathbf{k_I} - \mathbf{k_s}^- \qquad (3.1.15)$$

Equations (3.1.11), (3.1.14), and (3.1.15) show that the scattered electric field in the observer's direction $\mathbf{R}$ comes from two plane-wave components of the electric susceptibility whose wave vectors $\mathbf{q}^+$ and $\mathbf{q}^-$ satisfy Eqs. (3.1.14) and (3.1.15). In addition, the modulation produces a frequency shift whose magnitude is equal to the frequency of the *scattering* plane wave $(\pm\bar{\omega})$. In Fig. 3.1.2, we envisage light waves as being diffracted by propagating sound waves owing to local thermal fluctuations in the electric susceptibility and the Bragg law holds. The two wave vectors $\mathbf{q}^+$ and $\mathbf{q}^-$, as shown in Fig. 3.1.2, must satisfy Eqs. (3.1.14) and (3.1.15) and have magnitudes

$$|\,\mathbf{q}^+\,| = |\,\mathbf{q}^-\,| = k_s s \qquad (3.1.16)$$

where we have $k_s{}^+ \simeq k_s{}^- \simeq k_I$ for the case $\bar{\omega} \ll \omega_I$ since the velocity of sound is much smaller than that of light; $k_I = 2\pi/\lambda$; $s = 2\sin(\tfrac{1}{2}\theta)$; λ and θ are the wavelength of light in the medium and the scattering angle.

In our example, if the grating were fixed in space, the scattered light would have the incident frequency. However, our grating moves with a phase velocity v_s $(= \bar{\omega}/|\,\mathbf{q}\,|)$ so that the frequency of the *back-reflected* light is reduced by a Doppler shift of $(2v_s/c_m)\omega_I$. An analogous situation for a Doppler-shift effect is to consider the speed of a train by measuring the pitch of its whistle as it moves with respect to a fixed listener. Quantum mechanically, we may consider the scattering process as inelastic photon–phonon collisions. The incident photon has an energy $\hbar\omega_I$ and a momentum $\hbar\mathbf{k_I}$, and the sound wave may be described as a quasiparticle of energy $\hbar\bar{\omega}$ and quasimomentum $\hbar\mathbf{q}$. Conservations of energy and momentum in the

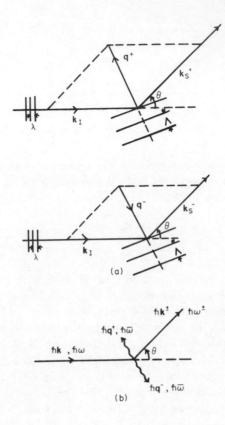

Fig. 3.1.2. Brillouin scattering. (a) Classical description $(v_s/c_m \ll 1)$; $q^+ = k_s^+ - k_I$, $k_s^+ = k_s^- = \hat{R}$, $q^- = k_I - k_s^-$. (b) Quantum description $(v_s/c_m \ll 1)$; $\hbar k_s = \hbar k_I \pm \hbar q$, $\hbar \omega_s = \hbar \omega_I \pm \hbar \bar{\omega}$.

scattering process require

$$\hbar k_s = \hbar k_I \pm \hbar q \qquad \text{(momentum conservation)} \qquad (3.1.17)$$

$$\hbar \omega_s = \hbar \omega_I \pm \hbar \bar{\omega} \qquad \text{(energy conservation)} \qquad (3.1.18)$$

The situation $q = k_s - k_I$ and $\bar{\omega} = \omega_s - \omega_I$ corresponds to $q^+ = k_s^+ - k_I$ and $\bar{\omega} = \omega^+ - \omega_I$, respectively, and represents "anti-Stokes" or phonon annihilation, while the situation $q = k_I - k_s$ and $\bar{\omega} = \omega_I - \omega_s$ corresponds to $q^- = k_I - k_s^-$ and $\bar{\omega} = \omega_I - \omega_s^-$, respectively, and represents "Stokes" or phonon creation. In phonon creation, the scattered photon has a lower frequency than that of the incident photon, so the shift is toward the red. The converse is true for phonon annihilation, where the shift is toward the blue. In practice, the idea of diffraction of light by ultrasonic waves

was first proposed by Debye (1932). Tunable lasers have been constructed successfully using this principle.

3.1.3. Scattered Electric Field in the Limit of Small Frequency Shifts

In the limit of small frequency shifts where $\bar{\omega} \ll \omega_I$, $\mathbf{k}_s = (\omega_I/c_m)\hat{\mathbf{R}}$, Eqs. (3.1.3) and (3.1.5) combine to give

$$\mathbf{E}_{(s)}(\mathbf{R}, t) = \frac{1}{4\pi R}\left(\frac{\epsilon_0}{\epsilon}\right) \nabla_R \times \{\nabla_R \times \mathbf{E}_1{}^0 \exp[i(k_sR - \omega_I t)]\}$$

$$\times \int_v \Delta\chi_e(\mathbf{r}', t) \exp[i(\mathbf{k}_I - \mathbf{k}_s)\cdot\mathbf{r}'] \, d\mathbf{r}' \quad (3.1.19)$$

The double-curl operation can be carried out explicitly. In spherical polar coordinates, the components of curl $\mathbf{p}_1$ are as follows:

$$(\nabla \times \mathbf{p}_1)_r = \frac{1}{r\sin\vartheta}\left(\frac{\partial(\sin\vartheta p_\phi)}{\partial\vartheta} - \frac{\partial p_\vartheta}{\partial\phi}\right) \quad (3.1.20)$$

$$(\nabla \times \mathbf{p}_1)_\vartheta = \frac{1}{r\sin\vartheta}\frac{\partial p_r}{\partial\phi} - \frac{1}{r}\frac{\partial(rp_\phi)}{\partial r} \quad (3.1.21)$$

$$(\nabla \times \mathbf{p}_1)_\phi = \frac{1}{r}\left(\frac{\partial(rp_\vartheta)}{\partial r} - \frac{\partial p_r}{\partial\vartheta}\right) \quad (3.1.22)$$

The problem corresponds to consideration of the electric dipole radiation. Let us set

$$\mathbf{\Pi} = \frac{1}{4\pi R}\left(\frac{\epsilon_0}{\epsilon}\right) \mathbf{E}_I{}^0 \exp[i(k_sR - \omega_I t)] \int_v \Delta\chi_e(\mathbf{r}', t) \exp[i(\mathbf{k}_I - \mathbf{k}_s)\cdot\mathbf{r}'] \, d\mathbf{r}'$$

$$= \frac{\exp[i(k_sR - \omega_I t)]}{4\pi\epsilon R} \mathbf{p}_1 \quad (3.1.23)$$

where

$$\mathbf{p}_1(t) = \epsilon_0\mathbf{E}_I{}^0 \int_v \Delta\chi_e(\mathbf{r}', t) \exp[i(\mathbf{k}_I - \mathbf{k}_s)\cdot\mathbf{r}'] \, d\mathbf{r}'$$

and is parallel to the polar axis as shown in Fig. 3.1.3. We denote the vectors as real even though the periodic fluctuations are represented by complex exponentials. We shall neglect the time dependence of $\mathbf{p}_1$ when compared with the optical frequencies. Then the Hertz potential has the

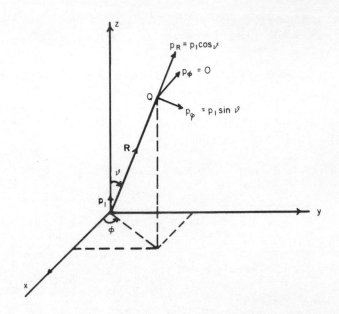

Fig. 3.1.3. Components of a vector oriented along the polar axis.

spherical polar components as (Panofsky and Phillips, 1955)

$$(\mathbf{\Pi})_R = \{\exp[i(k_s R - \omega_I t)]/4\pi\epsilon R\}p_1 \cos\vartheta \qquad (3.1.24)$$

$$(\mathbf{\Pi})_\vartheta = -\{\exp[i(k_s R - \omega_I t)]/4\pi\epsilon R\}p_1 \sin\vartheta \qquad (3.1.25)$$

$$(\mathbf{\Pi})_\phi = 0 \qquad (3.1.26)$$

By Eq. (2.3.9), we shall first compute **C**. Equations (3.1.20) and (3.1.21), together with Eqs. (3.1.24)–(3.1.26), show that C_ϕ is the only component of **C**:

$$C_\phi = \frac{1}{R}\left(\frac{\partial(-Rp_1 \sin\vartheta \exp[i(k_s R - \omega_I t)]/4\pi\epsilon R)}{\partial R}\right.$$

$$\left. - \frac{\partial(p_1 \cos\vartheta \exp[i(k_s R - \omega_I t)]/4\pi\epsilon R)}{\partial\vartheta}\right)$$

$$= \frac{1}{4\pi\epsilon R}\{\exp[i(k_s R - \omega_I t)]p_1 \sin\vartheta(-ik_s)$$

$$+ p_1 \sin\vartheta \exp[i(k_s R - \omega_I t)]/R\}$$

$$= \frac{\exp[i(k_s R - \omega_I t)]}{4\pi\epsilon R}\left(\frac{1}{R} - ik_s\right)p_1 \sin\vartheta \qquad (3.1.27)$$

From C_ϕ, we obtain the components of the electric field

$$E_R = \frac{1}{R \sin \vartheta} \frac{\partial}{\partial \vartheta} (\sin \vartheta C_\phi)$$

$$= \frac{1}{R \sin \vartheta} \frac{\partial}{\partial \vartheta} \left[\sin^2 \vartheta p_1 \frac{\exp[i(k_s R - \omega_I t)]}{4\pi\epsilon R} \left(\frac{1}{R} - ik_s \right) \right]$$

$$= \frac{p_1 \cos \vartheta}{2\pi\epsilon R^2} \left(\frac{1}{R} - ik_s \right) \exp[i(k_s R - \omega_I t)] \qquad (3.1.28)$$

and

$$E_\vartheta = -\frac{1}{R} \frac{\partial}{\partial R} (R C_\phi) = \frac{\exp[i(k_s R - \omega_I t)]}{4\pi\epsilon R}$$

$$\times \left(\frac{1}{R^2} - \frac{ik_s}{R} - k_s^2 \right) p_1 \sin \vartheta \qquad (3.1.29)$$

The ϑ component of the electric field has a static dipole field varying as $1/R^0$, a transition field varying as $1/R^2$, and a radiation field varying as $1/R$. The transition field contributes to the energy storage during oscillation but it does not contribute to the radiated energy. Using the far-field approximation, only the term involving $1/R$ is important. Furthermore, there is no contribution to the radiation field by E_R. Similarly, from Eq. (2.3.10), we have

$$H_\phi = \frac{B_\phi}{\mu} = \frac{-i\omega_I}{\mu} \left(\frac{\epsilon_0}{4\pi\epsilon} \right) E_I^0 \sin \vartheta \left(\frac{1}{R^2} - \frac{ik_s}{R} \right)$$

$$\times \left\{ \iint_v \Delta\chi_e(\mathbf{r}', t) \exp[i(\mathbf{k}_I - \mathbf{k}_s) \cdot \mathbf{r}'] \, d\mathbf{r}' \right\}$$

$$\cdot \frac{1}{c_m^2} \exp[i(k_s R - \omega_I t)] \qquad (3.1.30)$$

The *radiation* fields alone are

$$H_\phi = -\frac{\omega_I k_s \epsilon_0}{4\pi R} \sin \vartheta E_I^0 \exp[i(k_s R - \omega_I t)]$$

$$\times \int_v \Delta\chi_e(\mathbf{r}', t) \exp[i(\mathbf{k}_I - \mathbf{k}_s) \cdot \mathbf{r}'] \, d\mathbf{r}' \qquad (3.1.31)$$

$$E_\vartheta = -\frac{k_s^2 \sin \vartheta}{4\pi R} \left(\frac{\epsilon_0}{\epsilon}\right) E_I^0 \exp[i(k_sR - \omega_I t)]$$

$$\times \int_v \Delta\chi_e(\mathbf{r'}, t) \exp[i(\mathbf{k_I} - \mathbf{k_s})\cdot\mathbf{r'}]\,d\mathbf{r'} \quad (3.1.32)$$

In vector form, Eq. (3.1.32) becomes

$$\mathbf{E}_s(\mathbf{R}, t) = \mathbf{k}_s \times (\mathbf{k}_s \times \mathbf{E}_I^0) \left(\frac{\epsilon_0}{\epsilon}\right) \frac{\exp[i(k_sR - \omega_I t)]}{4\pi R}$$

$$\times \int_v \Delta\chi_e(\mathbf{r'}, t) \exp[i(\mathbf{k_I} - \mathbf{k_s})\cdot\mathbf{r'}]\,d\mathbf{r'} \quad (3.1.33)$$

where we recall that $\mathbf{k}_s = (\omega_I/c_m)\hat{R}$, and we have taken the radiation field $E_{(s)}$ as the scattered field E_s. The factor $\exp[i(k_sR - \omega_I t)]/R$ represents the wave scattered from the origin 0 while $\exp[i(\mathbf{k_I} - \mathbf{k_s})\cdot\mathbf{r'}]$ is the phase factor which measures the interference between the wavelets emitted by different volume elements $d\mathbf{r'}$.

The phase integral $\int_v \exp(i\mathbf{K}\cdot\mathbf{r'})\,d\mathbf{r'}$ can be evaluated by considering the function $g(w) = (\sin w)/w$ which peaks sharply at $w = 0$ and goes to unity as $w \to 0$, as shown in Fig. 3.1.4. The function $g(w)$ dies off in an oscillatory fashion for increasing w with an envelope of w^{-1}. Lastovka (1967)

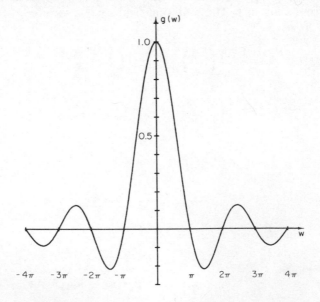

Fig. 3.1.4. A plot of the function $g(w) = (\sin w)/w$.

has approximated $g(w) = \sin w/w$ by a step function $g^*(w)$ with

$$g^*(w) = \begin{cases} 1 & -\Delta w \le w \le \Delta w \\ 0 & \text{otherwise} \end{cases} \quad (3.1.34)$$

The increment Δw is chosen by equating the areas under $g(w)$ and $g^*(w)$ such that the x, y, and z components of $\mathbf{K}$ satisfy the condition

$$\int_{-\infty}^{\infty} \frac{\sin w}{w}\, dw = \int_{-\pi/2}^{\pi/2} g^*(w)\, dw = \int_{-\pi/2}^{\pi/2} dw = \pi$$

If we choose the shape of the illuminated volume v to be a rectangular parallelepiped of dimensions L_x, L_y, and L_z, the integral as a function of $\mathbf{K}$ around $\mathbf{K} \simeq 0$ has the form

$$\int_{-\infty}^{\infty} dK_x\, dK_y\, dK_z \left\{ \int_v \exp(i\mathbf{K}\cdot\mathbf{r}')\, d\mathbf{r}' \right\}$$

$$= \int_{-\infty}^{\infty} dK_x\, dK_y\, dK_z v\, \frac{\sin(\tfrac{1}{2}K_xL_x)}{\tfrac{1}{2}K_xL_x}\, \frac{\sin(\tfrac{1}{2}K_yL_y)}{\tfrac{1}{2}K_yL_y}\, \frac{\sin(\tfrac{1}{2}K_zL_z)}{\tfrac{1}{2}K_zL_z}$$

$$= \frac{8v}{L_xL_yL_z} \int_{-\infty}^{\infty} \frac{\sin(\tfrac{1}{2}K_xL_x)}{\tfrac{1}{2}K_xL_x}\, d(\tfrac{1}{2}K_xL_x) \int_{-\infty}^{\infty} \frac{\sin(\tfrac{1}{2}K_yL_y)}{\tfrac{1}{2}K_yL_y}\, d(\tfrac{1}{2}K_yL_y)$$

$$\times \int_{-\infty}^{\infty} \frac{\sin(\tfrac{1}{2}K_zL_z)}{\tfrac{1}{2}K_zL_z}\, d(\tfrac{1}{2}K_zL_z)$$

$$= 8\pi^3 \quad (3.1.35)$$

or

$$\int_v \exp(i\mathbf{K}\cdot\mathbf{r}')\, d\mathbf{r}' = (2\pi)^3\delta(\mathbf{K}) \quad (3.1.36)$$

But for $\mathbf{K} \simeq 0$, we have

$$\int_{-\pi/L_x}^{\pi/L_x} dK_x \int_{-\pi/L_y}^{\pi/L_y} dK_y \int_{-\pi/L_z}^{\pi/L_z} dK_z = \frac{2\pi}{L_x} \times \frac{2\pi}{L_y} \times \frac{2\pi}{L_z} = \frac{8\pi^3}{v} \quad (3.1.37)$$

Thus,

$$\int_v \exp[i(\mathbf{k}_I - \mathbf{k}_s)\cdot\mathbf{r}']\, d\mathbf{r}'$$

$$= \begin{cases} v & \text{when} \begin{cases} -\pi/L_x \le (k_I - k_s + K)_x \le \pi/L_x \\ -\pi/L_y \le (k_I - k_s + K)_y \le \pi/L_y \\ -\pi/L_z \le (k_I - k_s + K)_z \le \pi/L_z \end{cases} \quad (3.1.38) \\ 0 & \text{otherwise} \end{cases}$$

From Eq. (3.1.38), we see that the radiation field observed at the point of observation $Q(\mathbf{R})$ comes from the plane wave components of $\Delta\chi_e$ having a wave vector $\mathbf{K}$. In other words, in order to get light scattered in the $\mathbf{k}_s$ direction, $\Delta\chi_e(\mathbf{r}', t)$ must have a Fourier component whose wave vector is such that the exponential factor in the phase integral is zero.

3.2. Fourier Decomposition of Susceptibility Fluctuations

Consideration of the phase integral (3.1.38) leads us to the realization that we must make a Fourier decomposition of the susceptibility fluctuations. More generally, we may write

$$P_\alpha = \epsilon_0 \chi_{e\alpha\beta} E_\beta \tag{3.2.1}$$

where $\chi_{e\alpha\beta}$ is the electric susceptibility tensor, i.e., the direction of the induced dipole and that of the external field may not be the same. In an isotropic medium, the electric susceptibility becomes a scalar quantity. The polarization field may also be expressed in terms of the polarizability α:

$$\mathbf{P} = N\mathbf{p} = N\epsilon_0 \alpha \mathbf{E}_{\text{eff}}$$

where N is the number of molecules per unit volume, and $\mathbf{E}_{\text{eff}}$ is the effective field which is the sum of the macroscopic external field and an internal field owing to the polarization of neighboring molecules. For example, in an isotropic medium, α is again a scalar and $\mathbf{E}_{\text{eff}} = \mathbf{E} + \mathbf{P}/3\epsilon_0$, which could lead to the Clausius–Messotti relation applicable to a wide class of solids and liquids.

In terms of a Fourier-series expansion, we have

$$\Delta\chi_e(\mathbf{r}, t) = \sum_K \Delta\chi_{eK}(t) \exp[i(\mathbf{K}\cdot\mathbf{r})] \tag{3.2.3}$$

where the allowed $\mathbf{K}$ values are found by applying the cyclic boundary conitions on the surface bounding v. For waves of different $\mathbf{K}$, we have from Eq. (3.1.38)

$$\int_v \exp[i(\mathbf{K}_1 - \mathbf{K}_2)\cdot\mathbf{r}']\, d\mathbf{r}' = v\delta(\mathbf{K}_1 - \mathbf{K}_2) \tag{3.2.4}$$

The Fourier amplitudes of $\Delta\chi_{eK}(t)$ can be obtained in terms of $\Delta\chi_e(\mathbf{r}, t)$:

$$\int_v \Delta\chi_e(\mathbf{r}', t) \exp(-i\mathbf{K}_2\cdot\mathbf{r}')\, d\mathbf{r}' = \int_v \sum_K \Delta\chi_{eK}(t) \exp(i\mathbf{K}\cdot\mathbf{r}')$$

$$\times \exp(-i\mathbf{K}_2\cdot\mathbf{r}')\, d\mathbf{r}'$$

$$= \int_v \sum_K \Delta\chi_{eK}(t) \exp[i(\mathbf{K} - \mathbf{K}_2)\cdot\mathbf{r}']\, d\mathbf{r}'$$

$$= \sum_K \Delta\chi_{eK}(t) v\delta(\mathbf{K} - \mathbf{K}_2)$$

$$= \Delta\chi_{eK_2}(t) v$$

or

$$\Delta\chi_{eK}(t) = (1/v) \int_v \Delta\chi_e(\mathbf{r}', t) \exp(-i\mathbf{K}\cdot\mathbf{r}')\, d\mathbf{r}' \qquad (3.2.5)$$

Since $\Delta\chi_e(\mathbf{r}, t)$ is real, we can rewrite Eq. (3.2.3) as a sum of explicitly real terms:

$$\Delta\chi_e(\mathbf{r}, t) = \tfrac{1}{2}[\Delta\chi_e(\mathbf{r}, t) + \Delta\chi_e^*(\mathbf{r}, t)]$$

$$= \tfrac{1}{2}[\sum_K \Delta\chi_{eK}(t) \exp(i\mathbf{K}\cdot\mathbf{r}) + \sum_K \Delta\chi_e^*(t) \exp(-i\mathbf{K}\cdot\mathbf{r})]$$

$$= \tfrac{1}{2} \sum_K [\Delta\chi_{eK}(t) \exp(i\mathbf{K}\cdot\mathbf{r}) + \Delta\chi_e^*(t) \exp(-i\mathbf{K}\cdot\mathbf{r})] \qquad (3.2.6)$$

By substituting Eq. (3.2.6) into (3.1.33), we get

$$\mathbf{E}_s \propto \tfrac{1}{2} \sum_K \Delta\chi_{eK}(t) \int_v \exp[i(\mathbf{k}_I - \mathbf{k}_s + \mathbf{K})\cdot\mathbf{r}']\, d\mathbf{r}'$$

$$+ \tfrac{1}{2} \sum_K \Delta\chi_{eK}^*(t) \int_v \exp[i(\mathbf{k}_I - \mathbf{k}_s - \mathbf{K})\cdot\mathbf{r}']\, d\mathbf{r}' \qquad (3.2.7)$$

From Eq. (3.2.4), we know that the first integral in Eq. (3.2.7) vanishes unless $\mathbf{K} = -(\mathbf{k}_I - \mathbf{k}_s)$. Similarly, for the second integral, we have $\mathbf{K} = +(\mathbf{k}_I - \mathbf{k}_s)$. Thus, the scattered electric field at $Q(R)$ is due to the plane-wave components of $\Delta\chi_e(\mathbf{r}, t)$ with wave vectors

$$\mathbf{K} = \pm(\mathbf{k}_I - \mathbf{k}_s) \qquad (3.2.8)$$

which agrees with our earlier conclusions of scattering from a traveling plane wave [Eqs. (3.1.14) and (3.1.15)]. By substituting Eqs. (3.2.7) and (3.2.8) into Eq. (3.1.33), we have

$$\mathbf{E}_s(\mathbf{R}, t) = \mathbf{k}_s \times (\mathbf{k}_s \times \mathbf{E}_{I}{}^0) \left(\frac{\epsilon_0}{\epsilon}\right) \{\exp[i(k_s R - \omega_I t)]/4\pi R\}$$

$$\times \tfrac{1}{2}v[\Delta\chi_{ek_I-k_s}{}^*(t) + \Delta\chi_{ek_s-k_I}(t)] \quad (3.2.9)$$

3.3. Intensity of Scattered Light

3.3.1. Poynting's Theorem

Poynting's theorem deals with energy and power relations in the electromagnetic field. If we take the scalar product of Eq. (2.1.4) with the electric field and integrate over a volume, we have

$$\int \mathbf{E}\cdot\mathbf{J}\, dv = \int \left(\mathbf{E}\cdot\nabla\times\mathbf{H} - \mathbf{E}\cdot\frac{\partial\mathbf{D}}{\partial t}\right) dv \quad (3.3.1)$$

Similarly, with Eq. (2.1.2), we have

$$\int \left(\mathbf{H}\cdot\nabla\times\mathbf{E} + \mathbf{H}\cdot\frac{\partial\mathbf{B}}{\partial t}\right) dv = 0 \quad (3.3.2)$$

By combining Eqs. (3.3.1) and (3.3.2), we get

$$-\int \mathbf{E}\cdot\mathbf{J}\, dv = \int (\mathbf{H}\cdot\nabla\times\mathbf{E} - \mathbf{E}\cdot\nabla\times\mathbf{H})\, dv + \int \left(\mathbf{H}\cdot\frac{\partial\mathbf{B}}{\partial t} + \mathbf{E}\cdot\frac{\partial\mathbf{D}}{\partial t}\right) dv$$

$$= \int \nabla\cdot(\mathbf{E}\times\mathbf{H})\, dv + \frac{1}{2}\int \frac{\partial}{\partial t}[(\mathbf{H}\cdot\mathbf{B}) + (\mathbf{E}\cdot\mathbf{D})]\, dv$$

$$= \int_S (\mathbf{E}\times\mathbf{H})\cdot d\mathbf{S} + \frac{1}{2}\int_v \frac{\partial}{\partial t}(\mathbf{H}\cdot\mathbf{B} + \mathbf{E}\cdot\mathbf{D})\, dv \quad (3.3.3)$$

since

$$\mathbf{H}\cdot\nabla\times\mathbf{E} - \mathbf{E}\cdot\nabla\times\mathbf{H} = \nabla\cdot(\mathbf{E}\times\mathbf{H})$$

and

$$\mathbf{H}\cdot\frac{\partial\mathbf{B}}{\partial t} + \mathbf{E}\cdot\frac{\partial\mathbf{D}}{\partial t} = \frac{1}{2}\frac{\partial}{\partial t}(\mathbf{H}\cdot\mathbf{B} + \mathbf{E}\cdot\mathbf{D})$$

Equation (3.3.3) is the Poynting theorem, which is a simple statement of conservation of energy. It means that the power being put into the system by the field on the sources within volume v is equal to the time rate at which energy is being stored in volume v plus the power which is flowing out through the surface S. The quantity

$$\mathbf{N} = \mathbf{E} \times \mathbf{H} \tag{3.3.4}$$

is known as the Poynting vector and has units of flux of power per unit area. The total scattered radiation can be obtained by integrating the time average of Poynting's vector over a sphere of large radius. Then the intensity of light scattered into the solid angle $d\Omega = \sin\vartheta \, d\vartheta \, d\phi$ around the field point $Q(\mathbf{R})$ as shown in Fig. 3.1.3 corresponds to the flow of power crossing a unit area along the direction of propagation $\mathbf{k}_s$:

$$I_s = \tfrac{1}{2} \operatorname{Re}\langle \mathbf{E}_s \times \mathbf{H}_s{}^* \rangle$$
$$= \tfrac{1}{2} \operatorname{Re}[\langle E_\vartheta H_\phi{}^* \rangle - \langle E_\phi H_\vartheta{}^* \rangle] \tag{3.3.5}$$

By substituting Eqs. (3.1.31) and (3.1.32) into Eq. (3.3.5), we get

$$I_s = \tfrac{1}{2} \operatorname{Re}\langle E_\vartheta H_\phi{}^* \rangle = \tfrac{1}{2}(\epsilon/\mu)^{1/2}\langle \mathbf{E}_s \cdot \mathbf{E}_s{}^* \rangle \tag{3.3.6}$$

It should be interesting to note that $(\mu/\epsilon)^{1/2}$ has the dimensions of resistance.

3.3.2. Scattered Intensity, Rayleigh Ratio, Turbidity

The quantity I_s represents the scattered intensity accepted by an element of the solid angle $d\Omega$ located at point $Q(\mathbf{R})$ with coordinates R, ϑ, ϕ. In Eq. (3.3.6), the factor $\tfrac{1}{2}$ occurs because the scattered fields and the incident waves are taken as complex. The incident intensity has the form

$$I_I = \tfrac{1}{2}(\epsilon/\mu)^{1/2} \, | E_I{}^0 |^2 \tag{3.3.7}$$

where I_I is the flow of power per unit area of the incoming light beam. By combining Eqs. (3.1.33), (3.3.6), and (3.3.7), we obtain for the scattered intensity

$$I_s = \frac{1}{2}\left(\frac{\epsilon}{\mu}\right)^{1/2} \frac{| \mathbf{k}_s \times (\mathbf{k}_s \times \mathbf{E}_I{}^0) |^2}{(4\pi R)^2}\left(\frac{\epsilon_0}{\epsilon}\right)^2$$

$$\times \left\langle \iint_v \Delta\chi_e(\mathbf{r}_1', t)\,\Delta\chi_e(\mathbf{r}_2', t)\,\exp[i(\mathbf{k}_I - \mathbf{k}_s)\cdot(\mathbf{r}_1' - \mathbf{r}_2')]\,d\mathbf{r}_1'\,d\mathbf{r}_2' \right\rangle$$

$$= I_I \frac{k_s{}^4 \sin^2\vartheta}{(4\pi R)^2}\left(\frac{\epsilon_0}{\epsilon}\right)^2 \iint_v \langle \Delta\chi_e(\mathbf{r}_1', t)\,\Delta\chi_e(\mathbf{r}_2', t) \rangle$$

$$\times \exp[i(\mathbf{k}_I - \mathbf{k}_s)\cdot(\mathbf{r}_1' - \mathbf{r}_2')]\,d\mathbf{r}_1'\,d\mathbf{r}_2' \tag{3.3.8}$$

With the far-field approximation, there is no scattering along the z axis, which is the direction of polarization of the incident wave. The $\sin^2 \vartheta$ angular dependence is characteristic of the dipole radiation.

We define the differential scattering cross section as the Rayleigh ratio:

$$\mathfrak{R} = I_s R^2 / I_I v \qquad (3.3.9)$$

where v is the scattering volume. The total scattering cross section, known as the turbidity τ^*, is related to the Rayleigh ratio by integration of $\mathfrak{R}$ over the whole solid angle. Then,

$$\tau^* = \int_\Omega \mathfrak{R} \, d\Omega(\vartheta, \phi) \qquad (3.3.10)$$

By substituting Eqs. (3.3.8) and (3.3.9) into Eq. (3.3.10), we have

$$\tau^* = \frac{k_s^4}{6\pi v} \left(\frac{\epsilon_0}{\epsilon}\right)^2 \iint_v \langle \Delta\chi_e(\mathbf{r}_1', t) \, \Delta\chi_e(\mathbf{r}_2', t) \rangle$$

$$\times \exp[i(\mathbf{k}_I - \mathbf{k}_s) \cdot (\mathbf{r}_1' - \mathbf{r}_2')] \, d\mathbf{r}_1' \, d\mathbf{r}_2' \quad (3.3.11)$$

where τ^* represents the total energy loss per second per scattering volume v and unit incident intensity. In the absence of absorption,

$$\tau^* = d^{-1} \ln(I_I/I_t) \qquad (3.3.12)$$

where I_t and d are the transmitted intensity and the optical path length through the scattering medium, respectively.

3.3.3. Thermal Fluctuations

The scattered intensity as expressed in Eq. (3.3.8) can be calculated if we know the behavior of local fluctuations of the electric susceptibility $\Delta\chi_e(\mathbf{r}, t)$. We shall limit our present discussion to the time and position dependence of $\Delta\chi_e(\mathbf{r}, t)$ arising from the thermal motions of molecules. These thermal motions or thermal fluctuations are local disturbances in the "thermodynamic" coordinates of the system about their respective equilibrium values. Thus, fluctuations in the electric susceptibility can be represented by statistical fluctuations in local density, temperature, pressure, entropy, etc. In general, changes in the electric susceptibility could also depend upon other effects, such as molecular orientation and vibrations. Coupling between fluctuations in these quantities and $\Delta\chi_e$ results in other light-scattering phenomena (Chu, 1970a). The Gaussian properties of hydrodynamic fluctuations and their relationship to the intensity correlation function of scattered light are discussed in Section 4.3.2.

In a one-component system, there are two independent thermodynamic variables such as (ρ_d, T), (P, T), and (V, T) pairs, which determine the thermodynamic state of the system. The symbols ρ_d, P, V, T denote the density, pressure, volume, and temperature of the system, respectively. In other words, if we know the values of two thermodynamic properties, then the values of all other thermodynamic properties of the closed homogeneous system are fixed. This does not mean that we know the values of all the other thermodynamic properties; rather, if we fix the values of any two of the properties and repeatedly measure the values of all other properties, we always get the same answers within the limits of experimental error.

Let us at the outset take the state variables as the entropy s and the pressure P, since thermal sound waves responsible for the Brillouin–Mandel'shtam components are *adiabatic pressure* disturbances. In this case, the fluctuations in the electric susceptibility are represented by local fluctuations in s and P around their equilibrium values s_0 and P_0, where s_0 and P_0 are the average entropy per unit volume and pressure of the system:

$$\Delta \chi_e(\mathbf{r}, t) = (\partial \chi_e / \partial s)_{P_0} [\Delta s_P(\mathbf{r}, t)] + (\partial \chi_e / \partial P)_{s_0} [\Delta P_s(\mathbf{r}, t)] \quad (3.3.13)$$

where $\Delta s_P(\mathbf{r}, t)$ are the local changes in entropy per unit volume from the equilibrium entropy per unit volume at constant pressure, and $\Delta P_s(\mathbf{r}, t)$ the local changes in pressure from the equilibrium pressure at constant entropy. The choice of s and P as the pair of state variables to represent the fluctuations in the electric susceptibility turns out to be an appropriate one. The problem then is to find the mean-square fluctuations in Δs_P and ΔP_s.

We need to evaluate $\langle \Delta \chi_e(\mathbf{r_1}', t) \Delta \chi_e(\mathbf{r_2}', t) \rangle$ in Eq. (3.3.8). By substituting Eq. (3.3.13) into $\langle \Delta \chi_e(\mathbf{r_1}', t) \Delta \chi_e(\mathbf{r_2}', t) \rangle$, we have

$$
\begin{aligned}
\langle \Delta \chi_e(\mathbf{r_1}', t) \Delta \chi_e(\mathbf{r_2}', t) \rangle = {} & (\partial \chi_e / \partial s)_{P_0}{}^2 \langle \Delta s_P(\mathbf{r_1}', t) \Delta s_P(\mathbf{r_2}', t) \rangle \\
& + (\partial \chi_e / \partial P)_{s_0} (\partial \chi_e / \partial s)_{P_0} [\langle \Delta P_s(\mathbf{r_1}', t) \Delta s_P(\mathbf{r_2}', t) \rangle \\
& + \langle \Delta s_P(\mathbf{r_1}', t) \Delta P_s(\mathbf{r_2}', t) \rangle] \\
& + (\partial \chi_e / \partial P)_{s_0}{}^2 \langle \Delta P_s(\mathbf{r_1}', t) \Delta P_s(\mathbf{r_2}', t) \rangle \quad (3.3.14)
\end{aligned}
$$

where Δs_P and ΔP_s are random functions of time and satisfy the ergodic hypothesis. Thus, the time average in the right-hand side of Eq. (3.3.14) is equivalent to an ensemble average in which the single sample is replaced by a large number of identical samples, and then the product

$$\Delta P_s(\mathbf{r_1}', t) \Delta P_s(\mathbf{r_2}', t)$$

is computed for each member of the ensemble. Now the time t is of no consequence:

$$\langle \Delta\chi_e(\mathbf{r_1}', t)\,\Delta\chi_e(\mathbf{r_2}', t) \rangle = (\partial\chi_e/\partial s)_{P_0}{}^2\overline{\Delta s_P(\mathbf{r_1}', t)\,\Delta s_P(\mathbf{r_2}', t)}$$

$$+ (\partial\chi_e/\partial P)_{s_0}(\partial\chi_e/\partial s)_{P_0}$$

$$\times\left[\overline{\Delta P_s(\mathbf{r_1}', t)\,\Delta s_P(\mathbf{r_2}', t)} + \overline{\Delta s_P(\mathbf{r_1}', t)\,\Delta P_s(\mathbf{r_2}', t)}\right]$$

$$+ (\partial\chi_e/\partial P)_{s_0}{}^2\overline{\Delta P_s(\mathbf{r_1}', t)\,\Delta P_s(\mathbf{r_2}', t)} \qquad (3.3.15)$$

Lastovka (1967) has further argued that the statistical or thermodynamic averages of an isotropic medium are independent of the origins of space coordinates as well as time. So the correlation function which is the average value of the product of two simultaneous fluctuations of a thermodynamic variable can only be a function of the separation distance between the two fluctuations at $\mathbf{r_1}'$ and $\mathbf{r_2}'$. Then

$$\overline{\Delta s_P(\mathbf{r_1}', t)\,\Delta s_P(\mathbf{r_2}', t)} = \overline{\Delta s_P(\mathbf{r_1}' - \mathbf{r_2}', 0)\,\Delta s_P(0, 0)}$$

$$= f(|\,\mathbf{r_1}' - \mathbf{r_2}'\,|) \qquad (3.3.16)$$

$$\overline{\Delta P_0(\mathbf{r_1}', t)\,\Delta P_s(\mathbf{r_2}', t)} = \overline{\Delta P_s(\mathbf{r_1}' - \mathbf{r_2}', 0)\,\Delta P_s(0, 0)}$$

$$= g(|\,\mathbf{r_1}' - \mathbf{r_2}'\,|) \qquad (3.3.17)$$

are the spatial correlation functions for fluctuations in Δs_P and ΔP_s, respectively. The spatial correlation function is a mathematical representation of the extension of local fluctuations in a system. The normalized spatial correlation function for entropy and pressure fluctuations may be defined as

$$F(\rho_r, 0) = \overline{\Delta s_P(\rho_r, 0)\,\Delta s_P(0, 0)}/\overline{\Delta s_P^2(0, 0)} \qquad (3.3.18)$$

$$G(\rho_r, 0) = \overline{\Delta P_s(\rho_r, 0)\,\Delta P_s(0, 0)}/\overline{\Delta P_s^2(0, 0)} \qquad (3.3.19)$$

More generally, the isotropic spatial correlation function has the form (Chu, 1967, 1970b)

$$C(\rho_r, 0) = \overline{\Delta_1\Delta_2}/\overline{\Delta^2} \qquad (3.3.20)$$

where Δ_i represents the local fluctuations in a random process at point $\mathbf{r_i}'$, and ρ_r is the distance between points $\mathbf{r_1}'$ and $\mathbf{r_2}'$. The bar indicates an equilibrium ensemble average. The local deviations from its equilibrium value Δ could mean fluctuations in pressure P, entropy per unit volume s, concentration C, dielectric constant κ_e, electric field $\mathbf{E}$, etc., depending upon the problem of interest. Physically we may interpret the correlation function as follows.

Let us imagine that we can measure the *instantaneous* dielectric constant on a line passing through the interior of a liquid, as shown schematically in Fig. 3.3.1. The quantity $\Delta_1\Delta_2$ represents a product of local fluctuations

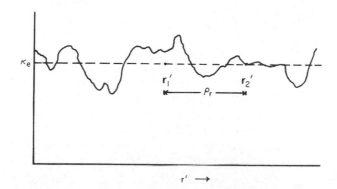

Fig. 3.3.1. Instantaneous dielectric constant as a function of separation distance ρ_r.

measured at r_1' and r_2' at a distance ρ_r ($\varrho_r = r_1' - r_2'$) apart. We may consider Δ_1 and Δ_2 as the observed local fluctuations measured at the two ends 1 and 2, located at r_1' and r_2' respectively, of a stick with length ρ_r. The ensemble average is obtained by throwing the stick at random into the liquid so as to allow the stick to take up all possible orientations and positions. The average square of the local fluctuations Δ^2 corresponds to the ensemble average of the local fluctuations measured with a stick of zero length. $C(\rho_r, 0)$ starts with 1 when $\rho_r = 0$, which corresponds to perfect correlation, and eventually approaches zero for large values of ρ_r when the fluctuations at r_1' and at r_2' are statistically independent because molecular interactions decrease with increasing distance. The correlation curve from a plot of $C(\rho_r, 0)$ vs ρ_r can have different shapes. We shall drop the zero in $C(\rho_r, 0)$.

Both $F(\rho_r)$ and $G(\rho_r)$ decrease rapidly to zero as ρ_r increases beyond correlation ranges r_s and r_P which are determined by the range of molecular pair-correlation functions. In a liquid, angular distribution of scattered x-ray intensity shows that the intermolecular distance is small when compared to the wavelength of visible light, so that we may set

$$\exp[i(\mathbf{k_I} - \mathbf{k_s}) \cdot (\mathbf{r_1}' - \mathbf{r_2}')] = \exp[i(\mathbf{k_I} - \mathbf{k_s}) \cdot \boldsymbol{\varrho}_r] \approx 1 \quad (3.3.21)$$

in Eq. (3.3.8). Then, by combining Eqs. (3.3.8) and (3.3.15)–(3.3.19) we have for the scattered intensity

$$I_s(\mathbf{R}) = I_I \frac{k_s^4 \sin^2 \vartheta}{(4\pi R)^2} \left(\frac{\epsilon_0}{\epsilon}\right)^2 v \left[\left(\frac{\partial \chi_e}{\partial s}\right)_{P_0}^2 \overline{\Delta s_P^2} v_F^* + \left(\frac{\partial \chi_e}{\partial P}\right)_{s_0}^2 \overline{\Delta P_s^2} v_G^*\right] \quad (3.3.22)$$

where v_F^* and v_G^* are the correlation volumes with

$$v_F^* = 4\pi \int_0^\infty \rho_r^2 F(\rho_r) \, d\rho_r \quad (3.3.23)$$

and

$$v_G{}^* = 4\pi \int_0 \rho_r{}^2 G(\rho_r) \, d\rho_r \qquad (3.3.24)$$

The correlation volumes represent the persistence of the regions over which essentially uniform fluctuations in Δs_P and ΔP_s take place. We have dropped out the cross terms involving $\Delta P_s(\mathbf{r}_1, t)\,\Delta s_P(\mathbf{r}_2, t)$ and $\Delta s_P(\mathbf{r}_1, t)\,\Delta P_s(\mathbf{r}_2, t)$ since the variables P and s are statistically independent. What do we mean by the statement of statistical independence? We shall discuss this question toward the end of the section. We may also take the density ρ_d and the temperature T as the state variables. Then, the fluctuations in the electric susceptibility are represented by local fluctuations in ρ_d and T around the average equilibrium values $\rho_{d,0}$ and T_0 of the system:

$$\Delta\chi_e(\mathbf{r}, t) = \left(\frac{\partial\chi_e}{\partial\rho_d}\right)_{T_0} [\Delta\rho_d(\mathbf{r}, t)] + \left(\frac{\partial\chi_e}{\partial T}\right)_{\rho_{d,0}} [\Delta T(\mathbf{r}, t)] \quad (3.3.25)$$

where $\Delta\rho_d(\mathbf{r}, t)$ are the local changes in density from the equilibrium density at constant temperature, and ΔT the local changes in temperature from the equilibrium temperature at constant density. Similarly, as in Eq. (3.3.15), we may write

$$\langle \Delta\chi_e(\mathbf{r}_1', t)\,\Delta\chi_e(\mathbf{r}_2', t) \rangle = \left(\frac{\partial\chi_e}{\partial\rho_d}\right)_{T_0}^2 \overline{\Delta\rho_d(\mathbf{r}_1', t)\,\Delta\rho_d(\mathbf{r}_2', t)}$$

$$+ \left(\frac{\partial\chi_e}{\partial\rho_d}\right)_{T_0} \left(\frac{\partial\chi_e}{\partial T}\right)_{\rho_{d,0}}$$

$$\times \left[\overline{\Delta\rho_d(\mathbf{r}_1', t)\,\Delta T(\mathbf{r}_2', t)} + \overline{\Delta\rho_d(\mathbf{r}_2', t)\,\Delta T(\mathbf{r}_1', t)} \right]$$

$$+ \left(\frac{\partial\chi_e}{\partial T}\right)_{\rho_{d,0}}^2 \overline{\Delta T(\mathbf{r}_1', t)\,\Delta T(\mathbf{r}_2', t)}$$

$$= \left(\frac{\partial\chi_e}{\partial\rho_d}\right)_{T_0}^2 \overline{\Delta\rho_d{}^2(0)}\,M(\rho_r) + \left(\frac{\partial\chi_e}{\partial T}\right)_{\rho_{d,0}}^2 \overline{\Delta T^2(0)}\,N(\rho_r)$$

$$+ \text{ cross terms} \qquad (3.3.26)$$

where

$$M(\rho_r, 0) = \overline{\Delta\rho_d(\rho_r)\,\Delta\rho_d(0)} \big/ \overline{\Delta\rho_d{}^2(0)} \qquad (3.3.27)$$

and

$$N(\rho_r, 0) = \overline{\Delta T(\rho_r)\,\Delta T(0)} \big/ \overline{\Delta T^2(0)} \qquad (3.3.28)$$

The computation of the mean-square fluctuations of the density and the temperature was first accomplished by Einstein (1910). We shall follow the discussions presented by Landau and Lifshitz (1958). In order to calculate the mean-square deviations from the average values of the density and temperature, we are confronted with the problem of finding the probability distribution of those deviations. At constant temperature and volume, the probability of having a fluctuation from the average value of those properties is related to the Helmholtz free-energy fluctuations.

For small deviations about the average, we can expand the Helmholtz free energy $A(x)$ in a Taylor series expansion:

$$A(x) = A(\bar{x}) + (1/2!)(\partial^2 A/\partial x^2)_{x=\bar{x}}(x - \bar{x})^2 + \cdots \quad (3.3.29)$$

where $(\partial A/\partial x)_{x=\bar{x}} = 0$, since the equilibrium Helmholtz free energy is a minimum under the specified constraints and x is a physical quantity such as temperature. By neglecting higher-order terms, we can identify the fluctuations in A as

$$\delta A(x) = \tfrac{1}{2}(\partial^2 A/\partial x^2)_{x=\bar{x}}(\delta x)^2 \quad (3.3.30)$$

If x follows a Gaussian distribution, the mean-square fluctuation of x is

$$\overline{x^2} = (\beta/2\pi)^{1/2} \int_{-\infty}^{\infty} x^2 \exp(-\tfrac{1}{2}\beta x^2) \, dx = 1/\beta \quad (3.3.31)$$

where $\beta = (\partial^2 A/\partial x^2)_{x=\bar{x}}/kT$ and we have set $\bar{x} = 0$ so that $\delta x = x - \bar{x} = x$. The normalization constant $(\beta/2\pi)^{1/2}$ is given by the condition

$$\left(\frac{\beta}{2\pi}\right)^{1/2} \int_{-\infty}^{\infty} \exp(-\tfrac{1}{2}\beta x^2) \, dx = 1 \quad (3.3.32)$$

so the Gaussian distribution can be expressed as

$$w(x) \, dx = (2\pi\overline{x^2})^{-1/2} \exp(-x^2/2\overline{x^2}) \, dx \quad (3.3.33)$$

The Gaussian function has moments of all orders:

$$\overline{x^0} \equiv \int_{-\infty}^{\infty} w(x) \, dx = 1, \qquad \overline{x^1} \equiv \int_{-\infty}^{\infty} xw(x) \, dx = 0$$

$$\overline{x^2} \equiv \int_{-\infty}^{\infty} x^2 w(x) \, dx = 1/\beta, \qquad \overline{x^3} \equiv \int_{-\infty}^{\infty} x^3 w(x) \, dx = 0$$

$$\overline{x^4} \equiv \int_{-\infty}^{\infty} x^4 w(x) \, dx = 3/\beta^2, \qquad \overline{x^5} \equiv \int_{-\infty}^{\infty} x^5 w(x) \, dx = 0, \ldots$$

The local changes in the Helmholtz free energy of a fluctuation could be expressed in terms of fluctuations in density and temperature. It turns out that the terms involving ΔT are small compared with the term involving $\Delta \rho_d$. By neglecting higher-order terms, we have

$$\delta A = \tfrac{1}{2}(\partial^2 A/\partial \rho_d{}^2)_0(\Delta \rho_d)^2 \qquad (3.3.34)$$

where the subscript 0 denotes equilibrium values. The mean-square value of $(\Delta \rho_d)^2$ at a single point in the medium can be obtained from the second moment of the Gaussian function:

$$\overline{(\Delta \rho_d)^2} = \frac{1}{\beta} = \frac{kT}{(\partial^2 A/\partial \rho_d{}^2)_0} \qquad (3.3.35)$$

From thermodynamics, we know $(\partial A/\partial V)_T = -P$. If we let $V = \text{const}/\rho_d$, then

$$(\partial A/\partial \rho_d)_T = \text{const } P/\rho_d{}^2 \qquad (3.3.36)$$

and

$$(\partial^2 A/\partial \rho_d{}^2)_T = V/\rho_d{}^2 K_T \qquad (3.3.37)$$

where $K_T \left[= (\partial \rho_d/\partial P)_T/\rho_d = -(\partial V/\partial P)_T/V \right]$ is the isothermal compressibility. Substituting Eq. (3.3.37) into (3.3.35), we obtain the mean-square amplitude of the density fluctuations at a single point in the medium:

$$\overline{(\Delta \rho_d)^2} = kTK_T \rho_d{}^2/v_M{}^* \qquad (3.3.38)$$

Thus, in the absence of correlations, and with negligibly small temperature fluctuations, we get

$$\langle \Delta \chi_e(\mathbf{r}_1, t)\, \Delta \chi_e(\mathbf{r}_2, t) \rangle = (\partial \chi_e/\partial \rho_d)_0{}^2 \overline{(\Delta \rho_d)^2} v_M{}^*$$

$$+ \text{ negligible temperature terms}$$

$$\approx (\partial \chi_e/\partial \rho_d)_0{}^2 kTK_T \rho_d{}^2 \qquad (3.3.39)$$

With Eqs. (3.3.39) and (3.3.22), where the thermodynamic variables have been changed to ρ_d and T instead of s and P, we get the differential scattering cross section due to only *density fluctuations*:

$$\mathcal{R} = \frac{I_s R^2}{I_I v} = \frac{k_s{}^4 \sin^2 \vartheta}{16\pi^2} \left(\frac{\epsilon_0}{\epsilon}\right)^2 \left(\frac{\partial \chi_e}{\partial \rho_d}\right)_0^2 \rho_d{}^2 kTK_T \qquad (3.3.40)$$

Equation (3.3.40) was first derived by Einstein (1910). In Einstein's formula, the scattered intensity is independent of the angle of observation θ if the polarized incident light has its electric field vector perpendicular to the plane of observation.

We shall now proceed to calculate the mean-square fluctuations of the fundamental thermodynamic quantities pertaining to a part of the system in a more general way (Benedek, 1968). Subsystem I is small compared to the whole, yet it is large enough to contain a sufficient number of molecules, so it is a macroscopic body. Subsystem I is subject to continuous interaction of the remaining parts of the system II that is the medium. From the second law of thermodynamics, subsystem I is in a state of equilibrium if (Kirkwood and Oppenheim, 1961)

$$dS_I \leq \delta q_I / T_0 \tag{3.3.41}$$

where T_0 is the uniform temperature of medium II and δq_I is the heat absorbed by the subsystem. For systems with only PV work, $\delta q_I = \delta E_2 + p\delta V_I$, so we have

$$\delta E_I + P_0 \delta V_I - T_0 \delta S_I \geq 0 \tag{3.3.42}$$

Equation (3.3.42) is the general criterion of equilibrium for closed systems. The criterion of equilibrium for a closed system at constant energy E and volume V is

$$(\delta S_I)_{E,V} \leq 0 \tag{3.3.43}$$

The subsystem may be considered as a quasiclosed system, and it interacts in various ways with the medium of the system in a complex and intricate manner. From Eq. (3.3.42), we take the probability for finding the system w_I in a state which may be reached reversibly from the equilibrium state to the nonequilibrium state by performing a minimum amount of work δW_{min} such that

$$w_I = \text{const} \exp[-(\delta W_{min}/kT)] \tag{3.3.44}$$

where $\delta W_{min} = \delta E_I + P\delta V_I - T\delta S_I$ and δ denotes deviation from the equilibrium value.

The difference in energy between states in a continuous change can be expanded in a Taylor's series in the form

$$\delta E = \left(\frac{\partial E}{\partial V}\right)_S \delta V + \left(\frac{\partial E}{\partial S}\right)_V \delta S + \frac{1}{2}\left[\left(\frac{\partial^2 E}{\partial S^2}\right)_V (\delta S)^2 + \left(\frac{\partial^2 E}{\partial V^2}\right)_S (\delta V)^2 \right.$$

$$\left. + 2\left(\frac{\partial^2 E}{\partial S\, \partial V}\right) \delta S\, \delta V\right] + \text{higher-order terms} \tag{3.3.45}$$

From thermodynamics, we have

$$\left(\frac{\partial E}{\partial V}\right)_S = -P_0 \quad \text{and} \quad \left(\frac{\partial E}{\partial S}\right)_V = T_0 \tag{3.3.46}$$

where the subscripts denote evaluation of the coefficients at equilibrium values of the thermodynamic quantities. T_0 and P_0 refer to the equilibrium property of the entire system. However, for simplicity, we shall drop the subscript zero from now on.

By combining Eqs. (3.3.45) and (3.3.46), we get

$$\delta E_I + P\,\delta V_I - T\,\delta S_I$$

$$= \frac{1}{2}\left[\left(\frac{\partial^2 E}{\partial S^2}\right)_V (\delta S)^2 + \left(\frac{\partial^2 E}{\partial V^2}\right)_S (\delta V)^2 + 2\left(\frac{\partial^2 E}{\partial V\,\partial S}\right)\delta S\,\delta V\right]_I \quad (3.3.47)$$

where we have neglected higher-order terms. The right-hand side of Eq. (3.3.47) can be simplified. In particular, we want to eliminate the cross term involving $\delta S\,\delta V$ by choosing two statistically independent thermodynamic variables such as T and V. With the use of Eq. (3.3.46), we get

$$\left(\frac{\partial^2 E}{\partial V^2}\right)_S = -\left(\frac{\partial P}{\partial V}\right)_S,\qquad \left(\frac{\partial^2 E}{\partial S^2}\right)_V = \left(\frac{\partial T}{\partial S}\right)_V \quad (3.3.48)$$

and

$$\left(\frac{\partial^2 E}{\partial S\,\partial V}\right) = \left(\frac{\partial T}{\partial V}\right)_S = -\left(\frac{\partial P}{\partial S}\right)_V \quad (3.3.49)$$

With

$$\delta S = \left(\frac{\partial S}{\partial V}\right)_T \delta V + \left(\frac{\partial S}{\partial T}\right)_V \delta T \quad (3.3.50)$$

we then have

$$\left(\frac{\partial^2 E}{\partial S^2}\right)_V (\delta S)^2 + \left(\frac{\partial^2 E}{\partial V^2}\right)_S (\delta V)^2 + 2\left(\frac{\partial^2 E}{\partial V\,\partial S}\right)\delta S\,\delta V$$

$$= \left(\frac{\partial S}{\partial T}\right)_V (\delta T)^2 + 2\left(\frac{\partial S}{\partial V}\right)_T \delta V\,\delta T + \left(\frac{\partial S}{\partial V}\right)_T^2 \left(\frac{\partial T}{\partial S}\right)_V (\delta V)^2$$

$$- \left(\frac{\partial P}{\partial V}\right)_S (\delta V)^2 + 2\left(\frac{\partial T}{\partial V}\right)_S \left(\frac{\partial S}{\partial T}\right)_V \delta T\,\delta V - 2\left(\frac{\partial P}{\partial S}\right)_V \left(\frac{\partial S}{\partial V}\right)_T (\delta V)^2$$

$$(3.3.51)$$

Since $(\partial T/\partial V)_S\,(\partial S/\partial T)_V\,(\partial V/\partial S)_T = -1$, the cross term is zero. Therefore, V and T are indeed statistically independent Gaussian random variables. The term involving the mean-square fluctuations in V can be simplified by utilizing the relation

$$\left(\frac{\partial P}{\partial V}\right)_T = \left(\frac{\partial P}{\partial V}\right)_S + \left(\frac{\partial P}{\partial S}\right)_V \left(\frac{\partial S}{\partial V}\right)_T \quad (3.3.52)$$

More specifically, we have

$$
\left(\frac{\partial S}{\partial V}\right)_T^2 \left(\frac{\partial T}{\partial S}\right)_V - 2\left(\frac{\partial P}{\partial S}\right)_V \left(\frac{\partial S}{\partial V}\right)_T - \left(\frac{\partial P}{\partial V}\right)_S
$$

$$
= -\left(\frac{\partial S}{\partial V}\right)_T \left(\frac{\partial T}{\partial V}\right)_S - 2\left(\frac{\partial P}{\partial S}\right)_V \left(\frac{\partial S}{\partial V}\right)_T - \left(\frac{\partial P}{\partial V}\right)_S
$$

$$
= -\left(\frac{\partial P}{\partial V}\right)_S - \left(\frac{\partial P}{\partial S}\right)_V \left(\frac{\partial S}{\partial V}\right)_T = -\left(\frac{\partial P}{\partial V}\right)_T \qquad (3.3.53)
$$

By definition,

$$
C_V = T\left(\frac{\partial S}{\partial T}\right)_V \quad \text{and} \quad K_T = -\frac{1}{V}\left(\frac{\partial V}{\partial P}\right)_T
$$

We then get

$$
w_1(\delta V, \delta T)\, d(\delta V)\, d(\delta T)
$$

$$
= \text{const} \exp\left[\left(-\frac{1}{VK_T}(\delta V)^2 - \frac{C_V}{T}(\delta T)^2\right)_I \Big/ 2kT\right] d(\delta V)\, d(\delta T)
$$

$$
(3.3.54)
$$

From Eq. (3.3.54) we can obtain the mean-square values of $(\delta V)^2$ and $(\delta T)^2$ for the *subsystem*:

$$
\overline{(\delta V)^2} = \frac{\displaystyle\int_{-\infty}^{\infty}(\delta V)^2 w_I(\delta V,\,\delta T)\, d(\delta V)\, d(\delta T)}{\displaystyle\int_{-\infty}^{\infty} w_I(\delta V,\,\delta T)\, d(\delta V)\, d(\delta T)} = kTK_T v_M^* \qquad (3.3.55)
$$

and

$$
\overline{(\delta T)^2} = kT^2/C_{V,\mathrm{I}} \qquad (3.3.56)
$$

where $C_{V,\mathrm{I}}$ is the specific heat at constant volume in the subsystem. Now the fluctuations spread throughout the medium, so we regard the medium as made up of many small subsystems. The minimum work done by all the subsystems is the sum of $\delta W_{\min}$ over the entire set of subsystems. Then,

$$
W_{\min} = \int_v \delta W_{\min}\, dv \qquad (3.3.57)
$$

With $(\delta V/V)^2 = (\delta \rho_d/\rho_d)^2$, we have for the differential scattering cross section of a dielectric medium due to density and temperature fluctuations:

$$\Re = \frac{k_s^4 \sin^2 \vartheta}{16\pi^2} \left(\frac{\epsilon_0}{\epsilon}\right)^2 \left[\rho_d^2 \left(\frac{\partial \chi_e}{\partial \rho_d}\right)_T^2 kTK_T + \left(\frac{\partial \chi_e}{\partial T}\right)_{\rho_d}^2 \frac{kT^2}{C_V'} \right] \quad (3.3.58)$$

The first term on the right-hand side of Eq. (3.3.58) corresponds to Eq. (3.3.40), where we have neglected the temperature fluctuations, and C_V' is the specific heat at constant volume per unit volume.

Instead of V and T, we can choose P and S as the two independent thermodynamic variables. The derivation, using a slightly different approach, has been presented by Benedek (1968). The $\Delta S \, \Delta P$ cross term is again zero, showing that S and P are independent Gaussian random variables. The differential scattering cross section of a dielectric medium due to entropy and pressure fluctuations is given by

$$\Re = \frac{k_s^4 \sin^2 \vartheta}{16\pi^2} \left(\frac{\epsilon_0}{\epsilon}\right)^2 \left[\left(\frac{\partial \chi_e}{\partial s}\right)_P^2 kC_P' + \left(\frac{\partial \chi_e}{\partial P}\right)_s^2 \frac{kT}{K_S} \right] \quad (3.3.59)$$

where C_P' is the specific heat at constant pressure per unit volume and $K_S \left[= -(1/V)(\partial V/\partial P)_s \right]$ is the adiabatic compressibility. It should be noted that we may define the isothermal bulk modulus as $-V(\partial P/\partial V)_T$ and the adiabatic bulk modulus as $-V(\partial P/\partial V)_S$. Equation (3.3.59) is again independent of the direction of observation except for the dipole radiation factor $\sin^2 \vartheta$, because we have assumed rapidly decreasing $F(\rho_r)$ and $G(\rho_r)$ as ρ_r increases beyond correlation ranges r_s and r_P.

The Rayleigh ratio may also be defined as (Lastovka, 1967)

$$\Re^* = \Re_s^* + \Re_P^* = (R^2/vI_{\mathrm{I}}) \left[(2\pi)^{-1} \int_0^{2\pi} I_s(\theta = 90°, \phi, \vartheta) \, d\vartheta \right] \quad (3.3.60)$$

which differs from our definition in Eq. (3.3.9). Then, with

$$\frac{1}{2\pi} \int_0^{2\pi} \sin^2 \vartheta \, d\vartheta = \frac{1}{2\pi} \left[-\tfrac{1}{2} \cos \vartheta \sin \vartheta + \tfrac{1}{2}\vartheta \ \right]_0^{2\pi} = \frac{1}{2\pi} \left[\pi \right] = \frac{1}{2}$$

we have

$$\Re_s^* = \left(\frac{\omega_{\mathrm{I}}}{c_0}\right)^4 \frac{1}{2(4\pi)^2} \left(\frac{\partial \chi_e}{\partial s}\right)_P^2 kC_P' \quad (3.3.61)$$

and

$$\Re_P^* = \left(\frac{\omega_{\mathrm{I}}}{c_0}\right)^4 \frac{1}{2(4\pi)^2} \left(\frac{\partial \chi_e}{\partial P}\right)_s^2 \frac{kT}{K_S} \quad (3.3.62)$$

From Eq. (3.3.59), if we take $\vartheta = 90°$, i.e., polarization perpendicular to the plane of observation, we have

$$\mathcal{R}_s = \left(\frac{\omega_I}{c_0}\right)^4 \frac{1}{(4\pi)^2} \left(\frac{\partial \chi_e}{\partial s}\right)_P^2 kC_P{}'$$

(3.3.63)

and

$$\mathcal{R}_P = \left(\frac{\omega_I}{c_0}\right)^4 \frac{1}{(4\pi)^2} \left(\frac{\partial \chi_e}{\partial P}\right)_s^2 \frac{kT}{K_S}$$

(3.3.64)

where we have used $\epsilon = \epsilon_0(1 + \langle \chi_e \rangle)$ and $\kappa_e = n^2$. Equations (3.3.61)–(3.3.64) differ by a factor of $\frac{1}{2}$, so we should be careful in our understanding of them.

We may express the scattered intensity in terms of $\mathcal{R}$ or $\mathcal{R}^*$:

$$I_s(\mathbf{R}) = \frac{I_I v}{R^2} \mathcal{R} = \frac{2I_I v}{R^2} \mathcal{R}^* \sin^2 \vartheta$$

(3.3.65)

By writing $A \times L =$ area of illuminated beam $\times$ length of beam = volume of illuminated region = v, we have for the power scattered into a solid angle Ω

$$P = 2P_I \mathcal{R}^* L(\sin^2 \vartheta)\Omega = P_I \mathcal{R} \Omega L$$

(3.3.66)

Thus, $\mathcal{R}$ is related to the fraction of the incident power P_I scattered into a solid angle Ω per unit length of the scattering volume.

3.3.4. Evaluation of Rayleigh's Ratio

The Rayleigh ratio can be estimated using Eqs. (3.3.61)–(3.3.64). With $n^2 = 1 + \langle \chi_e \rangle$, Lastovka (1967) has obtained the desired suscepti-bility derivatives in terms of the more readily measurable quantities $(\partial n/\partial P)_T$ and $(\partial n/\partial T)_P$:

$$\left(\frac{\partial \chi_e}{\partial s}\right)_P = \left(\frac{\partial n^2}{\partial s}\right)_P = 2n \left(\frac{\partial n}{\partial s}\right)_P = 2n \left(\frac{\partial n}{\partial T}\right)_P \left(\frac{\partial T}{\partial s}\right)_P$$

$$= 2n \left(\frac{T}{C_P{}'}\right) \left(\frac{\partial n}{\partial T}\right)_P = 2n \left(\frac{T}{\rho_d C_P{}^*}\right) \left(\frac{\partial n}{\partial T}\right)_P$$

(3.3.67)

where $C_P^* \left[= (T/\rho_d)(\partial s/\partial T)_P\right]$ is the specific heat at constant pressure per unit mass.

Similarly,

$$\left(\frac{\partial \chi_e}{\partial P}\right)_s = 2n \left[\left(\frac{T\alpha}{\rho_d C_P{}^*}\right) \left(\frac{\partial n}{\partial T}\right)_P + \left(\frac{\partial n}{\partial P}\right)_T\right]$$

(3.3.68)

Table 3.3.1

Computed Rayleigh ratios $\mathcal{R}_s^*$ and $\mathcal{R}_P^*$ for some liquids[a,b]

	H_2O	CS_2	Benzene	CCl_4	Toluene
ρ_d (gm/cm³)	1.00	1.263	0.879	1.595	0.867
n_{air}^T	1.3318	1.6232	1.4975	1.458	1.4925
C_P^* (J/gm °C)	4.185	0.994	1.699	0.841	1.673
$(\partial n/\partial T)_P^c$ (°C⁻¹)	-0.79×10^{-4}	-8.0×10^{-4}	-6.45×10^{-4}	-5.0×10^{-4}	-5.8×10^{-4}
K_S^{-1} (dyn/cm²)	2.23×10^{10}	1.69×10^{10}	1.52×10^{10}	1.41×10^{10}	1.503×10^{10}
$(\partial n/\partial P)_T^c$ (cm²/dyn)	1.50×10^{-11}	6.50×10^{-11}	5.03×10^{-11}	—	—
α (°C⁻¹)	0.207×10^{-3}	1.218×10^{-3}	1.237×10^{-3}	1.236×10^{-3}	—
$2\mathcal{R}_s^*$ (cm⁻¹)	0.0077×10^{-6}	3.92×10^{-6}	1.82×10^{-6}	1.17×10^{-6}	0.79×10^{-6}
$2\mathcal{R}_P^*$ (cm⁻¹)	0.87×10^{-6}	7.92×10^{-6}	4.07×10^{-6}	—	—
$\mathcal{R}_{total}^*$ (cm⁻¹)	0.44×10^{-6}	5.92×10^{-6}	2.95×10^{-6}	—	—
$(\mathcal{R}_{total}^* C_d)^d$ (cm⁻¹)	0.53×10^{-6}	38×10^{-6}	8.3×10^{-6}	—	—
$(2\mathcal{R}_{total}^*)_{expt}^e$ (cm⁻¹)	—	—	16.3×10^{-6}	5.88×10^{-6}	—

[a] $T = 20°C$; $P = 1$ atm; $\lambda_{air} = 632.8$ nm; $\vartheta = \frac{1}{2}\pi$.

[b] Lastovka, 1967.

[c] Measured at $\lambda_{air} = 589.3$ nm.

[d] The depolarization factor $C_d = (6 + 6\rho_u)/(6 - 7\rho_u)$. H_2O: $\rho_u = 0.088$, $C_d = 1.2$; benzene: $\rho_u = 0.42 \pm 0.02$, $C_d = 2.8 \pm 0.2$; CS_2: $\rho_u = 0.64 \pm 0.02$, $C_d = 6.5 \pm 0.7$ (Fabelinskii, I. L., 1965).

[e] Carr and Zimm, 1950. $\lambda_{air} = 546$ nm; $T = 25°C$.

where α $[=(1/V)(\partial V/\partial T)_P]$ is the thermal coefficient of expansion. Table 3.3.1 shows values of the susceptibility derivations and Rayleigh's ratio $\mathcal{R}^*$ for some typical liquids; all are computed at 20°C and 1 atm. Fabelinskii (1957) has reviewed the experimental data for $\mathcal{R}^*$ made before 1957. It should be noted that our computed Rayleigh's ratio according to Eqs. (3.3.61) and (3.3.62) or (3.3.63) and (3.3.04) has not included depolarization. The depolarization factor C_d almost always involves large uncertainties since depolarization is difficult to measure. Furthermore, we have used the adiabatic compressibility K_S from ultrasonic measurements. In fact, we need K_S in the hypersonic region.

3.4. Spectrum of Scattered Light

While the intensity of scattered light provides information on the mean-square amplitude of local fluctuations in the thermodynamic variables, the spectrum of scattered light tells us something about the time dependence of the fluctuations in the electric susceptibility $\Delta\chi_e(\mathbf{r}, t)$. By means of

$$\Delta\chi_e(\mathbf{r}, t) = \tfrac{1}{2}[\sum_K \Delta\chi_{eK}(t) \exp(i\mathbf{K}\cdot\mathbf{r}) + \sum_K \Delta\chi_{eK}{}^* \exp(-i\mathbf{K}\cdot\mathbf{r})] \quad (3.2.6')$$

we have, from Eq. (3.1.33), the scattered electric field in the form

$$\mathbf{E}_s(\mathbf{R}, t) = \mathbf{k}_s \times (\mathbf{k}_s \times \mathbf{E}_I{}^0) \left(\frac{\epsilon_0}{\epsilon}\right) \frac{\exp[i(k_sR - \omega_I t)]}{4\pi R} \int_v \Delta\chi_e(\mathbf{r}', t)$$

$$\times \exp[i(\mathbf{k}_I - \mathbf{k}_s)\cdot\mathbf{r}']\, d\mathbf{r}'$$

$$= \mathbf{f}(\mathbf{R}) \exp[i(k_sR - \omega_I t)]$$

$$\times \tfrac{1}{2}\left\{\int_v (\sum_K \Delta\chi_{eK}(t) \exp[i(\mathbf{k}_I - \mathbf{k}_s + \mathbf{K})\cdot\mathbf{r}'])\, d\mathbf{r}'\right.$$

$$\left. + \int_v (\sum_K \Delta\chi_{eK}{}^*(t) \exp[i(\mathbf{k}_I - \mathbf{k}_s - \mathbf{K})\cdot\mathbf{r}'])\, d\mathbf{r}'\right\}$$

$$= v\mathbf{f}(\mathbf{R}) \exp[i(k_sR - \omega_I t)]\tfrac{1}{2}[\Delta\chi_{ek_s-k_I} + \Delta\chi_{ek_I-k_s}{}^*] \quad (3.4.1)$$

where $\mathbf{f}(\mathbf{R})$ $[=\mathbf{k}_s \times (\mathbf{k}_s \times \mathbf{E}_I{}^0)(\epsilon_0/\epsilon)/4\pi R]$ is independent of time and $\mathbf{K}$ is fixed by the direction of $\mathbf{R}$ through $|K| = 2k_I \sin(\tfrac{1}{2}\theta)$ with k_I $[=n(2\pi/\lambda_{\text{air}})]$ being the incident wave vector in the scattering medium.

By substituting Eq. (3.3.13) into Eq. (3.4.1), we have expressed the scattered electric field due to entropy and pressure fluctuations

$$\mathbf{E}_s(\mathbf{R}, t) = v\mathbf{f}(\mathbf{R}) \exp[i(k_sR - \omega_I t)] \left(\frac{1}{2}\left(\frac{\partial \chi_e}{\partial s}\right)_P [\Delta s_{k_s-k_I}(t) + \Delta s_{k_I-k_s}{}^*(t)]\right.$$

$$\left. + \frac{1}{2}\left(\frac{\partial \chi_e}{\partial P}\right)_s [\Delta P_{k_s-k_I}(t) + \Delta P_{k_I-k_s}{}^*(t)]\right) \quad (3.4.2)$$

The spectrum of scattered light, expressible in terms of the scattered optical intensity per unit frequency interval, is related to the ordinary Fourier *time* transform of $\mathbf{E}_s(\mathbf{R}, t)$. Unfortunately, $\mathbf{E}_s(\mathbf{R}, t)$ is not mean-square integrable over the infinite time domain (Margenau and Murphy, 1956). Hence, we cannot use the ordinary Fourier integral. Furthermore, even if we could expand $\mathbf{E}_s$ in a large but finite time domain in a Fourier series, the exact time behavior of $\Delta s_K(t)$ and $\Delta P_K(t)$ could not be specified because both are random variables. How can we describe the time dependence of such random fluctuations?

3.4.1. Definitions of the Time Correlation Function and the Power Spectral Density*

We have discussed the spatial correlation function in Section 3.3 in which we have deliberately delayed our consideration on the time dependence of the correlation function. The time dependence of the correlation (or probability) function becomes important in problems involving random signals and noise.

Let x_1 and x_2 be random variables that refer to the possible values which can be assumed at time instants t_1 and t_2, respectively, by the sample function $x(\mathbf{r}, t)$ of a given random process. In our case, the random variables are (real-valued) *functions* defined on a sample space of points $\mathbf{r}$ for which a probability is defined. We could make measurements at N instants of time, say t_1–t_N giving sample values of the random variables x_1–x_N and obtain a measure of the joint probability density function $w(x_1, x_2, \ldots, x_N)$. A continuous-parameter random process is defined by the specification of all such sets of random variables and of their joint probability distribution functions for all values of N. For example, the output current of a photodetector as a function of time is a sample function of our continuous-parameter random process as shown in Fig. 3.4.1. We define the time correlation function of $x(t)$ as

$$R_x(\tau) = \lim_{T\to\infty}\frac{1}{2T}\int_{-T}^{T} x(t)x(t+\tau)\, dt = \langle x(t)x(t+\tau)\rangle \quad (3.4.3)$$

* Davenport and Root, 1958.

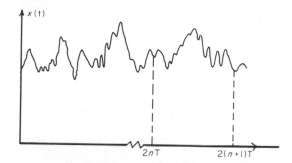

Fig. 3.4.1. A typical sample function of a continuous-parameter random process with periodograms of length $2T$.

The integral indicates a time average over all the starting time t inside the periodograms of length $2T$. Furthermore, we have taken the random process to be stationary so that the joint probability distribution for x_1 and x_2 depends only on the time difference $\tau = t_1 - t_2$ and not on the particular values of t_1 and t_2. The limit exists provided that the average "power" in $x(t)$, $R_x(0)$ ($\equiv \langle x^2(t) \rangle$), is finite. On the other hand, the requirement on $x(t)$ for the existence of a Fourier integral demands that $x(t)$ be mean-square integrable in the limit $T \to \infty$, or correspondingly that the total energy in $x(t)$ be bounded. We may consider the time correlation function as a mathematical representation on the persistence in time of a particular fluctuation before it dies out to zero. The time correlation function is obtained by computing $x(t)x(t + \tau)$ and then averaging the results over all starting times inside the periodogram, and it has similar properties as Eq. (3.3.20):

For time-invariant random processes, the correlation function

$$\langle x(t + \tau)x(t) \rangle = \langle x(\tau)x(0) \rangle$$

is independent of t. As

$$\tau \to 0, \qquad \langle x(t + \tau)x(t) \rangle \to \langle | x(t) |^2 \rangle$$

$$\tau \to \infty, \qquad \langle x(t + \tau)x(t) \rangle \to 0$$

If $R_x(\tau)$ exists and is absolutely integrable, the correlation function and the power spectral density $S_x(\omega)$ are connected through Fourier transforms:

In Fig. 3.4.1, we break the infinitely random fluctuations into equal periods of length $2T$, i.e., periodograms, and regard $x(t) = 0$ outside the interval $2nT < t < 2(n + 1)T$. Then, x_{2T} can be decomposed rigorously into its Fourier components

$$x_{2T}(t) = \int_{-\infty}^{\infty} \hat{x}_{2T}(\omega) \exp(-i\omega t) \, d\omega \qquad (3.4.4)$$

and

$$\hat{x}_{2T}(\omega) = \frac{1}{2\pi} \int_{-\infty}^{\infty} x_{2T}(t) \exp(i\omega t) \, dt \qquad (3.4.5)$$

with

$$2\pi\delta(\omega - \omega') = \int_{-\infty}^{\infty} \exp[i(\omega - \omega')t] \, dt \qquad (3.4.6)$$

Then, for complex x, we have

$$\langle x_{2T}(t + \tau) x_{2T}{}^*(t) \rangle = \lim_{T \to \infty} \frac{1}{2T} \int_{-T}^{T} x_{2T}(t + \tau) x_{2T}{}^*(t) \, dt$$

$$= \lim_{T \to \infty} \frac{1}{2T} \left\{ \int_{-T}^{T} dt \int_{-\infty}^{\infty} d\omega \int_{-\infty}^{\infty} d\omega' \hat{x}_{2T}(\omega) \hat{x}_{2T}{}^*(\omega') \right.$$

$$\left. \times \exp[-i\omega(t + \tau)] \exp(i\omega' t) \right\}$$

$$= \int_{-\infty}^{\infty} d\omega \int_{-\infty}^{\infty} d\omega' \lim_{T \to \infty} \left(\frac{\hat{x}_{2T}(\omega) \hat{x}_{2T}{}^*(\omega')}{2T} \right)$$

$$\times \exp(-i\omega\tau) \int_{-T}^{T} \exp[i(\omega' - \omega)t] \, dt$$

But, from Eq. (3.4.6) we have

$$\int_{-\infty}^{\infty} \hat{x}_{2T}{}^*(\omega') \, d\omega' \lim_{T \to \infty} \int_{-T}^{T} \exp[i(\omega' - \omega)t] \, dt$$

$$= \int_{-\infty}^{\infty} \hat{x}_{2T}{}^*(\omega') \, d\omega' [2\pi\delta(\omega' - \omega)]$$

$$= 2\pi\hat{x}_{2T}{}^*(\omega)$$

and

$$\langle x(t + \tau) x^*(t) \rangle = \int_{-\infty}^{\infty} d\omega \left(2\pi \lim_{T \to \infty} \frac{|\hat{x}_{2T}(\omega)|^2}{2T} \right) \exp(-i\omega\tau)$$

which gives

$$\langle x(t+\tau)x^*(t)\rangle = \int_{-\infty}^{\infty} S_x(\omega)\exp(-i\omega\tau)\,d\omega \qquad (3.4.7)$$

i.e., the correlation function is the inverse Fourier transform of the power spectral density $S_x(\omega)$ with

$$S_x(\omega) = \frac{1}{2\pi}\int_{-\infty}^{\infty}\langle x(t+\tau)x^*(t)\rangle\exp(i\omega\tau)\,d\tau \qquad (3.4.8)$$

and the power spectral density is the time Fourier transform of the correlation function. Equations (3.4.7) and (3.4.8) are called the *Wiener–Khintchine theorem*.

We may note that the total power contained under the spectral density curve is $\langle |x(t)|^2\rangle$, i.e.,

$$\int_{-\infty}^{\infty} S_x(\omega)\,d\omega = \int_{-\infty}^{\infty}\frac{1}{2\pi}\langle x(t+\tau)x^*(t)\rangle\int_{-\infty}^{\infty}\exp(i\omega\tau)\,d\omega\,d\tau$$

$$= \int_{-\infty}^{\infty}\langle x(t+\tau)x^*(t)\rangle\delta(\tau)\,d\tau = \langle |x(t)|^2\rangle \qquad (3.4.9)$$

Let $S_{x,N}(\omega)$ be the normalized power spectral density. Then we have

$$S_{x,N}(\omega) = \frac{1}{2\pi}\int\frac{\langle x(t+\tau)x^*(t)\rangle}{\langle |x(t)|^2\rangle}\exp(i\omega\tau)\,d\tau \qquad (3.4.10)$$

where

$$\int_{-\infty}^{\infty} S_{x,N}(\omega)\,d\omega = 1 \qquad (3.4.11)$$

Lastovka (1967) has noted that the normalization is performed in terms of "power" $\langle |x(t)|^2\rangle$ rather than "energy" which is "power" times time. This normalization permits us to treat the scattered field as a random variable since the average "power" is finite even though the total energy is infinite over infinite time. In addition, when we compute $R_x(\tau)$, we do not need a precise knowledge of the time evolution of $x(t)$. Rather, we need only to express an ensemble average of the time evolution of $x(t)$ from some fixed instant by invoking the ergodic hypothesis for the associated random processes.

3.4.2. Correlation for the Scattered Electric Field in Terms of Entropy and Pressure Fluctuations

We can obtain the correlation function for the scattered electric field by substituting Eq. (3.4.1) into Eq. (3.4.3),

$$R_{\mathbf{E}}(\tau) = \langle \mathbf{E}_s^*(\mathbf{R}, t) \cdot \mathbf{E}_s(\mathbf{R}, t + \tau) \rangle$$

$$= v^2 \mid \mathbf{f}(\mathbf{R}) \mid^2 \left\{ \left(\frac{\partial \chi_e}{\partial s} \right)_P^2 \exp(-i\omega_{\mathrm{I}}\tau) \langle \Delta s_K^*(t) \Delta s_K(t + \tau) \rangle \right.$$

$$\left. + \left(\frac{\partial \chi_e}{\partial P} \right)_s^2 \exp(-i\omega_{\mathrm{I}}\tau) \langle \Delta P_K^*(t) \Delta P_K(t + \tau) \rangle + \text{cross terms} \right\}$$

$$(3.4.12)$$

where we have used the relation $\Delta \chi_{ek_{\mathrm{I}}-k_s}^* = \Delta \chi_{eK}^* = \Delta \chi_{e-K}$. The cross terms are usually small because entropy and the pressure correlations are generally uncorrelated.

The form of the correlation functions for the pressure and the entropy fluctuations was first proposed by Brillouin (1914, 1922) and by Landau and Placzek (1934), respectively.

The time correlation functions for the entropy and the pressure fluctuations are

$$R_{\Delta s}(K, \tau) = \langle \Delta s_K^*(t) \Delta s_K(t + \tau) \rangle$$

and

$$R_{\Delta P}(K, \tau) = \langle \Delta P_K^*(t) \Delta P_K(t + \tau) \rangle$$

which could be evaluated in terms of their respective statistical averages.

If we take $x(t)$ to be ergodic and stationary in the strict sense (i.e., the probability distributions in the random processes are invariant under shifts of the time origin), then we have

$$\langle x(t)x(t + \tau) \rangle = \overline{x(t)x(t + \tau)} = \overline{x(0)x(\tau)} \qquad (3.4.13)$$

By definition,

$$\overline{x(t)x(t + \tau)} = \lim_{N \to \infty} \frac{1}{N} \sum_{i=1}^{N} x_i(t) x_i(t + \tau) \qquad (3.4.14)$$

where i is a particular ensemble member and N is the total number of members. The summation could be carried out in a different way. Suppose $n(x_1, x_2)$ is the number of times a particular product having $x(t) = x_1$ and $x(t + \tau) = x_2$ appears in N terms, then,

$$\overline{x(t)x(t + \tau)} = \lim_{N \to \infty} \frac{1}{N} \sum_{x_1, x_2} n(x_1, x_2) x_1 x_2 \qquad (3.4.15)$$

where the summation is carried out over all occurring values of x_1 and x_2. We define a joint probability density $w(x_1, x_2)$ for the continuous random variable $x(t)$:

$$w(x_1, x_2) \equiv \lim_{N \to \infty, \; dx_1 \to 0, \; dx_2 \to 0} \frac{n(x_1, x_2)}{N \, dx_1 \, dx_2} \qquad (3.4.16)$$

such that

$$\overline{x(t)x(t+\tau)} = \int_{x'=-\infty}^{\infty} dx' \int_{x''=-\infty}^{\infty} dx'' x'x''w[x'(t), x''(t+\tau)] \quad (3.4.17)$$

$w(x_1, x_2)$ is the ensemble average probability of finding $x_1 \leq x(t) \leq x_1 + dx_1$ and $x_2 \leq x(t+\tau) \leq x_2 + dx_2$ in a measurement on any particular member of the ensemble. We may factor $w(x_1, x_2)$ into a conditional probability density and a simple probability density

$$w[x'(t), x''(t+\tau)] = w[x''(t+\tau) \mid x'(t)]w(x'(t)) \quad (3.4.18)$$

where $w(x'(t)) \, dx'$ gives the probability of an ensemble member with $x' \leq x(t) \leq x' + dx'$, and $w(x''(t+\tau) \mid x'(t)) \, dx''$ is the probability of an ensemble member with $x'' \leq x(t+\tau) \leq x'' + dx''$ given $x(t) = x'$. Thus,

$$R_x(\tau) = \overline{x(0)x(\tau)}$$

$$= \int_{-\infty}^{\infty} \int_{-\infty}^{\infty} x'x''w[x''(\tau) \mid x'(0)]w[x'(0)] \, dx' \, dx'' \quad (3.4.19)$$

Let us consider the entropy fluctuations by means of Eq. (3.4.19):

$$R_{\Delta s}(K, \tau) = \langle \Delta s_K(t) \, \Delta s_K{}^*(t+\tau) \rangle$$

$$= \int_{-\infty}^{\infty} \int_{-\infty}^{\infty} (\Delta s_K{}''^*)(\Delta s_K{}') w[\Delta s_K{}''^*(\tau) \mid \Delta s_K{}'(0)]w[\Delta s_K{}'(0)]$$

$$\times d[\Delta s_K{}''^*] \, d[\Delta s_K{}'] \qquad (3.4.20)$$

in which we shall first consider the conditional probability

$$w[\Delta s_K{}''^*(t) \mid \Delta s_K{}'(0)] \, d[\Delta s_K{}''^*]$$

This probability requires us to prepare an ensemble of identical systems all having $\Delta s_K = \Delta s_K{}'$ at $t = 0$. Thus, the state is not in thermodynamic equilibrium since $\overline{\Delta s_K(0)} \neq 0$. Rather,

$$\overline{\Delta s_K(t)} = \int \Delta s_K{}''^* w[\Delta s_K{}''^*(t) \mid \Delta s_K{}'(0)] \, d(\Delta s_K{}''^*) = 0 \quad (3.4.21)$$

i.e., if we release an ensemble at $t = 0$, its members should reach thermo-dynamic equilibrium at some later time t.

The time dependence of the local entropy fluctuations at constant pressure is related to that of local temperature fluctuations:

$$\Delta s_P(\mathbf{r}, t) = (C_P'/T)\Delta T_P(\mathbf{r}, t) \qquad (3.4.22)$$

where C_P' is the heat capacity at constant pressure per unit volume. The space–time dependence of the local temperature fluctuations obeys the heat-flow equation of Fourier:

$$\int_v \frac{dq'}{dt}\, dv = \Lambda \int_S \boldsymbol{\nabla} T(\mathbf{r}, t)\cdot d\mathbf{S} \qquad (3.4.23)$$

where dq' $[= T\, ds = C_P'\, dT]$ is the heat absorbed by the system per unit volume, and Λ is the thermal conductivity. By application of Gauss's divergence theorem, we have

$$\int_v \frac{C_P'\, dT}{dt}\, dv = \Lambda \int_v \boldsymbol{\nabla}\cdot\boldsymbol{\nabla} T(\mathbf{r}, t)\, dv = \Lambda \int_v \nabla^2 T(\mathbf{r}, t)\, dv \qquad (3.4.24)$$

which gives us the equation

$$d(\overline{\Delta T_P(\mathbf{r}, t)})/dt = (\Lambda/C_P')\nabla^2(\overline{\Delta T_P(\mathbf{r}, t)}) \qquad (3.4.25)$$

governing the relaxation to equilibrium of the ensemble average in $\Delta T_P(\mathbf{r}, t)$. In Eq. (3.4.25), Λ/C_P' is the thermal diffusivity. By taking the spatial Fourier transform of Eq. (3.4.25), we find

$$d(\overline{\Delta T_{P,K}(t)})/dt = (\Lambda/C_P')(-K^2)\overline{\Delta T_{P,K}(t)} \qquad (3.4.26)$$

The initial condition requires that $\Delta T_K(0) = \Delta T_K'$. Thus, the solution to Eq. (3.4.26) is

$$\overline{\Delta T_{P,K}(t)} = \overline{\Delta T_{P,K}(0)}\exp(-\Gamma_c t) = \Delta T_{P,K}'\exp(-\Gamma_c t) \qquad (3.4.27)$$

where

$$\Gamma_c = \Lambda K^2/C_P' \qquad (3.4.28)$$

For the local entropy fluctuations,

$$\overline{\Delta s_{P,K}(t)} = \Delta s_{P,K}'\exp(-\Gamma_c t) \qquad (3.4.29)$$

The ensemble average entropy fluctuation relaxes back to equilibrium exponentially. Furthermore, it does not propagate. By substituting Eqs.

(3.4.29) and (3.4.21) into Eq. (3.4.20), we get

$$R_{\Delta s}(K, \tau) = \int_{-\infty}^{\infty} \int_{-\infty}^{\infty} (\Delta s_K''^*) (\Delta s_K') w[\Delta s_K''^*(\tau) \mid \Delta s_K'(0)]$$

$$\times w[\Delta s_K'(0)] d[\Delta s_K''^*] d[\Delta s_K']$$

$$= \exp(-\Gamma_c \tau) \int_{-\infty}^{\infty} \Delta s_K'^*(0) \Delta s_K'(0) w[\Delta s_K'(0)] d[\Delta s_K']$$

$$= \exp(-\Gamma_c \tau) \overline{\mid \Delta s_K(0) \mid^2} = \exp(-\Gamma_c \tau) \langle \mid \Delta s_K(t) \mid^2 \rangle$$

From Eq. (3.3.59), we have

$$\langle \mid \Delta s_K(t) \mid^2 \rangle = \overline{\mid \Delta s_K(0) \mid^2} = kC_P'/v \qquad (3.4.30)$$

where v is the illuminated volume. Therefore,

$$\boxed{R_{\Delta s}(K, \tau) = (kC_P'/v) \exp(-\Gamma_s \tau)} \qquad (3.4.31)$$

We shall now consider the pressure fluctuations which contribute to the scattered electric field:

$$R_{\Delta P}(K, \tau) = \langle \Delta P_K(t) \Delta P_K^*(t + \tau) \rangle$$

Earlier discussion on the scattered electric field from a propagating sound wave (Section 3.1.2) shows that local pressure fluctuations at constant entropy could be represented, to a good approximation, by sound waves. We *guess*

$$\Delta P_{s,K}(t) = \Delta P_{s,K}(0) \exp(\pm i\bar{\omega}_K t) \exp(-\Gamma_P t) \qquad (3.4.32)$$

where $\bar{\omega}$ is the frequency of the sound wave having wave vector $\mathbf{K}$, and Γ_P is the damping constant for the sound-wave amplitude. The $\pm$ sign corresponds to two sound waves with the same frequency running in opposite directions. The correlation function for the pressure fluctuations has the form:

$$\langle \Delta P_K(t) \Delta P_K^*(t + \tau) \rangle$$

$$= \langle \mid \Delta P_K(t) \mid^2 \rangle \tfrac{1}{2} [\exp(i\bar{\omega}_K \tau) + \exp(-i\bar{\omega}_K \tau)] \exp(-\Gamma_P \tau)$$

$$= \overline{\mid \Delta P_K(0) \mid^2} \tfrac{1}{2} [\exp(i\bar{\omega}_K \tau) + \exp(-i\bar{\omega}_K \tau)] \exp(-\Gamma_P \tau) \qquad (3.4.33)$$

where the factor $\tfrac{1}{2}$ is introduced to take into account that half of the mean-square pressure fluctuations belong to each of the two degenerate sound waves.

From Eq. (3.3.59), we have

$$\overline{|\,\Delta P_K\,|^2} = kT/vK_S$$

where K_S is the adiabatic compressibility.

In liquids, the hydrodynamic equations can be linearized for small fluctuations. Furthermore, the propagation of thermal sound waves produces negligible heat conduction effect and only longitudinal waves exist. Then, we have the usual Navier–Stokes equation (Landau and Lifshitz, 1959)

$$\rho_d \left(\frac{\partial u}{\partial t} \right) = - \frac{\partial P}{\partial q} + (\tfrac{4}{3}\eta + \eta') \frac{\partial^2 u}{\partial q^2} \qquad (3.4.34)$$

where u is the fluid velocity in the direction of q; η and η' are the shear and compressional viscosities, respectively. We choose q to be in the direction of **K**. A more detailed discussion on the related hydrodynamic equations has been presented by Benedek (1968).

For a liquid, we have

$$K_S(\partial P/\partial t) = -(\partial u/\partial q) \qquad (3.4.35)$$

By substituting Eq. (3.4.35) into Eq. (3.4.34) and taking partial derivatives with respect to q we get a damped-wave equation for P:

$$\rho_d K_S \frac{\partial^2 P}{\partial t^2} = \frac{\partial^2 P}{\partial q^2} + K_S(\tfrac{4}{3}\eta + \eta') \frac{\partial^3 P}{\partial q^2 \, \partial t} \qquad (3.4.36)$$

Again, we take the spatial Fourier transform of Eq. (3.4.36) and consider the local pressure fluctuations by using δP instead of P:

$$\rho_d K_S \frac{\partial^2 [\delta P_K(t)]}{\partial t^2} = -K^2 [\delta P_K(t)] - K_S K^2 (\tfrac{4}{3}\eta + \eta') \frac{\partial (\delta P_K(t))}{\partial t} \qquad (3.4.37)$$

The solution to Eq. (3.4.37) can be obtained by assuming

$$\Delta P_K(t) = \exp(ht) \qquad (3.4.38)$$

Substituting Eq. (3.4.38) into Eq. (3.4.37) gives

$$\rho_d K_S h^2 = -K^2 - K_S K^2 (\tfrac{4}{3}\eta + \eta') h \qquad (3.4.39)$$

Thus, we have a quadratic equation in h whose roots are

$$h = \frac{-K_S K^2 (\tfrac{4}{3}\eta + \eta') \pm [(K_S K^2 (\tfrac{4}{3}\eta + \eta'))^2 - 4\rho_d K_S K^2]^{1/2}}{2\rho_d K_S} \qquad (3.4.40)$$

In the limit of small damping, Eq. (3.4.40) reduces to

$$h = -(K^2/2\rho_d)(\tfrac{4}{3}\eta + \eta') \pm i(\rho_d K_S)^{-1/2} K \qquad (3.4.41)$$

with the corresponding solution for $\Delta P_K(t)$:

$$\Delta P_K(t) = \exp[-(K^2/2\rho_d)(\tfrac{4}{3}\eta + \eta')t]\exp[\pm i(\rho_d K_S)^{-1/2}Kt] \quad (3.4.42)$$

The adiabatic pressure fluctuations are damped propagating sound waves with a frequency

$$\bar{\omega}_K = (\rho_d K_S)^{-1/2}K \quad (3.4.43)$$

traveling in both directions of $\mathbf{K}$ and a phase velocity

$$v_s = (\bar{\omega}_K/K) = (\rho_d K_S)^{-1/2} \quad (3.4.44)$$

We define a damping rate Γ_P with

$$\Gamma_P = (K^2/2\rho_d)(\tfrac{4}{3}\eta + \eta') = (\bar{\omega}_K^2/2\rho_d v_s^2)(\tfrac{4}{3}\eta + \eta') \quad (3.4.45)$$

such that the spatial decay constant α_P has the form

$$\alpha_P = \Gamma_P/v_s = (\bar{\omega}_K^2/2\rho_d v_s^3)(\tfrac{4}{3}\eta + \eta') \quad (3.4.46)$$

which implies negligible damping of the sound wave in a distance of one acoustic wavelength. α_P can be measured using ultrasonic techniques except for the fact that our light-scattering experiments deal with hypersonic frequencies which are beyond the range of present-day ultrasonic experiments; on the other hand, the hypersonic frequencies are low compared with the frequency of visible light.

With these results we can now write the expression for the pressure–time correlation function $R_{\Delta P}(K, \tau)$ as

$$R_{\Delta P}(K, \tau) = \langle \Delta P_K(t)\, \Delta P_K^*(t + \tau)\rangle$$
$$= (kT/vK_S)\tfrac{1}{2}\exp(-\Gamma_P\tau)\{\exp[(i\bar{\omega}_K\tau) + \exp(-i\bar{\omega}_K\tau)]\}$$

or

$$\boxed{\begin{aligned}
R_{\Delta P}(K, \tau) &= \frac{kT}{vK_S}\tfrac{1}{2}\exp\left[-\frac{K^2}{2\rho_d}(\tfrac{4}{3}\eta + \eta')\tau\right] \\
&\times \left[\exp\left(i\,\frac{K}{(\rho_d K_S)^{1/2}}\tau\right) + \exp\left(-i\,\frac{K}{(\rho_d K_S)^{1/2}}\tau\right)\right]
\end{aligned}}$$

$$(3.4.47)$$

3.4.3. Spectrum of Scattered Electric Field

The power spectral density of the scattered radiation has the form

$$S_{\mathbf{E_s}, N}(\omega) = \frac{1}{2\pi}\int_{-\infty}^{\infty}\frac{\langle \mathbf{E_s}^*(\mathbf{R}, t)\cdot\mathbf{E_s}(\mathbf{R}, t + \tau)\rangle}{\langle |\,\mathbf{E_s}(\mathbf{R}, t)\,|^2\rangle}\exp(i\omega\tau)\, d\tau \quad (3.4.48)$$

by using Eq. (3.4.10). By substituting Eqs. (3.4.12), (3.4.31), and (3.4.47) into Eq. (3.4.48), we get

$$S_{E_s,N}(\omega) = \frac{1}{2\pi} \int_{-\infty}^{\infty} \left\{ \left(\frac{\partial \chi_e}{\partial s}\right)_P^2 \frac{kC_{P'}}{v} \exp\left(\frac{-\Lambda K^2}{C_{P'}}\tau\right) + \left(\frac{\partial \chi_e}{\partial P}\right)_s^2 \frac{kT}{vK_S} \right.$$

$$\times \frac{1}{2} \left\{ \exp\left[i\frac{K\tau}{(\rho_d K_S)^{1/2}}\right] + \exp\left[-i\frac{K\tau}{(\rho_d K_S)^{1/2}}\right] \right\}$$

$$\times \exp\left[-\frac{K^2\tau}{2\rho_d}\left(\tfrac{4}{3}\eta + \eta'\right)\right] \left\} \left[\left(\frac{\partial \chi_e}{\partial s}\right)_P^2 \frac{kC_{P'}}{v} + \left(\frac{\partial \chi_e}{\partial P}\right)_s^2 \frac{kT}{vK_S}\right]^{-1}$$

$$\times \exp[i(\omega - \omega_I)\tau]\,d\tau \qquad\qquad (3.4.49)$$

The power spectral density produced by Eq. (3.4.49) has three Lorentzians. Since the correlation function must satisfy the condition

$$R(\tau) = R(-\tau)$$

we obtain the power spectral density by taking the Fourier *cosine* transform

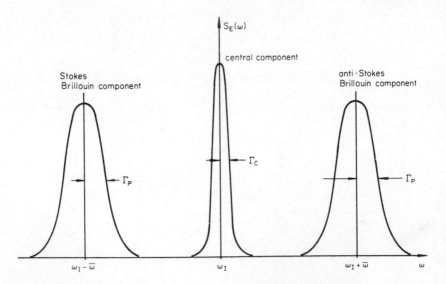

Fig. 3.4.2. Theoretical spectrum for the light scattered by thermal fluctuations in liquids according to Eq. (3.4.50). $\bar{\omega}_K = v_s K = K/(\rho_d K_S)^{1/2}$; $\Gamma_c = (\Lambda/C_{P'})K^2$; $\Gamma_P = \alpha_p v_s = (\bar{\omega}_K^2/2\rho_d v_s^2)(\tfrac{4}{3}\eta + \eta') = (K^2/2\rho_d)(\tfrac{4}{3}\eta + \eta')$.

(the real part of the Fourier transform of the time correlation function)

$$\int_{-\infty}^{\infty} \exp(i\omega\tau) \exp(-\Gamma\tau)\, d\tau = \int_{-\infty}^{\infty} \exp(-\Gamma\tau) \cos \omega\tau\, d\tau$$

$$= 2 \int_{0}^{\infty} \exp(-\Gamma\tau) \cos \omega\tau\, d\tau$$

$$= 2 \left(\frac{\Gamma}{\Gamma^2 + \omega^2} \right)$$

So, the normalized power spectral density consists of three Lorentzians symmetrically split around the center:

$$S_{E_s,N}(\omega) = \frac{\left(\dfrac{\partial \chi_e}{\partial s}\right)_P^2 \dfrac{C_P' k}{v}}{\left(\dfrac{\partial \chi_e}{\partial s}\right)_P^2 \dfrac{C_P' k}{v} + \left(\dfrac{\partial \chi_e}{\partial P}\right)_s^2 \dfrac{T}{K_S} \dfrac{k}{v}} \frac{1}{\pi} \left(\frac{\dfrac{\Lambda K^2}{C_P'}}{(\omega - \omega_I)^2 + \left(\dfrac{\Lambda}{C_P'} K^2\right)^2} \right)$$

$$+ \frac{\left(\dfrac{\partial \chi_e}{\partial P}\right)_s^2 \dfrac{T}{K_S}}{\left(\dfrac{\partial \chi_e}{\partial s}\right)_P^2 C_P' + \left(\dfrac{\partial \chi_e}{\partial P}\right)_s^2 \dfrac{T}{K_S}} \frac{1}{2\pi}$$

$$\times \left\{ \frac{\dfrac{1}{2\rho_d}\left(\tfrac{4}{3}\eta + \eta'\right) K^2}{\left(\omega - \omega_I - \dfrac{K}{(\rho_d K_S)^{1/2}}\right)^2 + \left(\dfrac{1}{2\rho_d}\left(\tfrac{4}{3}\eta + \eta'\right) K^2\right)^2} \right.$$

$$\left. + \frac{\dfrac{1}{2\rho_d}\left(\tfrac{4}{3}\eta + \eta'\right) K^2}{\left(\omega - \omega_I + \dfrac{K}{(\rho_d K_S)^{1/2}}\right)^2 + \left(\dfrac{1}{2\rho_d}\left(\tfrac{4}{3}\eta + \eta'\right) K^2\right)^2} \right\} \quad (3.4.50)$$

Equation (3.4.50) is a heuristic formula for the spectrum of scattered light of a simple fluid where the central and the Brillouin components do not overlap so that the cross terms, e.g., $\langle \Delta P_K(t)\,\Delta S_K(t+\tau) \rangle = 0$, vanish for all τ, and we have neglected depolarization effects. Figure 3.4.2 shows a theoretical spectrum of scattered light according to Eq. (3.4.50). There is a pair of Doppler shifted lines, called Brillouin doublets, located at frequencies $\omega \pm \bar\omega$, as we have discussed in Fig. 3.1.2. Equations (3.1.16) and (3.4.44) represent the zeroth approximation where we have taken $k_s^+ \simeq k_s^- \simeq k_I$ for the case $\bar\omega \ll \omega_I$. Let us now consider the case involving higher orders of v_s/c (Chiao, 1965).

We shall establish the angular dependence of the splitting of Brillouin's doublets by using Eqs. (3.1.17) and (3.1.18):

$$\mathbf{k}_s = \mathbf{k}_I \pm \mathbf{K} \qquad\qquad (3.1.17')$$

and

$$\omega_s = \omega_I \pm \bar\omega \qquad\qquad (3.1.18')$$

where we have set $\mathbf{K} \equiv \mathbf{q}$. In taking the law of cosines from Fig. 3.4.3, we get

$$K^2 = k_s{}^2 + k_I{}^2 - 2k_s k_I \cos\theta$$

Now we use $K = \bar\omega/v_s$, $k_s = \omega_s/c_m$, and $k_I = \omega_I/c_m$ where we have implicitly taken $n = n_I = n_s$. Then,

$$\bar\omega^2 = (v_s/c_m)^2 \big[\omega_s{}^2 + \omega_I{}^2 - 2\omega_I\omega_s(1 - 2\sin^2(\tfrac{1}{2}\theta)) \big]$$

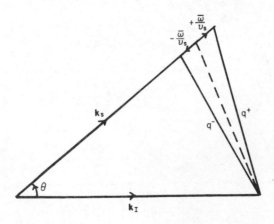

Fig. 3.4.3.   The law of cosines: $k_I = \omega_I/c_m$; $\mathbf{k}_s = \mathbf{k}_I \pm \mathbf{q}$.

which can be expressed as a quadratic equation for $\bar{\omega}$:

$$[1 - (v_s/c_m)^2]\bar{\omega}^2 \mp 4[(v_s/c_m)^2\omega_I \sin^2(\tfrac{1}{2}\theta)]\bar{\omega} - 4(v_s/c_m)^2\omega_I^2 \sin^2(\tfrac{1}{2}\theta) = 0 \tag{3.4.51}$$

where we should recall that c_m is the speed of light in the medium. The solutions to Eq. (3.4.51) are

$$\bar{\omega} = \left\{\pm 4\left[\left(\frac{v_s}{c_m}\right)^2 \omega_I \sin^2(\tfrac{1}{2}\theta)\right]\right.$$

$$+ \left(16\left(\frac{v_s}{c_m}\right)^4 \omega_I^2 \sin^4(\tfrac{1}{2}\theta) + 16\left[1 - \left(\frac{v_s}{c_m}\right)^2\right]\right.$$

$$\left.\times \left(\frac{v_s}{c_m}\right)^2 \omega_I^2 \sin^2(\tfrac{1}{2}\theta)\right)^{1/2}\right\}\left\{2\left[1 - \left(\frac{v_s}{c_m}\right)^2\right]\right\}^{-1}$$

$$= \frac{v_s}{c_m}\omega_I\left[1 - \left(\frac{v_s}{c_m}\right)^2\right]^{-1}\left\{\pm 2\frac{v_s}{c_m}\sin^2(\tfrac{1}{2}\theta)\right.$$

$$\left.+ \left[4\sin^2(\tfrac{1}{2}\theta) - \left(\frac{v_s}{c_m}\right)^2 \sin^2\theta\right]^{1/2}\right\} \tag{3.4.52}$$

where we have used the relation

$$\sin^2\theta = 4\sin^2(\tfrac{1}{2}\theta)\cos^2(\tfrac{1}{2}\theta) = 4\sin^2(\tfrac{1}{2}\theta)[1 - \sin^2(\tfrac{1}{2}\theta)]$$

The plus $(+)$ sign is for sound waves with an up-shifted frequency, referred to as anti-Stokes component of the scattered radiation. As $v_s/c_m \to 0$, $\bar{\omega}$ must be positive. So, we have

$$\bar{\omega} = \frac{v_s}{c_m}\omega_I\left[1 - \left(\frac{v_s}{c_m}\right)^2\right]^{-1}\left\{2\frac{v_s}{c_m}\sin^2(\tfrac{1}{2}\theta) + \left[4\sin^2(\tfrac{1}{2}\theta) - \left(\frac{v_s}{c_m}\right)^2 \sin^2\theta\right]^{1/2}\right\}$$

$$\approx \frac{v_s}{c_m}\omega_I\left[1 - \left(\frac{v_s}{c_m}\right)^2\right]^{-1}\left[2\frac{v_s}{c_m}\sin^2(\tfrac{1}{2}\theta) + 2\sin(\tfrac{1}{2}\theta) - \left(\frac{v_s}{c_m}\right)^2 \sin(\tfrac{1}{2}\theta)\cos^2(\tfrac{1}{2}\theta)\right.$$

$$\left.+ O\left(\frac{v_s}{c_m}\right)^4 + \cdots\right] \tag{3.4.53}$$

Thus, both the Stokes (down-shifted in frequency) and the anti-Stokes (up-shifted in frequency) lines are shifted up to the blue very slightly by $\delta\bar{\omega}$

in the amount

$$\delta\bar{\omega} \approx \frac{v_\text{s}}{c_\text{m}}\,\omega_\text{I}\left[2\,\frac{v_\text{s}}{c_\text{m}}\sin^2(\tfrac{1}{2}\theta)\right] = \frac{1}{2}\left[2\,\frac{v_\text{s}}{c_\text{m}}\sin(\tfrac{1}{2}\theta)\right]^2\omega_\text{I} = \frac{\bar{\omega}_K^2}{2\omega_\text{I}} \quad (3.4.54)$$

with $\bar{\omega}_K = (v_\text{s}/c_\text{m})\omega_\text{I}(2\sin(\tfrac{1}{2}\theta))$ from Eq. (3.1.16).

Thus the Brillouin shifts have a slight asymmetry of the order of v_s/c_m (e.g., 10^{-6} for liquids and 10^{-5} for solids) which has not yet been detected.

Equation (3.4.53) also tells us that the frequencies of sound responsible for Brillouin scattering has the magnitude $(v_\text{s}/c_\text{m} \ll 1)$

$$\bar{\omega} \approx \omega_\text{I}(v_\text{s}/c_\text{m})2\sin(\tfrac{1}{2}\theta) \quad (3.4.55)$$

With $v_\text{s} \approx 10^5$ cm/sec for liquids, $\bar{\omega}$ ranges from 0 for $\theta = 0$ to $\sim 10^{10}$ Hz for $\theta = \pi$. Such high frequencies are orders of magnitude larger than those of ultrasonic measurements. Furthermore, the measurements require no external acoustic excitation. Table 3.4.1 shows estimates of the linewidth of the central component and Doppler shifts for some liquids using v_s from ultrasonic measurements. Since Γ_c has a K^2 dependence, the linewidths for the central component of simple fluids can only be measured with difficulty by conventional spectroscopy even at $\theta = \pi$. At smaller values of K, it becomes essential to use optical mixing spectroscopy (Lastovka and Benedek, 1966). The computation of Γ_P using Eq. (3.4.46) is less certain since K_S, η, and η' may be functions of frequency for some liquids. Similarly, v_s could change with frequency. More generally, the shifted Brillouin lines are not Lorentzians as they would be for scattering from a freely decaying

Table 3.4.1

Computed linewidths and splittings for some liquids[a,b]

	H_2O	CS_2	Benzene	CCl_4	Toluene
Λ (W/cm °C)	6.18×10^{-3}	1.61×10^{-3}	1.32×10^{-3}	1.06×10^{-3}	1.38×10^{-3}
Γ_c $(\theta = \pi)/2\pi$ (MHz)	16.4	21.2	12.4	10.5	13.3
v_s (cm/sec)	1.49×10^5	1.16×10^5	1.32×10^5	0.94×10^5	1.32×10^5
$\bar{\omega}_K$ $(\theta = \pi)/2\pi$ (MHz)	6.28×10^3	5.94×10^3	6.23×10^3	4.33×10^3	6.21×10^3

[a] α, ρ_d, $n_{\lambda\text{air}}{}^T$, and $C_P{}^*$ are listed in Table 3.3.1, and

$$\Gamma_c = \frac{\Lambda}{C_P'}\,K^2 \quad (3.4.28), \qquad \bar{\omega}_K = v_\text{s}K \quad (3.4.44)$$

[b] From Lastovka, 1967.

system. The scattered light is modulated by thermal acoustic waves characteristic of the liquid and the Brillouin peaks in the scattered light spectrum have been found to be thermally driven resonance lines (Montrose *et al.*, 1968). This means that one cannot identify the Brillouin frequency as the phase velocity times the wave vector of a temporarily damped acoustic wave [Eq. (3.4.55)]. Theory and measurements have been extended to relaxing liquids (Montrose *et al.*, 1968; Pinnow *et al.*, 1968) where the interpretation of the spectrum is more complicated. Instrumental effects on Brillouin line shapes have also been discussed (Leidecker and La Macchia, 1968).

3.4.4. The Landau–Placzek Intensity Ratio

In computing the Landau–Placzek intensity ratio from Eq. (3.4.50), we assume that the optical electric susceptibility, in fact, the dielectric constant is mainly a function of density so that $(\partial \chi_e / \partial T)_{\rho_d} = 0$. Then,

$$(\partial \chi_e / \partial P)_s = (\partial \chi_e / \partial \rho_d)_T (\partial \rho_d / \partial P)_s \qquad (3.4.56)$$

and

$$(\partial \chi_e / \partial s)_P = (\partial \chi_e / \partial \rho_d)_T (\partial \rho_d / \partial s)_P \qquad (3.4.57)$$

We recall

$$\frac{1}{\rho_d} \left(\frac{\partial \rho_d}{\partial} \right)_P = -\frac{1}{V} \left(\frac{\partial V}{\partial} \right)_P$$

So,

$$\frac{1}{\rho_d} \left(\frac{\partial \rho_d}{\partial s} \right)_P = -\frac{1}{V} \left(\frac{\partial V}{\partial s} \right)_P = -\left(\frac{\partial V}{\partial S} \right)_P = \left(\frac{\partial T}{\partial P} \right)_S$$

$$= \frac{T}{C_P} \left(\frac{\partial V}{\partial T} \right)_P = \frac{T\alpha}{C_P'}$$

Finally,

$$\left(\frac{\partial \chi_e}{\partial P} \right)_s^2 = \left[\left(\frac{\partial \chi_e}{\partial \rho_d} \right)_T \left(\frac{\partial \rho_d}{\partial P} \right)_s \right]^2$$

$$= \left[\rho_d \left(\frac{\partial \chi_e}{\partial \rho_d} \right)_T \right]^2 \left(\frac{1}{\rho_d} \left(\frac{\partial \rho_d}{\partial P} \right)_s \right)^2$$

$$= \left[\rho_d \left(\frac{\partial \chi_e}{\partial \rho_d} \right)_T \right]^2 K_S^2 \qquad (3.4.58)$$

and

$$\left(\frac{\partial \chi_e}{\partial s}\right)_P^2 = \left[\rho_d \left(\frac{\partial \chi_e}{\partial \rho_d}\right)_T\right]^2 \frac{T^2 \alpha^2}{C_{P'}^2}$$

$$= \left[\rho_d \left(\frac{\partial \chi_e}{\partial \rho_d}\right)_T\right]^2 \left(\frac{C_{P'} - C_{V'}}{C_{P'}^2}\right) TK_T \qquad (3.4.59)$$

In Eq. (3.4.59), we have used the general thermodynamic relation $C_{P'} - C_{V'} = T\alpha^2/K_T$ where $C_{P'}$ and $C_{V'}$ are the heat capacities per unit volume (Bearman and Chu, 1967). With $C_P/C_V = K_T/K_S$ (Bearman and Chu, 1967), Eq. (3.4.60) gives

$$S_{E_s,N}(\omega) = \frac{[(C_P - C_V)/C_P]K_T}{K_S + [(C_P - C_V)/C_P]K_T} \frac{1}{\pi} \frac{\Gamma_c}{(\omega - \omega_I)^2 + \Gamma_c^2}$$

$$+ \frac{K_S}{K_S + [(C_P - C_V)/C_P]K_T} \frac{1}{2\pi}$$

$$\times \left\{\frac{\Gamma_P}{(\omega - \omega_I - \bar{\omega}_K)^2 + \Gamma_P^2} + \frac{\Gamma_P}{(\omega - \omega_I + \bar{\omega}_K)^2 + \Gamma_P^2}\right\}$$

$$= \frac{(C_P - C_V)/C_V}{1 + [(C_P - C_V)/C_V]} \mathcal{L}_c + \frac{1}{2\{1 + [(C_P - C_V)/C_V]\}}$$

$$\times \{\mathcal{L}_P(\bar{\omega}) + \mathcal{L}_P(-\bar{\omega})\}$$

$$= \frac{C_P - C_V}{C_P} \mathcal{L}_c + \frac{1}{2(C_P/C_V)} \{\mathcal{L}_P(\bar{\omega}) + \mathcal{L}_P(-\bar{\omega})\} \qquad (3.4.60)$$

where

$$\mathcal{L}_C = \frac{1}{\pi} \frac{\Gamma_c}{(\omega - \omega_I)^2 + \Gamma_c^2} \qquad (3.4.61)$$

and

$$\mathcal{L}_P(\bar{\omega}) = \frac{1}{\pi} \frac{\Gamma_P}{(\omega - \omega_I + \bar{\omega}_K)^2 + \Gamma_P^2} \qquad (3.4.62)$$

The Lorentzian functions $\mathcal{L}_C$ and $\mathcal{L}_P$ have been normalized such that

$$\int_{-\infty}^{\infty} \mathcal{L}_c(\Gamma_c, \omega - \omega_I) \, d\omega = \int_{-\infty}^{\infty} \mathcal{L}_P(\bar{\omega}, \Gamma_P, \omega - \omega_I) \, d\omega = 1 \qquad (3.4.63)$$

which agrees with the earlier normalization for $S_{E_s}(\omega)$

$$\int_{-\infty}^{\infty} S_{E_s,N}(\omega)\, d\omega = \frac{C_P - C_V}{C_P} + \frac{C_V}{C_P} = 1$$

From Eq. (3.4.60), we see that the intensity of the central component is related to $[(C_P - C_V)/C_V]K_S$ while that of the Brillouin component varies with K_S. Thus,

$$\boxed{I_c/2I_B = (C_P - C_V)/C_V} \tag{3.4.64}$$

where I_c is the relative intensity of central component and I_B is that of one of the two Brillouin components. Equation (3.4.64) is the Landau–Placzek ratio, and may be written in the form

$$(I_c + 2I_B)/2I_B = C_P/C_V \tag{3.4.65}$$

In comparing Eq. (3.4.65) with experiments, it is essential to take into account the dispersion effects. Then, the Landau–Placzek ratio is in substantial agreement with experiments (Cummins and Gammon, 1966).

References

Bearman, R. J., and Chu, B. (1967). "Problems in Chemical Thermodynamics," pp. 77–78, 80–81. Addison-Wesley, Reading, Massachusetts.

Benedek, G. B. (1968). *In* "Statistical Physics, Phase Transitions and Superfluidity" (M. Cretien, E. P. Gross, and S. Deser, eds.). Gordon and Breach, New York.

Brillouin, L. (1914). *C.R.H. Acad. Sci.* **158**, 1331.

Brillouin, L. (1922). *Ann. Phys. (Paris)*, **17**, 88.

Chiao, R. (1965). Ph.D. thesis. MIT, Cambridge, Massachusetts.

Carr, C. I., and Zimm, B. H. (1950). *J. Chem. Phys.* **18**, 1616.

Chu, B. (1970a). *Ann. Rev. Phys. Chem.* **21**, 145.

Chu, B. (1970b). *In* "Advances in Macromolecular Chemistry" (W. M. Pasika, ed.), pp. 89–121. Academic Press, New York and London.

Chu, B. (1967). "Molecular Forces Based on the Baker Lectures of Peter J. W. Debye." Wiley, New York.

Cummins, H. Z., and Gammon, R. W. (1966). *J. Chem. Phys.* **44**, 2785.

Davenport, J., W. B., and Root, W. L. (1958) "An Introduction to the Theory of Random Signals and Noise," Chaps. 2 and 3. McGraw-Hill, New York.

Debye, P. (1932) "The Collected Papers of Peter J. W. Debye." Interscience, New York, 1954.

Einstein, A. (1910). *Ann. Phys.* (*Leipzig*) **38**, 1275.

Fabelinskii, I. L. (1957). *Usp. Fiz. Nauk* **63**, 355.

Fabelinskii, I. L. (1965). "Molecular Scattering of Light." Plenum, New York. [Transl. (1968). Nauka, Moscow.]

Kirkwood, J. G., and Oppenheim, I. (1961). "Chemical Thermodynamics," Chap. 6. McGraw-Hill, New York.

Landau, L. D., and Lifshitz, E. M. (1958). "Statistical Physics." Chap. XII. Addison-Wesley, Reading, Massachusetts.

Landau, L. D., and Lifshitz, E. M. (1959). "Fluid Mechanics." Addison-Wesley, Reading, Massachusetts.

Landau, L., and Placzek, G. (1934). *Phys. Z. Sowjetunion* **5**, 172.

Lastovka, J. B. (1967). "Light Mixing Spectroscopy and the Spectrum of Light Scattered by Thermal Fluctuations in Liquids," Ph.D. thesis. MIT, Cambridge, Massachusetts.

Lastovka, J. B., and Benedek, G. (1966). *Phys. Rev. Lett.* **17**, 1039.

Leidecker, Jr., H. W., and La Macchia, J. T. (1968). *J. Acoust. Soc. Amer.* **43**, 143.

Margenau, H. and Murphy, G. M. (1956). "The Mathematics of Physics and Chemistry," pp. 247ff. Van Nostrand-Reinhold, Princeton, New Jersey.

Montrose, C. J., Solovyev, V. A., and Litovitz, T. A. (1968). *J. Acoust. Soc. Amer.* **43**, 117.

Pinnow, D. A., Candau, S. J., La Macchia, J. T., and Litovitz, T. A. (1968). *J. Acoust. Soc. Amer.* **43**, 131.

Panofsky, W. K. H., and Phillips, M. (1955). "Classical Electricity and Magnetism." Addison-Wesley, Reading, Massachusetts.

Chapter IV
LIGHT MIXING SPECTROSCOPY

4.1. Coherence Properties of the Scattered Electric Field

4.1.1. Introduction

Optical coherence theory is concerned with the whole field of statistical optics. The correlations associated with optical fields can be measured by means of photoelectric detectors. Thus, in practice, the studies deal with correlations between *photoelectrons* which can be related to the correlations between *photons*. Furthermore, such correlations can be treated semiclassically, i.e., we may use the classical electromagnetic wave theory even when the interactions have to be treated quantum mechanically (Mandel *et al.*, 1964; Mandel and Wolf, 1965). Glauber (1963, 1964) has developed quantum-mechanical analogs of the correlation functions. His quantum correlation functions indeed provide a more basic approach to optical coherence theory since the radiation field should be treated as a quantum-mechanical system. In general, classical and quantum-mechanical descriptions could lead to different results. However, we shall take the valid assumption that the semiclassical theory provides us with correct predictions in laser light scattering. Sudarshan (1963a,b) has shown the existence of a phase-space representation of the density operator of the electromagnetic field which leads to a correspondence between the classical and quantum-mechanical descriptions, at least for a stationary, ergodic field and in the case of thermal light in which the ensemble distribution of the complex field amplitude is Gaussian. The equivalence of classical (Mandel) and quantal (Glauber) treatment in photocount statistics will be discussed briefly in Section 4.2.

4.1.2. Classical Description of Second-Order Coherence

Spatial coherence deals with correlation between temporal behaviors of the instantaneous electric field observed at two spatially separated points r_1 and r_2. Such considerations are essential for later discussions on optical mixing spectroscopy. As we shall learn, the total scattering power is unimportant; rather the amount of power scattered into a "coherence solid angle" determines the signal-to-noise ratio of our optical mixing spectrometers.

Consider a beam of polarized quasimonochromatic light. Photodetectors are not capable of measuring experimentally the very rapid time variations of the (electric) field with mean optical periods of the order of 10^{-15} sec. However, we can make measurements of the correlations of the field at *two or more* space–time points. To a first approximation, the instantaneous electric field reaching point $Q(R)$ [or $Q(x_\alpha)$ as shown in Fig. 3.1.1] on the photocathode of a photomultiplier tube from two volume elements in the scattering volume as shown in Fig. 4.1.1, is given by

$$\mathbf{E}_s(\mathbf{R}, t) = \mathbf{E}_s(\mathbf{r}_1', t - t_1') + \mathbf{E}_s(\mathbf{r}_2', t - t_2') \qquad (4.1.1)$$

where t_1' ($= r_1/c$) and t_2' ($= r_2/c$) are the times needed for the light to travel from $d\mathbf{r}_1'$ and $d\mathbf{r}_2'$ to Q, respectively.

The instantaneous intensity $I_{inst}(\mathbf{R}, t)$ at the point $Q(R)$ and time t is

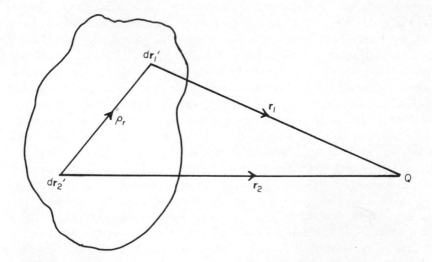

Fig. 4.1.1. Second-order coherence functions illustrated with the help of scattering from two spatially separated "volume" elements.

related to the electric field by Eq. (3.3.6):

$$I_{\text{inst}}(\mathbf{R}, t) = \tfrac{1}{2}(\epsilon/\mu)^{1/2}\mathbf{E}_s^*(\mathbf{R}, t) \cdot \mathbf{E}_s(\mathbf{R}, t)$$

$$\propto [\mathbf{E}_s^*(\mathbf{r}_1', t - t_1') + \mathbf{E}_s^*(\mathbf{r}_2', t - t_2')]$$

$$\cdot [\mathbf{E}_s(\mathbf{r}_1', t - t_1') + \mathbf{E}_s(\mathbf{r}_2', t - t_2')]$$

$$\propto I_{1,\text{inst}}(\mathbf{r}_1', t - t_1') + I_{2,\text{inst}}(\mathbf{r}_2', t - t_2')$$

$$+ \text{const} \cdot [\mathbf{E}_s^*(\mathbf{r}_1', t - t_1') \cdot \mathbf{E}_s(\mathbf{r}_2', t - t_2')] \qquad (4.1.2)$$

where $I_{1,\text{inst}}$ and $I_{2,\text{inst}}$ are the instantaneous intensities at positions $\mathbf{r}_1'$ and $\mathbf{r}_2'$ and times $(t - t_1')$ and $(t - t_2')$, respectively.

For stationary fields, the ensemble averages are independent of the origin of time, and by invoking the ergodic hypothesis, the averaged intensity of the light at Q has the form

$$\langle I(\mathbf{R}, t) \rangle = \langle I(\mathbf{r}_1', t) \rangle + \langle I(\mathbf{r}_2', t) \rangle + \text{const} \cdot [\Gamma_E(\mathbf{r}_1', \mathbf{r}_2', \tau)] \qquad (4.1.3)$$

where the mutual coherence function for the scattered electric field $\Gamma_E(\mathbf{r}_1', \mathbf{r}_2', \tau)$ represents correlations between the field at $\mathbf{r}_2'$, and the complex conjugate field at $\mathbf{r}_1'$, at times t_2' and t_1' which are τ ($= t_2' - t_1'$) apart. Under the assumption of stationarity and ergodicity,

$$\Gamma_E(\mathbf{r}_1', \mathbf{r}_2', \tau) = \langle E_s^*(\mathbf{r}_1', t) E_s(\mathbf{r}_2', t + \tau) \rangle$$

$$= \lim_{T \to \infty} \frac{1}{2T} \int_{-T}^{T} E_s^*(\mathbf{r}_1', t) E_s(\mathbf{r}_2', t + \tau)\, dt$$

$$= \langle E_s^*(\mathbf{r}_1', 0) E_s(\mathbf{r}_2', \tau) \rangle = \overline{E_s^*(\mathbf{r}_1', 0) E_s(\mathbf{r}_2', \tau)}$$

$$= \overline{E_s^*(\mathbf{r}_2' + \varrho_r, 0) E_s(\mathbf{r}_2', \tau)} \qquad (4.1.4)$$

with $\varrho_r = \mathbf{r}_1' - \mathbf{r}_2'$. Equation (4.1.3) tells us that if $\Gamma_E(\mathbf{r}_1', \mathbf{r}_2', \tau) \neq 0$, the superposition of the two beams from $\mathbf{r}_1'$ and $\mathbf{r}_2'$ will produce an interference effect. The normalized mutual coherence function has a form similar to that of Eq. (3.3.20):

$$\gamma_E^t(\mathbf{r}_1', \mathbf{r}_2', \tau) = \frac{\Gamma_E(\mathbf{r}_1', \mathbf{r}_2', \tau)}{[\Gamma_E(\mathbf{r}_1', \mathbf{r}_1', 0)]^{1/2}[\Gamma_E(\mathbf{r}_2', \mathbf{r}_2', 0)]^{1/2}}$$

$$\propto \frac{\Gamma_E(\mathbf{r}_1', \mathbf{r}_2', \tau)}{\langle I(\mathbf{r}_1', 0) \rangle^{1/2}\langle I(\mathbf{r}_2', 0) \rangle^{1/2}} \qquad (4.1.5)$$

In Eq. (4.1.5) we have expressed a normalization factor different from that of Eq. (3.3.20) in order to account for possible variations between $I(\mathbf{r}_1', 0)$ and $I(\mathbf{r}_2', 0)$. Following Eq. (4.1.5), we may define the *spatial* correlation function of the scattered electric field as (Lastovka, 1967)

$$\gamma_E(\mathbf{r}', \varrho_r) = \frac{\langle \mathbf{E}_s{}^*(\mathbf{r}' + \varrho_r, t) \cdot \mathbf{E}_s(\mathbf{r}', t) \rangle}{\langle | \mathbf{E}_s(\mathbf{r}', t) |^2 \rangle^{1/2} \langle | \mathbf{E}_s(\mathbf{r}' + \varrho_r, t) |^2 \rangle^{1/2}} \qquad (4.1.6)$$

where we have dropped the subscript 2 and taken t as some arbitrary time. The angular brackets could represent an ensemble average since it is unnecessary to distinguish between time and ensemble averages for a stationary ergodic process. The numerator in Eq. (4.1.6) may be expressed using the probability density function of Eq. (3.4.17):

$$\overline{\mathbf{E}_s{}^*(\mathbf{r}' + \varrho_r, t) \cdot \mathbf{E}_s(\mathbf{r}', t)} = \overline{\mathbf{E}_s{}^*(\mathbf{r}' + \varrho_r, 0) \cdot \mathbf{E}_s(\mathbf{r}', 0)}$$

$$= \int_{E_s{}^*(\mathbf{r}'+\varrho_r)} \int_{E_s(\mathbf{r}')} \mathbf{E}_s{}^*(\mathbf{r}' + \varrho_r, 0)$$

$$\cdot \mathbf{E}_s(\mathbf{r}', 0) w[\mathbf{E}_s{}^*(\mathbf{r}' + \varrho_r, 0), \mathbf{E}_s(\mathbf{r}', 0)]$$

$$\times d[\mathbf{E}_s{}^*(\mathbf{r}' + \varrho_r, 0)] d[\mathbf{E}_s(\mathbf{r}', 0)] \quad (4.1.7)$$

where $w[\mathbf{E}_s{}^*(\mathbf{r}' + \varrho_r, 0), \ \mathbf{E}_s(\mathbf{r}', 0)]$ is the joint probability density which gives the ensemble average probability that in a "measurement" we will find $\mathbf{E}_s(\mathbf{r}', 0)$ at $\mathbf{r}'$ and $\mathbf{E}_s{}^*(\mathbf{r}' + \varrho_r, 0)$ at $\mathbf{r}' + \varrho_r$. According to Eq. (3.4.18), the joint probability density may again be factored into a conditional probability density and a simple probability density:

$$w[\mathbf{E}_s{}^*(\mathbf{r}' + \varrho_r, 0), \mathbf{E}_s(\mathbf{r}', 0)] = w[\mathbf{E}_s{}^*(\mathbf{r}' + \varrho_r, 0) \mid \mathbf{E}_s(\mathbf{r}', 0)] w[\mathbf{E}_s(\mathbf{r}', 0)]$$

$$(4.1.8)$$

where $w[\mathbf{E}_s{}^*(\mathbf{r}' + \varrho_r, 0) \mid \mathbf{E}_s(\mathbf{r}', 0)]$ is the conditional probability density that the scattered field has $\mathbf{E}_s(\mathbf{r}' + \varrho_r, 0)$ at $\mathbf{r}' + \varrho_r$ *given* $\mathbf{E}_s(\mathbf{r}', 0)$ at $\mathbf{r}'$, while $w[\mathbf{E}_s(\mathbf{r}', 0)] \ d[\mathbf{E}_s(\mathbf{r}', 0)]$ is the simple probability of finding $\mathbf{E}_s(\mathbf{r}', 0)$.

In the absence of correlation, we have

$$w[\mathbf{E}_s{}^*(\mathbf{r}' + \varrho_r, 0) \mid \mathbf{E}_s(\mathbf{r}', 0)] = w[\mathbf{E}_s{}^*(\mathbf{r}' + \varrho_r, 0)]$$

Then, Eq. (4.1.7) reduces to

$$\overline{\mathbf{E}_s{}^*(\mathbf{r}' + \varrho_r) \cdot \mathbf{E}_s(\mathbf{r}')}$$

$$= \int_{E_s{}^*(\mathbf{r}'+\varrho_r)} \mathbf{E}_s{}^*(\mathbf{r}' + \varrho_r) w[\mathbf{E}_s{}^*(\mathbf{r}' + \varrho_r)] d[\mathbf{E}_s{}^*(\mathbf{r}' + \varrho_r)]$$

$$\cdot \int_{E_s(\mathbf{r}')} \mathbf{E}_s(\mathbf{r}') w[\mathbf{E}_s(\mathbf{r}')] d[\mathbf{E}_s(\mathbf{r}')]$$

$$= \overline{\mathbf{E}_s{}^*(\mathbf{r}' + \varrho_r)} \cdot \overline{\mathbf{E}_s(\mathbf{r}')} = 0 \qquad (4.1.9)$$

since the first moment of a Gaussian distribution function is zero. From Schwarz's inequality, we know that the normalization factor ensures the condition

$$0 \leq | \gamma_E(\mathbf{r}_1', \mathbf{r}_2', 0) | \leq 1 \tag{4.1.10}$$

In Eq. (3.1.38), we recall that the scattered electric field observed at the point of observation $Q(\mathbf{R})$ comes from the plane-wave components of $\Delta\chi_e$ having a wave vector $\mathbf{K}$:

$$J(\mathbf{R}, \mathbf{K}) = \int_v \exp[i(\mathbf{k}_\mathrm{I} - \mathbf{k}_\mathrm{s}) \cdot \mathbf{r}'] \, d\mathbf{r}' = \begin{cases} v & \begin{cases} -\dfrac{\pi}{L_x} \leq (k_\mathrm{I} - k_\mathrm{s} + K)_x \leq \dfrac{\pi}{L_x} \\[2mm] -\dfrac{\pi}{L_y} \leq (k_\mathrm{I} - k_\mathrm{s} + K)_y \leq \dfrac{\pi}{L_y} \\[2mm] -\dfrac{\pi}{L_z} \leq (k_\mathrm{I} - k_\mathrm{s} + K)_z \leq \dfrac{\pi}{L_z} \end{cases} \\[8mm] 0, & \text{otherwise} \end{cases} \tag{3.1.38}$$

This implies that the scattering occurs in the direction $\mathbf{R}$ or $\mathbf{k}_\mathrm{s}$, as shown in Fig. 4.1.2, and $\mathbf{k}_\mathrm{I} + \mathbf{K}$ falls inside a rectangular parallelepiped cell ξ^* centered at $\mathbf{k}_\mathrm{s}$ and with dimensions Δk_x, Δk_y, $\Delta k_z (= 2\pi/L_x, 2\pi/L_y, 2\pi/L_z)$, i.e., $\mathbf{K}$ comes to within $(\Delta k_x, \Delta k_y, \Delta k_z)$ of satisfying the condition $\mathbf{k}_\mathrm{I} - \mathbf{k}_\mathrm{s} + \mathbf{K} = 0$. Furthermore, $J(\mathbf{R}, \mathbf{K}) \neq 0$ only for those orientations on $Q(\mathbf{R})$ around the direction $\mathbf{k}_\mathrm{I} + \mathbf{K}$ for which $\mathbf{k}_\mathrm{s}$ falls inside the cell ξ^*. If we apply the Born–Von Kármán boundary conditions (Zinman, 1964), the lattice points in reciprocal space are given by

$$K_x = \frac{2\pi \bar{l}}{L_x}, \qquad K_y = \frac{2\pi \bar{m}}{L_y}, \qquad K_z = \frac{2\pi \bar{n}}{L_z} \tag{4.1.11}$$

with $\bar{l}, \bar{m}, \bar{n} = 0, \pm 1, \pm 2, \ldots$.

The Ewald sphere has a finite thickness equivalent to the dimensions of the unit cell ξ^* in reciprocal space because of the finite size of the scattering volume which produces the uncertainty in momentum $[(\Delta k_x, \Delta k_y, \Delta k_z) = \pm(\pi/L_x, \pi/L_y, \pi/L_z)]$, or, by examining Eq. (3.1.38), we note that the conservation of momentum condition is not sharp, and the light scattered in the direction $Q(\mathbf{R})$ is produced by a single Fourier component $\mathbf{K}_{\bar{l}\bar{m}\bar{n}}$ of the fluctuations falling inside the unit cell ξ^* in reciprocal

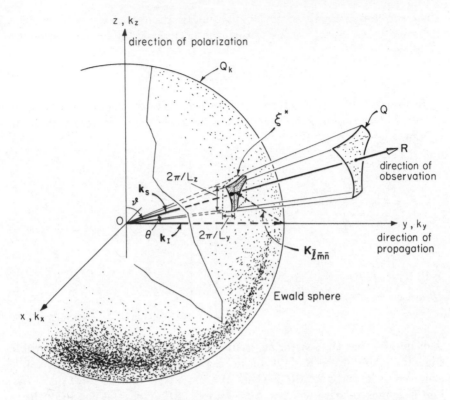

Fig. 4.1.2. Reciprocal space associated with Fourier-series expansion of the electric susceptibility fluctuations (Lastovka, 1967).

space. Furthermore, the unit cells associated with all possible vectors $\mathbf{k}_I + \mathbf{K}_{l\bar{m}\bar{n}}$ form a nonoverlapping net filling all k space.

4.1.3. Calculation of the Coherence Solid Angle*

If $\mathbf{k}_s$ is allowed to assume all possible orientations *on* the Ewald sphere Q_k, then a shell-like volume is swept out by the unit cell ξ^* as shown in Fig. 4.1.3. Since the momentum uncertainty gives the dimensions of the unit cell, we have

$$\Delta \mathbf{k} = \frac{2\pi}{L_x} \frac{\mathbf{x}}{|x|} + \frac{2\pi}{L_y} \frac{\mathbf{y}}{|y|} + \frac{2\pi}{L_z} \frac{\mathbf{z}}{|z|} \qquad (4.1.12)$$

* Lastovka, 1967.

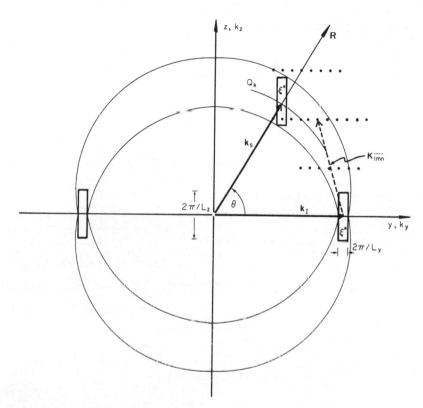

Fig. 4.1.3. Shell swept out by unit cell ξ^* if $\mathbf{k}_s$ takes up all orientations on the Ewald sphere Q_k (Lastovka, 1967).

Thus, the shell thickness in spherical polar coordinates has the form

$$\Delta\mathbf{k} \cdot \frac{\mathbf{k}_s}{|\,k_s\,|} = 2\pi \left[\frac{\sin\vartheta\cos\phi}{L_x} + \frac{\sin\vartheta\sin\phi}{L_y} + \frac{\cos\vartheta}{L_z} \right] \quad (4.1.13)$$

and the volume of the shell in k space is

$$v_k = |\,\mathbf{k}_\mathrm{I}\,|^2 (\Delta\mathbf{k}\cdot\mathbf{k}_s/|\,k_s\,|)\Omega \quad (4.1.14)$$

where Ω is a solid angle.

From Eq. (3.1.37), we get the density of cells in reciprocal k space:

$$\rho_k = \left(\int_{-\pi/L_x}^{+\pi/L_x} dK_x \int_{-\pi/L_y}^{+\pi/L_y} dK_y \int_{-\pi/L_z}^{+\pi/L_z} dK_z \right)^{-1} = \frac{L_x L_y L_z}{(2\pi)^3} = \frac{v}{8\pi^3} \quad (4.1.15)$$

Thus, the number of cells per unit solid angle is

$$\frac{dN}{d\Omega} = \frac{v}{8\pi^3} \mid \mathbf{k_I} \mid^2 2\pi \left(\frac{\sin \vartheta \cos \phi}{L_x} + \frac{\sin \vartheta \sin \phi}{L_y} + \frac{\cos \vartheta}{L_z} \right)$$

$$= \frac{v}{\lambda^2} \left(\frac{\sin \vartheta \cos \phi}{L_x} + \frac{\sin \vartheta \sin \phi}{L_y} + \frac{\cos \vartheta}{L_z} \right)$$

$$= \frac{1}{\lambda^2} (L_y L_z \sin \vartheta \cos \phi + L_x L_z \sin \vartheta \sin \phi + L_x L_y \cos \vartheta) \quad (4.1.16)$$

and the coherence solid angle Ω_{coh} is

$$\Omega_{\text{coh}} = \frac{d\Omega}{dN} = \frac{\lambda^2}{[L_y L_z \sin \vartheta \cos \phi + L_x L_z \sin \vartheta \sin \phi + L_x L_y \cos \vartheta]} \quad (4.1.17)$$

We recall that the power scattered into a solid angle Ω has the form

$$P = 2P_I \Re^* L(\sin^2 \vartheta)\Omega \quad (3.3.66)$$

By substituting Eq. (4.1.17) into Eq. (3.3.66) and with $\mathbf{k_I}$ in the y direction we obtain for the scattered power per coherence solid angle, P_{coh}:

$$P_{\text{coh}} = 2P_I \Re^* L_y (\sin^2 \vartheta) \frac{\lambda^2}{(L_y L_z \sin \vartheta \cos \phi + L_x L_z \sin \vartheta \sin \phi + L_x L_y \cos \vartheta)}$$

$$(4.1.18)$$

For $\vartheta = 90°$, we then have

$$P_{\text{coh}} = 2P_I \Re^* L_y \frac{\lambda^2}{L_z(L_x \sin \phi + L_y \cos \phi)} \quad (4.1.19)$$

where ϑ is the angle between the incident polarization vector and the direction of observation and ϕ is the angle on the x,y plane. Equation (4.1.19) shows that P_{coh} depends upon the geometry of the scattering volume:

$$P_{\text{coh}} \propto \{L_z[\cos \phi + (L_x/L_y) \sin \phi]\}^{-1}$$

By varying the dimensions of L_x, L_y, and L_z, we may maximize P_{coh}. In terms of the scattering angle θ, we have according to Fig. 4.1.2:

$$P_{\text{coh}} = 2P_I \Re^* L_y \frac{\lambda^2}{L_z(L_y \sin \theta + L_x \cos \theta)}, \quad \text{for} \quad \vartheta = 90° \quad (4.1.20)$$

since the angles ϕ and θ are defined from the x and y axes, respectively.

It should be noted that Eq. (4.1.20) depends on the directions of polarization and the incident beam. If we take $\mathbf{k_I}$ to be in the z direction and the direction of polarization to be in the x direction, then Eq. (4.1.20) is changed to

$$P_{\text{coh}} = 2P_{\text{I}}\Re^* L_z \frac{\lambda^2}{L_x(L_z \sin\theta + L_y \cos\theta)} \qquad (4.1.21)$$

We shall follow the geometry for Eq. (4.1.21) in subsequent discussions. Let us first examine the half-angle of coherence in the x,k_s plane as shown in Fig. 4.1.4:

$$(\Delta\vartheta)_{\text{coh}} = \frac{1}{2}\left(\frac{2\pi}{L_x}\right)\frac{1}{|\,\mathbf{k}_s\,|} = \frac{\lambda}{2L_x} \qquad (4.1.22)$$

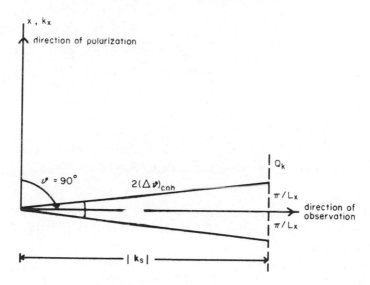

Fig. 4.1.4. Coherence angle of the scattering volume in the x,k_s plane.

Similarly in the y,z plane, the half-angle of coherence

$$(\Delta\theta)_{\text{coh}} = \frac{1}{2}\frac{\lambda}{(L_z \sin\theta + L_y \cos\theta)} \qquad (4.1.23)$$

as shown in Fig. 4.1.5. Thus, L_x should be made as small as possible so as to maximize the coherence angle $(\Delta\vartheta)_{\text{coh}}$ ($=\lambda/2L_x$) and the ratio of L_y to L_z should be minimized, since L_y is in the scattering plane and L_z in the direction of the incident beam. The scattering volume should have (1) small L_x

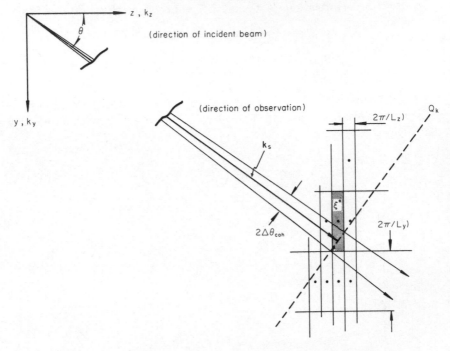

Fig. 4.1.5. Coherence angle in the y,z plane (Lastovka, 1967).

with $(\Delta\vartheta)_{coh} = \lambda/2L_x$ in the direction of the incident polarization vector; (2) small L_y in the direction of the scattering plane; (3) large L_z in the direction of the incident beam.

A simple rule is to observe the scattering process by means of a *thin narrow* incident beam and a *long* scattering volume.

On closer examination of Eq. (4.1.23), we see that there are two limiting behaviors:

$$(\Delta\theta)_{coh} = \frac{\lambda}{2L_z \sin\theta}, \qquad \text{when} \quad L_z \sin\theta \gg L_y \cos\theta \quad \text{or} \quad \tan\theta \gg L_y/L_z$$

$$(4.1.24)$$

and

$$(\Delta\theta)_{coh} = \frac{\lambda}{2L_y \cos\theta}, \qquad \text{when} \quad L_y \cos\theta \gg L_z \sin\theta \quad \text{or} \quad \tan\theta \ll L_y/L_z$$

$$(4.1.25)$$

The $(\Delta\theta)_{\text{coh}}$ dependence on $\sin\theta$ and $\cos\theta$ tells us that

$$P_{\text{coh}} \propto \begin{cases} \dfrac{1}{L_x \sin\theta} & \text{when} \quad \tan\theta \gg L_y/L_z \quad (4.1.26) \\[2mm] \dfrac{L_z}{L_x L_y \cos\theta} & \text{when} \quad \tan\theta \ll L_y/L_z \quad (4.1.27) \\[2mm] \dfrac{1}{2L_x \sin\theta} & \text{when} \quad \tan\theta_c = L_y/L_z \quad (4.1.28) \end{cases}$$

From Eqs. (4.1.22) and (4.1.23), we retrieve the coherence solid angle for $\vartheta = 90°$:

$$\Omega_{\text{coh}}(\vartheta = 90°) = 4(\Delta\theta)_{\text{coh}}(\Delta\vartheta)_{\text{coh}} = \frac{\lambda^2}{L_x(L_z \sin\theta + L_y \cos\theta)} \quad (4.1.29)$$

Thus, for fixed dimensions of L_x, L_y, and L_z, we see from Eqs. (4.1.21) and (4.1.29) that $P_{\text{coh}} \propto L_z \Omega_{\text{coh}} \propto \Omega_{\text{coh}}$. Figure 4.1.6 shows a plot of $1/L_x[\sin\theta + (L_y/L_z)\cos\theta]$ and Ω_{coh} vs θ for two flat scattering cells whose

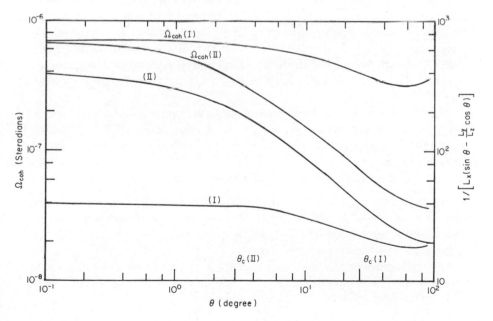

Fig. 4.1.6. A plot of $1/L_x[\sin\theta + (L_y/L_z)\cos\theta]$ and Ω_{coh} vs θ. Cell I has $L_x = L_y = 0.05$ cm, $L_z = 0.10$ cm; cell II has $L_x = L_y = 0.05$ cm, $L_z = 1.0$ cm.

scattering volumes have the following dimensions:

	L_x (cm)	L_y (cm)	L_z (cm)	$\tan \theta_c$	θ_c
Cell I:	0.05	0.05	0.10	0.50	26°34′
Cell II:	0.05	0.05	1.0	0.05	2°52′

With $\lambda_{air} = 632.8$ nm and $n = 1.5$, $(\Delta\theta)_{coh}$ varies from 0.02° to 0.01° for cell I and from 0.014° to 0.001° for cell II, between $\theta = 2°$ to 70°.

Thus we can draw the following conclusions:

(1) Dimensions of 0.05 cm form the upper limit for L_x and L_y. In fact, we should focus the laser beam down to smaller dimensions in order to obtain larger coherence angles. For example, a reduction of beam diameter down to 0.01 cm could increase $(\Delta\vartheta)_{coh}$ by a factor of 5. An angular aperture of about 0.25° for the detector is fairly easy to construct for a light-scattering photometer. The reduction in beam diameter should not be performed with a diaphragm but with a lens which increases the power density of the incident beam since ordinary continuous wave (cw) He–Ne or argon-ion lasers have beam diameters of 0.1–0.3 cm corresponding to a factor of about 10 to 30 too large for our purposes. In conventional light scattering we often use mercury arcs as light sources where the incident beam has cross sections in the neighborhood of 0.1 cm². If we replace the mercury arc lamp by a laser source *without focusing*, and try to do light-beating experiments, we shall be losing a factor of at least about 30 in P_{coh} when compared with a focused laser incident beam.

(2) An increase in the dimension of L_z becomes less important soon after $\theta < \theta_c$. A good criterion is $\tan \theta_c = L_y/L_z$ from Eq. (4.1.28). Then we need only to compare the sizes of effective scattering volumes between different L_x, L_y, and L_z.

(3) For fixed L_y, θ_c becomes smaller with increasing L_z.

If we have a long thin scattering volume (as in cell II), the most favorable measurements should be done at very small scattering angles ($\theta < \theta_c \approx 2°52′$) even though dust could then become a serious problem. At larger angles, the gain in P_{coh} decreases.

Let us now consider the case of a scattering volume having the shape of a parallelepiped. The effective scattering volume v_{eff} for a *very narrow* beam at a scattering angle θ is

$$v_{eff,\theta} = v_{\theta=90°}/\sin\theta = L_x L_y L_{z,90°}/\sin\theta \qquad (4.1.30)$$

where $L_x L_y$ = cross section of the incident beam normal to the direction of propagation z and $L_{z,90°}$ is the length dimension of the effective scattering volume as observed by the detector at $\theta = 90°$. If we take $\tan \theta \gg L_y/L_z$, then

$$(\Delta\theta)_{coh} = \frac{\lambda}{2(L_z \sin \theta)} = \frac{\lambda}{2L_{z,90°}} \qquad (4.1.31)$$

and

$$\Omega_{coh}(\vartheta = 90°) = 4(\Delta\vartheta)_{coh}(\Delta\theta)_{coh} = \frac{\lambda^2}{L_x L_{z,90°}} \qquad (4.1.32)$$

which is a constant, independent of the scattering angle θ so long as $\tan \theta \gg L_y/L_z$, and $L_z \ (= L_{z,90°}/\sin \theta)$ is less than or equal to the thickness of the cell in the direction of the incident beam. More generally, we know that Eq. (4.1.32) holds for a scattering volume with the shape of a parallelepiped. However, in the y,z plane, the half-angle of coherence $(\Delta\theta)_{coh}$ behaves differently.

The path-length increments Δ_1 and Δ_2, as shown in Fig. 4.1.7, are

$$\Delta_1 = L_z \cos \theta \qquad (4.1.33)$$

$$\Delta_2 = L_y/\sin \theta = L_y \csc \theta \qquad (4.1.34)$$

The relative phase at the position of the detector Q between waves origi-

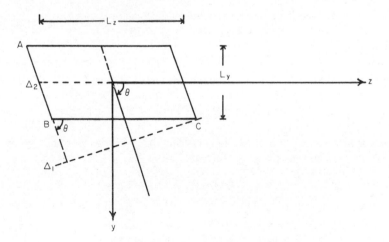

Fig. 4.1.7. Effective scattering area in the y,z plane.

nating at A and C changes with θ at a rate

$$\frac{d(\text{relative phase})}{d\theta} = \frac{2\pi}{\lambda}\frac{d(\Delta_1 + \Delta_2)}{d\theta}$$

$$= \frac{2\pi}{\lambda}\left(L_z \sin\theta + L_y \frac{\cos\theta}{\sin^2\theta}\right)$$

For a maximum change of π in relative phase, we have

$$(\Delta\theta)_{\text{coh}} = \frac{\lambda}{2(L_z \sin\theta + L_y \cos\theta/\sin^2\theta)} \tag{4.1.35}$$

In substituting Eq. (4.1.35) into Eq. (3.3.66), and in remembering $L_z = L_{z,90°}/\sin\theta$ where $L_{z,90°}$ is determined by the detector geometry, we have the power scattered into a coherence solid angle for a parallelepiped at $\vartheta = 90°$:

$$P_{\text{coh,parallelepiped}} = 2P_I\Re^* L_{z,90°} \frac{\lambda^2}{L_x \sin\theta[L_{z,90°} + (L_y \cos\theta/\sin^2\theta)]}$$

$$= \frac{2P_I\Re^*\lambda^2}{L_x \sin\theta \mid 1 + (L_y \cos\theta/L_{z,90°}\sin^2\theta) \mid} \tag{4.1.36}$$

4.2. Photoelectric Detection of the Scattered Electric Field

4.2.1. Introduction

We use photoelectric detectors to measure correlations in photoelectrons which in turn can be related to correlations of the scattered electric field. In laser light scattering, we are concerned mainly with the visible spectrum in the range from about 400 to 700 nm. Table 4.2.1 conveniently relates the various units of wavelength, frequency, wave numbers, and color. Often, we are interested in knowing the relationships between percentage changes in frequency and wavelength. Since we have $\nu = c/\lambda$,

$$\mid \Delta\nu \mid/\nu \approx \mid \Delta\lambda \mid/\lambda \tag{4.2.1}$$

which is the bandwidth. The best available grating spectrometer has a bandwidth of about 10^{-6} while Fabry–Perot interferometers have bandwidths of about 10^{-7}. On the other hand, for example, the linewidth of the central Rayleigh component for a one-component system in the neighborhood of its critical point becomes very small (Chu, 1970), so we need a

Table 4.2.1
Wavelength, frequency, wave number, color

λ (nm)	$\bar{\nu}$ $(=1/\lambda)$ (10^4 cm^{-1})	ν $(=c/\lambda)^a$ (10^{14} Hz)	ω $(=2\pi\nu)$ $(10^{14} \text{ rad/sec})$	Color
380–480	2.63–2.08	7.90–6.25	49.6–39.3	Violet
480–520	2.08–1.92	6.25–5.77	39.3–36.2	Blue
520–560	1.92–1.78	5.77–5.36	36.2–33.7	Green
560–610	1.78–1.64	5.36–4.92	33.7–30.9	Yellow
610–630	1.64–1.59	4.92–4.76	30.9–29.9	Orange
630–720	1.59–1.39	4.76–4.17	29.9–26.2	Red

$^a c = 3 \times 10^{10}$ cm/sec.

detection scheme with an extremely high resolving power which is about a million times more than the narrowest bandpass filter in the optical frequencies. The *direct* detection receiver, in which the signal is detected with no prior translation of the incident signal energy to another frequency, is not appropriate. Instead, we should shift the frequency down to a sufficiently low value prior to filtering so that the desired bandpass filters, which are no longer optical filters, may be used at the new center frequency. This technique is called *heterodyne detection* which always requires a local oscillator. *Homodyne* detection (or self-beating technique), where the local oscillator frequency and the input signal frequency have the same value, is a special case of heterodyne detection. While optical spectrometers filter at the optical frequency, the optical *mixing* spectrometer filters only after the light carrier wave has been shifted down, by means of a nonlinear element (a mixer, such as a photomultiplier tube), to a much lower frequency where very narrow bandpass filters are available. The photosensitive element (mixer) detects light intensity in terms of the number of photoelectrons or a photocurrent which is proportional to the *square* of the electric field falling on the photosensitive surface.

Before describing the two optical mixing spectrometers (self-beating and heterodyne), we need to know that the photoelectric detection process has its own probabilistic nature. The relationship between the photoelectric current spectrum and the optical spectrum depends crucially on the statistical nature of optical signals as well as the detection process itself. Furthermore, photodetectors are not able to follow the optical frequency but only the modulation due to motions of molecules in our scattering process as shown in Fig. 4.2.1. The photodetector output signal contains informa-

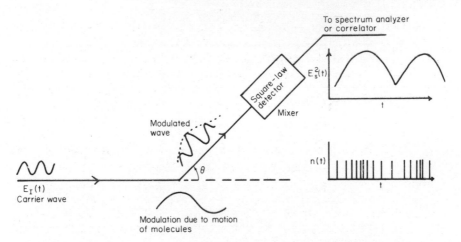

Fig. 4.2.1.   Pictorial representation of the self-beating technique.

tion on the modulation frequency which is the slowly varying envelope of a rapidly oscillating optical field.

We may consider the resulting time variation of the photocurrent as beatings (differences) between closely spaced optical frequencies from a nonlinear (square-law) mixer. The net result is a transposition of the optical *field* spectrum centered at $\nu_I \approx 5 \times 10^{14}$ Hz to a *current* spectrum at frequencies centered at 0 Hz, where a 1-Hz band filter is easily available. The advantages in the translation of the center frequency may be visualized as follows:

(1)   In the self-beating technique, if the spectrum has a Lorentzian linewidth of Γ_c, and the band filter is $\Delta\nu_0 = 1$ Hz, then the effective resolving power is

$$\left(\frac{\omega_I}{\Delta\omega}\right)_{\text{eff}} = \left(\frac{\omega_I}{\Gamma_c}\right)\left(\frac{\Gamma_c}{\Delta\omega_0}\right) = \frac{\omega_I}{\Delta\omega_0} = 5 \times 10^{14}$$

(2)   In the heterodyning procedure, if the local oscillator has a frequency ω_{LO}, the beat signals between ω_{LO} and the frequency components of the input signal give a spectrum which is identical to the spectrum of the input signal except for a shift in the center frequency from ω_I to $\omega_{if} = \omega_I - \omega_{LO}$. $\Delta\omega_{if}$ is the bandwidth of the tuned filter in the intermediate frequency (if) range. The effective resolving power for $\Delta\nu_{if} = 1$ Hz is

$$\left(\frac{\omega_I}{\Delta\omega}\right)_{\text{eff}} = \left(\frac{\omega_I}{\omega_{if}}\right)\left(\frac{\omega_{if}}{\Delta\omega_{if}}\right) = \frac{\omega_I}{\Delta\omega_{if}} = 5 \times 10^{14}$$

Figure 4.2.1 also shows that the photocurrent output can be expressed in terms of photopulses. The deviation of the counting distribution from a purely Poisson distribution provides us with the same information on the spectrum of light. However, the information is in digital form. Thus, in principle, it is easier to design a more precise instrument using the photon-count method even though it contains no more information.

4.2.2. Probability Distribution for Emitted Photopulses

The probability distribution $w[n, t, T]$ is defined as the probability that n photoelectrons are emitted in a period of time T after an initial starting time t per area element dS at $\mathbf{R}$. The probability that one photoelectron is emitted in a very short time period δT after an initial time t per area element dS at $\mathbf{R}$ is $w[1, t, \delta T]$. We may choose δT so short that we are not likely to find a photopulse within the time interval δT. Then,

$$w[1, t, \delta T] \ll 1 \qquad (4.2.2)$$

and the probability of having more than one emitted photoelectron during the time interval δT is negligible, i.e.,

$$w[n \geq 2, t, \delta T] \approx 0 \qquad (4.2.3)$$

It seems reasonable to assume that the probability of emission of an electron during a given time interval δT, $w[1, t, \delta T]$, is proportional to the short-time (st) average intensity $\langle I(\delta T) \rangle_{st}$ and the length of the time interval δT, i.e., as $\delta T \to 0$,

$$w[1, t, \delta T] = \alpha \left[\int_t^{t+\delta T} E^2(\mathbf{R}, t') \, dt' \right] \delta T = a \langle I(\delta T) \rangle_{st} \, \delta T \qquad (4.2.4)$$

where

$$\langle I(\delta T) \rangle_{st} \propto \int_t^{t+\delta T} E^2(\mathbf{R}, t') \, dt'$$

and a and α are undetermined proportionality constants. The short-time average denotes that δT is much smaller than the coherence time but much larger than the period of the light. Equations (4.2.3) and (4.2.4) imply that, for small δT,

$$w[0, t, \delta T] + w[1, t, \delta T] = 1 \qquad (4.2.5)$$

where $w[0, t, \delta T]$ is the probability that no photoelectrons are emitted within the short-time interval δT after time t from an area element dS at $\mathbf{R}$.

In terms of $w[n, t, \delta T]$, we have

$$
w[n, t, \delta T] = \begin{cases} 1 - w[1, t, \delta T], & n = 0 \\ w[1, t, \delta T], & n = 1 \\ 0, & n \geq 2 \end{cases} \qquad (4.2.6)
$$

The probability that *no* photoelectrons are emitted within the time interval T may be determined as follows. Consider a sampling period of length $T + \delta T$ to be broken up into two subintervals T and δT. If we assume that the emission of photoelectrons is statistically independent of the number of previously emitted photoelectrons, we have

$$
w[0, t, T + \delta T] = w[0, t, T]w[0, t + T, \delta T] \qquad (4.2.7)
$$

By substituting Eqs. (4.2.4) and (4.2.5) into Eq. (4.2.7), we get for small δT the result

$$
w[0, t, T + \delta T] = w[0, t, T](1 - a\langle I(\delta T) \rangle_{st}\delta T)
$$

or

$$
\frac{w[0, t, T + \delta T] - w[0, t, T]}{\delta T} = -a\langle I(\delta T) \rangle_{st}w[0, t, T] \qquad (4.2.8)
$$

As $\delta T \to 0$, the difference equation (4.2.8) becomes the differential equation:

$$
dw[0, t, T]/w[0, t, T] = -a\langle I(\delta T) \rangle_{st} \, dT \qquad (4.2.9)
$$

which has the solution

$$
w[0, t, T] = \exp\left(-a \int_t^{t+T} \langle I(\delta T') \rangle_{st} \, dT'\right) \qquad (4.2.10)
$$

where the boundary condition

$$
w[0, t, 0] = \lim_{\delta T \to 0} w[0, t, \delta T] = 1 \qquad (4.2.11)
$$

follows from Eqs. (4.2.2) and (4.2.5). In a stationary process, the starting time is unimportant so that

$$
w[0, T] = \exp\left(-a \int_0^T \langle I(\delta T') \rangle_{st} \, dT'\right) \qquad (4.2.12)
$$

Equation (4.2.10) could also be obtained if we divide the total time interval T into N very small time intervals δT_i such that $T = \sum_{i=1}^N \delta T_i$. Then the probability that no photoelectrons are emitted within time interval T is the product of the probabilities that there are no photoelectrons emitted in each of the short-time interval δT_i, i.e.,

$$w[0, t, T] = w[0, t_1, \delta T_1]w[0, t_2, \delta T_2]\cdots w[0, t_N, \delta T_N]$$

$$= (1 - a\langle I(\delta T_1)\rangle_{\text{st}}\,\delta T_1)\,(1 - a\langle I(\delta T_2)\rangle_{\text{st}}\,\delta T_2)\cdots$$

$$\cdot (1 - a\langle I(\delta T_N)\rangle_{\text{st}}\,\delta T_N)$$

or

$$\ln w[0, t, T] = \ln(1 - a\langle I(\delta T_1)\rangle_{\text{st}}\,\delta T_1) + \ln(1 - a\langle I(\delta T_2)\rangle_{\text{st}}\,\delta T_2)$$

$$+ \cdots + \ln(1 - a\langle I(\delta T_N)\rangle_{\text{st}}\,\delta T_N)$$

$$\approx -a\sum_{i=1}^{N}\langle I(\delta T_i)\rangle_{\text{st}}\,\delta T_i$$

$$= -a\int_{t}^{t+T}\langle I(\delta T')\rangle_{\text{st}}\,dT'$$

since $\ln(1 - x) = -x$ for $x < 1$ and we have $w(1, t, \delta T) \ll 1$ from Eq. (4.2.2). Thus, we have again obtained Eq. (4.2.10).

In order to compute the probability $w[n, t, T]$ that there are n photoelectrons emitted during an interval of time T after an initial starting time t, we shall next consider the probability that there are n photoelectrons emitted during a time interval $T + \delta T$ after an initial starting time t. The time interval $T + \delta T$ can again be broken into two intervals T and δT. By means of Eq. (4.2.2) there can be either one or no electron emitted during the short-time interval δT. It follows that, for small δT, in a stationary process,

$$w[n, T + \delta T] = w[n - 1, T; 1, \delta T] + w[n, T; 0, \delta T] \quad (4.2.13)$$

Again, with the assumption that the emission of photoelectrons during time interval δT is statistically independent of the photoelectrons emitted during time period T, we have for small δT:

$$w[n, T + \delta T] = w[n - 1, T]w[1, \delta T] + w[n, T]w[0, \delta T] \quad (4.2.14)$$

By substituting Eqs. (4.2.4) and (4.2.5) into Eq. (4.2.14), we get

$$w[n, T + \delta T] = w[n - 1, T]a\langle I(\delta T)\rangle_{\text{st}}\,\delta T$$

$$+ w[n, T][1 - a\langle I(\delta T)\rangle_{\text{st}}\,\delta T]$$

or

$$\frac{w[n, T + \delta T] - w[n, T]}{\delta T} + a\langle I(\delta T)\rangle_{\text{st}}w[n, T]$$

$$= a\langle I(\delta T)\rangle_{\text{st}}w[n - 1, T] \quad (4.2.15)$$

As $\delta T \to 0$, the difference equation (4.2.15) becomes the differential equation

$$dw[n, T]/dT + a\langle I(\delta T)\rangle_{st} w[n, T] = a\langle I(\delta T)\rangle_{st} w[n - 1, T] \quad (4.2.16)$$

which is a recursion equation relating $w[n, T]$ to $w[n - 1, T]$. The solution to Eq. (4.2.16) with the boundary condition $w[n, 0] = 0$ is

$$w[n, T] = a\left[\exp\left(-a\int_0^T \langle I(\delta T')\rangle_{st}\, dT'\right)\right]\int_0^T \langle I(\delta T')\rangle_{st}$$

$$\times \exp\left(a\int_0^{T'} \langle I(\delta T'')\rangle_{st}\, dT''\right) w[n - 1, T']\, dT'$$

Thus, if we take $n = 1, 2, \ldots, n$, we get

$$w[1, T] = a\left[\exp\left(-a\int_0^T \langle I(\delta T')\rangle_{st}\, dT'\right)\right]\int_0^T \langle I(\delta T')\rangle_{st}$$

$$\times \exp\left[a\int_0^{T'} \langle I(\delta T'')\rangle_{st}\, dT''\right] w[0, T']\, dT'$$

$$= a\int_0^T \langle I(\delta T')\rangle_{st}\, dT' \left\{\exp\left[-a\int_0^T \langle I(\delta T')\rangle_{st}\, dT'\right]\right\}$$

$$w[2, T] = \left[a\int_0^T \langle I(\delta T')\rangle_{st}\, dT'\right]^2 \left\{\exp\left[-a\int_0^T \langle I(\delta T')\rangle_{st}\, dT'\right]\right\}\bigg/ 2!$$

$$w[n, T] = \frac{1}{n!}\left[a\int_0^T \langle I(\delta T')\rangle_{st}\, dT'\right]^n \exp\left[-a\int_0^T \langle I(\delta T')\rangle_{st}\, dT'\right]$$

$$(4.2.17)$$

The term $n!$ is introduced to allow for the reordering of the times. The probability that there be n photoelectrons emitted in a finite time interval from t to $t + T$ is a Poisson distribution.

We shall consider $\langle I(\delta T)\rangle_{st}$ as (1) a constant I_0 and (2) a random variable.

(1)   In the limit when T becomes extremely large, all the fluctuations in the intensity are smoothed out on integration. W may be regarded as a constant with

$$W = \int_t^{t+T} \langle I(\delta T)\rangle_{st}\, dT = I_0 T \quad \text{and} \quad P(W) = \delta(W - \langle W\rangle)$$

where $P(W)$ is the probability density of the light intensity and is expected to be appropriate for light from an incandescent lamp. Then the probability distribution of registering n photoelectrons by an ideal detector in a time interval $t, t + T$, is

$$p(n, t, T) = (1/n!) \exp(-aI_0T)(aI_0T)^n \qquad (4.2.18)$$

where we have identified $w[n, t, T]$ with $p(n, t, T)$. The average number of photoelectrons emitted during the sampling period T is

$$\langle n(T) \rangle = \sum_{n=0}^{\infty} \frac{n(aI_0T)^n}{n!} \exp(-aI_0T) = \sum_{n=1}^{\infty} \frac{1}{(n-1)!} \exp(-aI_0T)(aI_0T)^n$$

$$= \exp(-aI_0T)(aI_0T) \sum_{n=1}^{\infty} \frac{(aI_0T)^{n-1}}{(n-1)!}$$

$$= \exp(-aI_0T)(aI_0T) \exp(aI_0T) = aI_0T$$

where we can identify a as the quantum efficiency of the detector. In general, a is proportional to the averaged gain of the photodetector as well as the quantum efficiency with which the photons are able to eject photoelectrons. Thus, we may write

$$p(n, t, T) = \frac{1}{n!} \exp[-\langle n(T) \rangle]\langle n(T) \rangle^n \qquad (4.2.19)$$

which is normalized since

$$\sum_{n=0}^{\infty} \frac{1}{n!} \exp[-\langle n(T) \rangle]\langle n(T) \rangle^n = \exp[-\langle n(T) \rangle] \sum_{n=0}^{\infty} \frac{\langle n(T) \rangle^n}{n!}$$

$$= \exp[-\langle n(T) \rangle + \langle n(T) \rangle] = 1$$

For $n = 1$ and $\langle n(T) \rangle = 0$, $\exp[-\langle n(T) \rangle] \rightarrow 1$. Equation (4.2.19) reduces approximately to $w[1, \delta T] \approx a\langle I(\delta T) \rangle_{st} \delta T$ which checks with Eq. (4.2.4).

Using Sterling's approximation for large n:

$$n! = (2\pi n)^{1/2} n^n e^{-n} (1 + 1/12n + \cdots)$$

we obtain for the probability of finding $\langle n(T) \rangle$ over the sample period T

$$p(\langle n(T) \rangle, t, T) = [1/\langle n(T) \rangle!] \exp[-\langle n(T) \rangle]\langle n(T) \rangle^{\langle n(T) \rangle}$$

$$\approx [1/\langle n(T) \rangle!]\{\langle n(T) \rangle!/[2\pi\langle n(T) \rangle]^{1/2}\}$$

$$= \{1/[2\pi\langle n(T) \rangle]^{1/2}\} \qquad (4.2.20)$$

and for the mean-square fluctuation in the number of photopulses

$$\langle[n - \langle n(T)\rangle]^2\rangle_{T,\text{Poisson}} = \sum_{n=0}^{\infty} [n - \langle n(T)\rangle]^2 p(n, t, T)$$

$$= \sum_{n=0}^{\infty} [n^2 - 2n\langle n(T)\rangle + \langle n(T)\rangle^2] p(n, t, T)$$

$$= \sum_{n=0}^{\infty} [n^2 - \langle n(T)\rangle^2] p(n, t, T)$$

$$= \sum_{n=0}^{\infty} n^2 p(n, t, T) - \langle n(T)\rangle^2 \sum_{n=0}^{\infty} p(n, t, T)$$

$$= \left(\sum_{n=0}^{\infty} \frac{n}{(n-1)!} \langle n(T)\rangle^n \exp[-\langle n(T)\rangle]\right)$$
$$- \langle n(T)\rangle^2$$

$$= \left[\sum_{n=1}^{\infty} \left(\frac{(n-1)}{(n-1)!} + \frac{1}{(n-1)!}\right)\right.$$
$$\left. \times \langle n(T)\rangle^n \exp[-\langle n(T)\rangle]\right] - \langle n(T)\rangle^2$$

$$= \sum_{n=2}^{\infty} \frac{\exp[-\langle n(T)\rangle]\langle n(T)\rangle^{n-2}\langle n(T)\rangle^2}{(n-2)!}$$

$$+ \sum_{n=1}^{\infty} \frac{\exp[-\langle n(T)\rangle](\langle n(T)\rangle^{n-1})\langle n(T)\rangle}{(n-1)!}$$
$$- \langle n(T)\rangle^2$$

$$= \langle n(T)\rangle^2 + \langle n(T)\rangle - \langle n(T)\rangle^2 = \langle n(T)\rangle$$

$$(4.2.21)$$

(2)   If $\langle I(\delta T')\rangle_{\text{st}}$ is a random variable, the integral

$$W = \int_t^{t+T} \langle I(\delta T')\rangle_{\text{st}} \, dT' \qquad (4.2.22)$$

is a random variable with a nonzero mean. Then, the *probability distribution* $p(n, t, T)$ of registering n photoelectrons by an ideal detector in a time interval from t to $t + T$ is also a random variable and its average over the probability density of the light intensity $P(W)$ is

$$p(n, t, T) = \int_0^\infty \frac{(aW)^n}{n!} e^{-aW} P(W) \, dW \qquad (4.2.23)$$

Equation (4.2.23) was first derived by Mandel (1958, 1959) using classical arguments.

Jakeman and Pike (1968) have computed $P(W)$ under the conditions that the light field is a Gaussian random variable and that T is small compared to the coherence time T_{coh} so that $W = IT$. Hence we may write

$$P(W) = (1/\langle W \rangle) \exp(-W/\langle W \rangle) \qquad (4.2.24)$$

where $\langle W \rangle = \langle I \rangle T$. Substituting Eq. (4.2.24) into Eq. (4.2.23), we get

$$p(n, t, T) = \int_0^\infty \exp(-aW)[(aW)^n/n!](1/\langle W \rangle) \exp(-W/\langle W \rangle) \, dW$$

The integral can be performed by a change of variable:

$$x = aW[1 + (a\langle W \rangle)^{-1}]; \qquad dx = a \, dW[1 + (a\langle W \rangle)^{-1}]$$

$$p(n, t, T) = \frac{1}{n!} \int_0^\infty \exp[-(aW + W/\langle W \rangle)](aW)^n \frac{dW}{\langle W \rangle}$$

$$= \frac{1}{n!} \int_0^\infty e^{-x} \frac{x^n}{[1 + (a\langle W \rangle)^{-1}]^n} \, dx \frac{1}{a\langle W \rangle[1 + (a\langle W \rangle)^{-1}]}$$

$$= \frac{1}{n!} \frac{1}{[1 + (a\langle W \rangle)^{-1}]^n} \frac{1}{(1 + a\langle W \rangle)} \int_0^\infty x^n e^{-x} \, dx$$

$$= \frac{1}{(1 + a\langle W \rangle)} \frac{1}{[1 + (a\langle W \rangle)^{-1}]^n} \qquad (4.2.25)$$

where

$$\Gamma(n + 1) = n! = \int_0^\infty x^n e^{-x} \, dx$$

since

$$\langle n(T) \rangle = \sum_n n p(n, t, T) = a\langle W(t, T) \rangle \qquad (4.2.26)$$

which is the average number of photoelectrons emitted during the interval T. Then,

$$p(n, t, T) = \frac{1}{[1 + \langle n(T) \rangle][1 + (\langle n(T) \rangle)^{-1}]^n} \qquad (4.2.27)$$

Equation (4.2.27) is the Bose–Einstein distribution which corresponds to the probability that there be n bosons in a single cell in phase space.

By definition, the *statistical average* of n in a Bose–Einstein distribution has the form:

$$\overline{n(T)} = \sum_{n=0}^{\infty} n(T) p(n, t, T) = \frac{1}{[1 + \langle n(T) \rangle]} \sum_{n=0}^{\infty} \frac{n}{[1 + (\langle n(T) \rangle)^{-1}]^n}$$

$$(4.2.28)$$

If we let $x = 1/[1 + \langle n(T) \rangle^{-1}]$, Eq. (4.2.28) changes to

$$\overline{n(T)} = \frac{1}{1 + \langle n(T) \rangle} \sum_{n=0}^{\infty} n x^n$$

$$= \frac{1}{1 + \langle n(T) \rangle} (x + 2x^2 + 3x^3 + \cdots)$$

$$= \frac{1}{1 + \langle n(T) \rangle} x \frac{\partial}{\partial x} (x + x^2 + x^3 + x^4 + \cdots)$$

$$= \frac{1}{1 + \langle n(T) \rangle} x \frac{\partial}{\partial x} \left(\frac{1}{1 - x} \right) = \frac{1}{1 + \langle n(T) \rangle} \frac{x}{(1 - x)^2}$$

$$= \frac{1}{1 + \langle n(T) \rangle} \frac{\langle n(T) \rangle}{1 + \langle n(T) \rangle} (1 + \langle n(T) \rangle)^2 = \langle n(T) \rangle \quad (4.2.29)$$

Thus, according to the Bose–Einstein distribution, the statistical average of n, $\bar{n}$, is equal to average number of photoelectrons $\langle n(T) \rangle$ in a period T. We now compute the second moment of n according to Eq. (4.2.27):

$$\overline{n^2} = \sum_{n=0}^{\infty} n^2 p(n, t, T) = \frac{1}{1 + \langle n(T) \rangle} \sum_{n=0}^{\infty} n^2 x^n$$

$$= \frac{1}{1 + \langle n(T) \rangle} x \frac{\partial}{\partial x} [x(1 + 2x + 3x^2 + \cdots)]$$

$$= \frac{1}{1 + \langle n(T) \rangle} x \frac{\partial}{\partial x} \left[x \left(\frac{\partial}{\partial x} \left(\frac{1}{1 - x} \right) \right) \right] = \frac{1}{1 + \langle n(T) \rangle} \frac{x + x^2}{(1 - x)^3}$$

$$= \frac{1}{1 + \langle n(T) \rangle} (1 + \langle n(T) \rangle)^3 \left(\frac{\langle n(T) \rangle + \langle n(T) \rangle^2 + \langle n(T) \rangle^2}{(1 + \langle n(T) \rangle)^2} \right)$$

$$= \langle n(T) \rangle^2 + \langle n(T) \rangle [\langle n(T) \rangle + 1]$$

$$= \langle n(T) \rangle + 2 \langle n(T) \rangle^2 \quad (4.2.30)$$

Now according to the Bose–Einstein distribution, the mean-square fluctuation of the photoelectrons in a period T can readily be obtained from Eqs. (4.2.29) and (4.2.30):

$$\langle (n - \langle n \rangle)^2 \rangle_{T,\text{Bose–Einstein}} = \langle n \rangle^2 - \langle n \rangle^2 + \langle n \rangle [\langle n \rangle + 1]$$

$$= \langle n \rangle [\langle n \rangle + 1] \qquad (4.2.31)$$

provided that the light field is a Gaussian random variable and $T \ll T_{\text{coh}}$. Alkemade (1959) first pointed out that the optical spectrum could be determined from an electronic spectral analysis of this excess noise in the photocurrent spectrum. The expression for the variance was first given by Mandel et al. (1964). Freed and Haus (1965) and Arecchi (1965) observed that the photocount distribution of a Gaussian light field obeyed the Bose–Einstein statistics while Arecchi (1969) found that the direct laser beam followed the Poisson distribution.

In general, $P(W)$ is not a positive definite function. However, for radiation fields produced from most of the available sources, we may take $P(W)$ as a probability function.

The theory of photoelectron counting has been reviewed extensively by Mehta (1970) who has also discussed briefly the relationship between the classical and quantal treatment of the statistical description of optical fields.

Quantum-mechanical derivations of photoelectron counting have been given by Kelley and Kleiner (1964), Glauber (1966), Korenman (1967), and Lehmberg (1968). The final result may be expressed in a form similar to Eq. (4.2.23). The probability of counting n photoelectrons in a time interval $t, t + T$ is given by

$$p(n, t, T) = \left\langle : \frac{(a\hat{W})^n}{n!} \exp(-a\hat{W}) : \right\rangle \qquad (4.2.32)$$

where the colons denote normal ordering and the angular brackets denote the quantum expectation value $\langle \vartheta \rangle \equiv \text{Tr}(\hat{\rho}\vartheta)$ with $\hat{\rho}$ being the density operator of the radiation field:

$$\hat{W} = \int_S dS \int_t^{t+T} dt' \, \hat{A}^+(\mathbf{r}, t') \cdot \hat{A}(\mathbf{r}, t') \qquad (4.2.33)$$

where $\hat{A}(\mathbf{r}, t)$ is the positive frequency part of the field operator (vector potential) and the integration dS is performed over the surface of the detector. The proof of equivalence of Eqs. (4.2.23) and (4.2.32) has been shown by Mehta (1970) in pp. 381–382 of his excellent review article. The field operators can be expanded in the form

$$\hat{A}(\mathbf{r}, t) = \sum_\lambda \hat{a}_\lambda \mathbf{u}_\lambda(\mathbf{r}, t), \qquad \hat{A}^+(\mathbf{r}, t) = \sum_\lambda \hat{a}_\lambda^+ \mathbf{u}_\lambda^*(\mathbf{r}, t)$$

where the operators $\hat{a}_\lambda$, $\hat{a}_\lambda^+$ are the annihilation and creation operators, respectively, of the photon with mode label λ.

By making use of the diagonal representation of the density operator

$$\hat{\rho} = \int \phi(\{v_\lambda\}) \mid \{v_\lambda\} \rangle\langle\{v_\lambda\} \mid d^2\{v_\lambda\} \qquad (4.2.34)$$

where $\mid \{v_\lambda\} \rangle$ is an eigenstate of $\hat{A}(\mathbf{r}, t)$:

$$\hat{A}(\mathbf{r}, t) \mid \{v_\lambda\} \rangle = \mathbf{V}(\mathbf{r}, t) \mid \{v_\lambda\} \rangle$$

and

$$\mathbf{V}(\mathbf{r}, t) = \sum_\lambda v_\lambda \mathbf{u}_\lambda(\mathbf{r}, t)$$

Eq. (4.2.32) has the form

$$p(n, t, T) = \int \phi(\{v_\lambda\}) \langle\{v_\lambda\} \mid : (a\hat{W})^n \exp(-a\hat{W})/n! : \mid \{v_\lambda\} \rangle \, d^2\{v_\lambda\}$$

$$= \int \phi(\{v_\lambda\}) [(aW')^n/n!] \exp(-aW') \, d^2\{v_\lambda\} \qquad (4.2.35)$$

where

$$W' \equiv W'(t, T) = \int_S dS \int_t^{t+T} dt' \, \mathbf{V}^*(\mathbf{r}, t') \cdot \mathbf{V}(\mathbf{r}, t') \qquad (4.2.36)$$

with

$$I(t') = \mathbf{V}^*(t) \cdot \mathbf{V}(t)$$

If we define

$$P(W) = \int \phi(\{v_\lambda\}) \, \delta(W - W') \, d^2\{v_\lambda\} \qquad (4.2.37)$$

we may rewrite Eq. (4.2.35) for an ideal detector in the form

$$p(n, t, T) = \int P(W) [(aW)^n/n!] e^{-aW} \, dW$$

which is Eq. (4.2.23).

Let us consider correlations in the photoelectron counting with two or more detectors. The joint probability of registering n_1 counts by the first detector and n_2 counts by the second detector is given by

$$w(n_1, n_2) = \prod_{k=1}^{2} [(a_k W_k)^{n_k}/n_k!] \exp(-a_k W_k) \qquad (4.2.38)$$

where a_k is the quantum efficiency of the kth detector and

$$W_k = \int_{t_k}^{t_k + T_k} I_k(t) \, dt \qquad (4.2.39)$$

with $I_k(t)$ $(\equiv \langle I_k(\delta T) \rangle_{st})$ being the intensity at time t of the light incident on the kth detector. The joint probability for N detectors is given by

$$p(n_1, n_2, \ldots, n_N; T) = \int_0^{\infty} \cdots \int_0^{\infty} P(W_1, W_2, \ldots, W_N)$$

$$\times \prod_{k=1}^{N} [(a_k W_k)^{n_k}/n_k!] \exp(-a_k W_k) \, dW_1 \cdots dW_N \qquad (4.2.40)$$

while the equivalent quantal formula has the form

$$p(n_1, n_2, \ldots, n_N; T) = \left\langle \ : \prod_{k=1}^{N} [(a_k \ddot{W}_k)^{n_k}/n_k!] \exp(-a_k \hat{W}_k) : \ \right\rangle \qquad (4.2.41)$$

4.3. Optical Mixing Spectrometers

4.3.1. Introduction

Several reviews (Benedek, 1969; Cummins and Swinney, 1970; and Chu, 1970) have discussed the technique of optical mixing spectroscopy in some detail. The use of the photoelectric effect for nonlinear detection was first demonstrated in an experiment of Forrester et al. (1955) and then confirmed by the fluctuation correlation experiments of Brown and Twiss (1956). However, correlation experiments were very difficult because of the broad linewidth and low power density of conventional light sources. In 1961, Forrester suggested the use of lasers as a light source and pointed out that photoelectric mixing is analogous to the mixing of ac electrical signals in nonlinear circuit elements. Thus, optical mixing spectrometers are the analogs of the super heterodyne and the monodyne receivers. The nonlinear detector or mixer in an optical mixing spectrometer is a photoelectric device such as a photomultiplier tube or a photodiode, which produces a photocurrent proportional to the *square* of the total electric field falling on the photosensitive surface of the device.

With the advent of lasers, Javan *et al.* (1961) first obtained intermode beats of a He–Ne laser using a radio-frequency spectrum analyzer. When combined with lasers, photoelectric mixing is particularly suitable for quasielastic light scattering resulting from various time-dependent non-propagating local thermodynamic fluctuations. Several closely related experimental approaches have been developed. These include spectrum analysis as well as signal correlation. Two schemes have been used: the heterodyne detection and the homodyne (or monodyne or self-beating) detection. In signal correlation, the emphasis has been on photon-counting statistics.

According to the Wiener–Khintchine theorem [Eqs. (3.4.7) and (3.4.8)] the power spectrum $S_j(\omega)$ of the photocurrent density and the current–density correlation function $R_j(\tau)$ *at one point of the photocathode surface* are related through the equations:

$$R_j(\tau) = \langle j(t + \tau)j(t) \rangle = \int_{-\infty}^{\infty} S_j(\omega) \cos \omega\tau \, d\omega \qquad (4.3.1)$$

$$S_j(\omega) = \frac{1}{2\pi} \int_{-\infty}^{\infty} R_j(\tau) \cos \omega\tau \, d\tau \qquad (4.3.2)$$

The total anode current from a photodetector, $i(t)$, is

$$i(t) = \int_S j(\mathbf{R}, t) \, dS$$

with S being the illuminated photocathode area. More rigorously speaking, correlation of the current output of the photodetector has the form

$$R_i(\tau) = \langle \langle i(t + \tau)i(t) \rangle_{\text{st}} \rangle$$

$$= \int_S \int_S \langle j(\mathbf{R}_2, t + \tau)j(\mathbf{R}_1, t) \rangle_{\text{st}} \, d^2R_2 \, d^2R_1 \qquad (4.3.3)$$

where $d^2R_p = dS_p$. Equation (4.3.3) requires us to consider the spatial characteristics of the mixing process in the double surface integral. Furthermore, the time behavior of $R_i(\tau)$ is contained in $R_j(\tau) = \langle \langle j(\mathbf{R}_2, t + \tau) \times j(\mathbf{R}_1, t) \rangle_{\text{st}} \rangle$, the current density correlation function which, in turn, may be computed using the joint probability distribution $w(n, t_2, \delta t_2, \mathbf{R}; m, t_1, \delta t_1, \mathbf{R})$ for $\mathbf{R}_2 = \mathbf{R}_1$. The instantaneous intensity $I(t)$ $[\propto E^*(t)E(t)]$ is responsible for the photoelectric current at a single point of the photocathode surface or the photocurrent density $j(\mathbf{R}, t)$:

$$j(\mathbf{R}, t) = eaI(\mathbf{R}, t) = eW^{(1)}(t) \qquad (4.3.4)$$

where e is the electronic charge and a is a suitably defined quantum efficiency. $W^{(1)}(t)$ is the probability per unit time per unit area of photoelectron emission from a photocathode and has the form (Mandel *et al.*, 1964)

$$W^{(1)}(t) = \alpha E^*(t) E(t) = aI(t) \qquad (4.3.5)$$

In Eqs. (4.3.4) and (4.3.5) we have dropped the short-time average notation and taken a [$\backsim a$] as the same suitably defined quantum efficiency after an appropriate correction in units according to Eq. (3.3.6). The joint probability per unit time per unit area that one photoelectron is emitted at time t and another at time $t + \tau$ is

$$W^{(2)}(t, t + \tau) = \alpha^2 E^*(t) E(t) E^*(t + \tau) E(t + \tau) \qquad (4.3.6)$$

For stationary fields, the averages of $j(t)$ and $W^{(2)}(t)$ are as follows:

$$\langle j(t) \rangle = e\langle W^{(1)}(t) \rangle = ea\langle I(t) \rangle = e\alpha\langle E^*(t) E(t) \rangle \qquad (4.3.7)$$

and

$$\langle W^{(2)}(t, t + \tau) \rangle = \alpha^2\langle E^*(t) E(t) E^*(t + \tau) E(t + \tau) \rangle$$
$$= \alpha^2\langle E^*(t) E(t) \rangle^2 g^{(2)}(\tau) \qquad (4.3.8)$$

where

$$g^{(2)}(\tau) = \frac{\langle E^*(t) E(t) E^*(t + \tau) E(t + \tau) \rangle}{\langle E^*(t) E(t) \rangle^2}$$

is the normalized correlation function.

Now if we take the photocurrent to be actually consisting of a series of infinitely narrow discrete pulses, $R_j(\tau)$ has two distinct contributions:

$$\langle W^{(1)}(t) W^{(1)}(t + \tau) \rangle = \langle W^{(2)}(t, t + \tau) \rangle$$
$$= \alpha^2\langle E^*(t) E(t) E^*(t + \tau) E(t + \tau) \rangle$$
$$= a^2\langle I(t) \rangle^2 g^{(2)}(\tau)$$

If the *same* electron occurs at t and $t + \tau$,

$$\langle W^{(1)}(t) W^{(1)}(t + \tau) \rangle = \langle W^{(1)}(t) \rangle \delta(\tau) = a\langle I(t) \rangle \delta(\tau)$$

Thus, we again obtain

$$R_j(\tau) = \langle j(t) j(t + \tau) \rangle = e^2\langle W^{(1)}(t) W^{(1)}(t + \tau) \rangle$$
$$= e^2 a\langle I(t) \rangle \delta(\tau) + e^2 a^2\langle I(t) \rangle^2 g^{(2)}(\tau)$$
$$= e\langle j \rangle \delta(\tau) + \langle j \rangle^2 g^{(2)}(\tau) \qquad (4.3.9)$$

Similarly, the spectrum of a light wave is related to the time dependence of its electric field through a statistical average quantity, the autocorrelation function $R_E(\tau)$ defined by:

$$R_E(\tau) = \langle E^*(t) E(t + \tau) \rangle = \langle E^*(t) E(t) \rangle g^{(1)}(\tau) \qquad (4.3.10)$$

where $g^{(1)}(\tau)$ is the normalized first-order correlation function for the electric field.

4.3.2. The Self-Beating Spectrometer

The self-beating spectrometer considers the spectrum of the photocurrent with the detector illuminated only by the field understudy. For an optical field which obeys *Gaussian* statistics, the normalized first- and second-order correlation functions $g^{(2)}(\tau)$ and $g^{(1)}(\tau)$ are related (Mandel, 1963):

$$g^{(2)}(\tau) = 1 + |g^{(1)}(\tau)|^2 \tag{4.3.11}$$

Then

$$R_j(\tau) = e\langle j\rangle\,\delta(\tau) + \langle j\rangle^2(1 + |g^{(1)}(\tau)|^2) \tag{4.3.9'}$$

If $g^{(1)}(\tau)$ has the form

$$g^{(1)}(\tau) = \exp(-i\omega_0\tau)\,\exp(-\Gamma|\tau|)$$

the optical spectrum of a *field* described by [Eq. (4.3.10)] is

$$S_E(\omega) = \frac{1}{2\pi}\int_{-\infty}^{\infty} R_E(\tau)e^{i\omega\tau}\,d\tau$$

$$= \frac{a}{\alpha}\langle I(t)\rangle\frac{1}{2\pi}\int_{-\infty}^{\infty}\exp[i(\omega-\omega_0)\tau]\exp(-\Gamma|\tau|)\,d\tau$$

$$= \frac{a}{\alpha}\langle I(t)\rangle\frac{\Gamma/\pi}{(\omega-\omega_0)^2 + \Gamma^2} \tag{4.3.12}$$

Equation (4.3.12) is a Lorentzian with a half-width at half-maximum $\Delta\omega_{1/2} = \Gamma$, centered at $\omega = \omega_0$. However, it does not represent the spectrum we measure using a square-law detector, such as a photomultiplier tube, which detects $I(t)$ $[\propto E^*(t)E(t)]$, not the electric field. Therefore, we should consider the power spectrum of the photocurrent $S_j(\omega)$ at a single point of the photocathode surface using Eqs. (4.3.2), (4.3.9), and (4.3.11):

$$S_j(\omega) = \frac{1}{2\pi}\int_{-\infty}^{\infty} e^{i\omega\tau}[e\langle j\rangle\,\delta(\tau) + \langle j\rangle^2(1 + e^{-2\Gamma|\tau|})]\,d\tau$$

$$= \frac{1}{2\pi}e\langle j\rangle + \langle j\rangle^2\,\delta(\omega) + \langle j\rangle^2\frac{2\Gamma/\pi}{\omega^2 + (2\Gamma)^2} \tag{4.3.13}$$

The power spectrum $S_j(\omega)$ is symmetric about $\omega = 0$. We can obtain a power spectrum for positive frequencies only. By combining the positive and negative frequency parts, we get

$$S_j{}^+(\omega) \underset{\omega \geq 0}{=} \frac{e\langle j \rangle}{\pi} + \langle j \rangle^2 \,\delta'(\omega) + 2\langle j \rangle^2 \frac{(2\Gamma/\pi)}{\omega^2 + (2\Gamma)^2}$$

$$S_j{}^-(\omega) \underset{\omega < 0}{=} 0 \qquad (4.3.13')$$

where the δ function is normalized for positive frequencies,

$$\int_0^\infty \delta'(\omega) \, d\omega = 1$$

Equation (4.3.13) has three components: a shot-noise term $e\langle j \rangle/\pi$, a dc component $\langle j \rangle^2 \,\delta'(\omega)$, and a light-beating spectrum which, with our present form for $g^{(1)}(\tau)$, is a Lorentzian of half-width $\Delta\omega_{1/2}$ (photocurrent) = 2Γ, centered at $\omega = 0$, with total *power* density $\langle j \rangle^2$. Figure 4.3.1 shows the

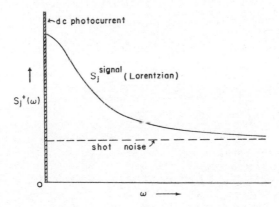

Fig. 4.3.1. General features of the photocurrent power spectrum; showing the dc photocurrent $[\langle j^2 \rangle \delta'(\omega)]$, the power spectrum of the signal which includes the background shot noise $(e\langle j \rangle)/\pi$ (Chu, 1970).

general features of the photocurrent power spectrum. It should be emphasized that Eq. (4.3.11) is valid only for optical fields with Gaussian statistics and Eq. (4.3.13) is a special case in which the correlation function has the form $e^{-\Gamma|\tau|}$. We may relax the form for $g^{(1)}(\tau)$ and express $S_j(\omega)$ as a convolution of the optical spectrum with itself:

$$S_j(\omega) = \frac{e}{2\pi} \langle j \rangle + \langle j \rangle^2 \,\delta(\omega)$$

$$+ \alpha^2 \int_{-\infty}^\infty S_E(\omega') [S_E(\omega' + \omega) + S_E(\omega' - \omega)] \, d\omega \qquad (4.3.14)$$

where we have taken $S_E(\omega)$ to be a symmetric function. However, for non-Gaussian fields, there is no simple connection between the optical spectrum $S_E(\omega)$ and the photocurrent power spectrum $S_j(\omega)$. In a self-beating spectrometer the phase information connected with the correlation function is also lost. Instead of a spectrum analyzer which is related to $S_j(\omega)$, the photocurrent time-dependent autocorrelation function $R_j(\tau)$, as expressed in Eq. (4.3.9), can be related directly to measurements from a signal correlator. Figure 4.3.2 shows the general features of the photocurrent

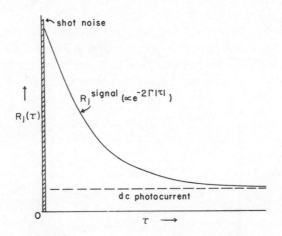

Fig. 4.3.2. General features of the photocurrent autocorrelation function; showing the dc photocurrent, shot noise, and the current correlation function. Note: the shot noise is now represented by a δ function, and the dc current forms the background. The R_j signal is represented by an exponential form in agreement with our special consideration of a Lorentzian power spectrum of the photocurrent $S_j{}^+$ signal as shown in Fig. 4.3.1 (Chu, 1970).

(density) correlation function which has a shot-noise term, a dc component, and the desired correlation signal. In signal correlation, the shot-noise term, instead of the dc component, becomes the δ function. Signal correlation is a much more efficient way of obtaining the desired information since the rate of data collection with a correlation-function computer is faster than that of data collection with a spectrum analyzer by a factor which is of the order of the number of bandwidths swept. On the other hand, signal correlators are often limited to relatively long relaxation times (or low frequencies). With fast shift registers, we expect to extend the ranges to less than 20 nsec per channel so that linewidth of the order of megahertz is within reach. The intensity should become a serious problem beyond the megahertz range, since by then we need more than 10^6–10^7 counts/sec which is near the limit of photoelectron counting rates of ordinary photo-multiplier tubes. Fortunately, we have already achieved an overlap between optical mixing spectroscopy and high-resolution interferometry so that the entire frequency range from 1 to 10^{+12} Hz is within the capability of our present-day laser-light-scattering techniques. There also exist commercial real-time spectrum analyzers which simultaneously sample many fre-quency intervals. Using a "time-compression" technique, such "real-time" spectrum analyzers have essentially the same efficiency as signal correlators. However, improvements have been achieved using digital photon counting in signal correlation while real-time spectrum analyzers, designed mainly for other purposes, such as vibration and acoustic analysis, are devices which accept only analog inputs. Thus, it appears that future instrumenta-tion in laser light scattering lies with the digital photon correlation tech-nique.

In specific applications, Arecchi *et al.* (1967) have measured the ensemble distribution of the scattered field within a coherence area and time, us-ing dilute solutions of monodisperse polystyrene (latex) spheres, by means of photocount distributions and have showed that the field distribution is *Gaussian* in the Bose limit. Pusey and Goldberg (1968) designed a single-channel correlation spectrometer, which is similar to that used by Morgan and Mandel (1966). The instrument operates as a delayed coincidence counter and measures the intensity autocorrelation function. It corresponds to a wave or spectrum analyzer which looks at one band-width [equivalent to one (τ)] at a time, although the spectrometer is a digital (instead of an analog) device. Another improvement for measuring the conditional probability function, defined as the probability of detecting a photon at $t = \tau$ within an interval $d\tau$ having first detected a photon at $t = 0$, for many values of τ simultaneously, has been accomplished by Chen and Polonsky-Ostrowsky (1969a,b) using a fast multichannel scaler. The scattered light was focused on a photomultiplier tube whose photoelectric pulses were amplified, standardized, and then fed *simultaneously* into the trigger and the signal inputs of a multichannel scaler. An arbitrary pulse which triggers the time base of the analyzer determines the arbitrary origin of time $(t = 0)$. The pulses arriving afterwards are stored in successive channels of the analyzer. After the sweep has reached the last channel, the analyzer automatically resets back to the first channel and waits for the next pulse to trigger again. In fact, the measurements represent first studies of the single clipped photocurrent autocorrelation function with clipping level k set at zero, $\langle n_{k=0}(t) n(t + \tau) \rangle$, even though no theory (see Chapter 6) for clipping existed at the time. Digital signal correlation offers the best future potential in optical mixing spectroscopy as the tech-nique utilizes virtually every photocount to compute the time-dependent correlation function. Theoretical applications of the photocounting method have been carried out for the case of a dense one-component classical fluid (Bertolotti *et al.* 1967, 1969) and for determining correlations in a plasma (Crosignani *et al.*, 1968). Earlier, Pike and his co-workers (1965, 1968) presented the theory of the intensity fluctuations of Gaussian light having a Lorentzian spectrum of finite linewidth and gave photocounting distributions for such light as a function of counting rate and linewidth. Subsequently, they measured the optical linewidth of 0.6-μm-diam polystyrene spheres undergoing Brownian motion in water at room temperature by photon-counting statistics and reported results of photon-counting experiments which demonstrated the factorization properties of the correlation functions, up to sixth order, of coherent and incoherent optical fields (Jakeman *et al.*, 1968). Arecchi *et al.* (1966) and Bedard (1967) have shown that optical linewidths can be determined from measurements of higher-order joint probability distributions. In actual applications, photon-counting statistics has been in its initial stages of development with many noteworthy contributions from Pike and his co-workers. Wolf (1966), Arecchi (1969), and Mehta (1970) have reviewed photoelectron statistics in detail. On an elementary level, laser-beat-frequency spectroscopy has been reviewed by French *et al.* (1969), who emphasized measurements on biomolecules in solution, and by Berge (1967), who discussed the principle of photon beating in the case of homodyne as well as heterodyne spectroscopy.

In intensity correlation spectroscopy it should be noted that the applicability of Eq. (4.3.11) depends on an ansatz that the scattered field $E(t)$ is a Gaussian random variable. In other words,

$$\frac{\langle I(t_1) I(t_2) \rangle}{\langle I \rangle^2} = 1 + \left| \frac{\langle E^*(t_1) E(t_2) \rangle}{\langle | E(t_1) |^2 \rangle} \right|^2 \qquad (4.3.11')$$

holds only for the scattered field which obeys Gaussian statistics. However, for light scattering from hydrodynamic fluctuations,

$$\mathbf{E}(\mathbf{K}, t) = \lambda \mathbf{A}(\mathbf{K}, t) \qquad (4.3.15)$$

where λ is a constant and $A(K, t)$ is the particular hydrodynamic mode which is coupled with the scattered electric field. Then we have

$$\frac{\langle I(t_1) I(t_2) \rangle}{\langle I \rangle^2} = 1 + \left| \frac{\langle A^*(K, t_1) A(K, t_2) \rangle}{\langle | A(K, t_1) |^2 \rangle} \right|^2 \qquad (4.3.16)$$

which relates the measured intensity correlation function to the correlation function of the hydrodynamic fluctuations. Although the scattered electric field $E(t)$ represents a summation of a large number of individual wave fields scattered from many scattering centers in the fluid, the "plausible" Gaussian nature of $E(t)$ is not strictly true in practice because the scattering centers can be highly correlated locally. Mandel (1969) showed that $E(t)$ is not a Gaussian random variable with a realistic incident laser beam even if we take $A(K, t)$ to be a Gaussian random process. However, Eq. (4.3.16) remains true by a rather fortuitous circumstance. In fact the assumption that $E(t)$ be a Gaussian random variable is too restrictive. The important point is to examine the right-hand side of Eq. (4.3.17) which is given by

$$\langle I(t_1) I(t_2) \rangle = \lambda^4 \langle A^*(K, t_1) A(K, t_1) A^*(K, t_2) A(K, t_2) \rangle \quad (4.3.17)$$

Tartaglia and Chen (1973) used the so-called "fluctuating hydrodynamic equations" (fhe), as described in Chapter 17 of Landau and Lifshitz (1959):

$$\frac{\partial}{\partial t} \mathbf{A}(\mathbf{K}, t) = - \mathbf{L}(\mathbf{K}) \mathbf{A}(\mathbf{K}, t) + \mathbf{f}(\mathbf{K}, t) \quad (4.3.18)$$

where $\mathbf{L}(\mathbf{K})$ is a symmetric matrix and $\mathbf{f}(\mathbf{K}, t)$ are the random forces which vary in time much faster than variables $\mathbf{A}(\mathbf{K}, t)$. Evaluation of the second-order correlation function in Eq. (4.3.17) does give Eq. (4.3.16). However, only weaker conditions, instead of the assumption that $A(K, t)$ is a Gaussian random variable, are required. These conditions are that the equilibrium distribution of $A(K, 0)$ is Gaussian and that the slowly varying $A(K, t)$ is uncorrelated with the rapidly varying random force $f(K, t)$, while in the formulation of the fluctuating hydrodynamic equations by Fox and Uhlenbeck (1970), they assumed $f(K, t)$ to be a Gaussian–Markovian process and hence also $A(K, t)$. Tartaglia and Chen (1973) showed that Eq. (4.3.16) holds even for fluids near the critical point as the so-called non-Gaussian terms (see Section 6.5) are too small to be observed. The same consideration has been extended to the case of clipped intensity correlation function.

We have stated that Eqs. (4.3.9) and (4.3.13) represent the photocurrent autocorrelation function and its corresponding power spectral density at a single point of the photocathode surface. The *total* photocurrent autocorrelation function from the entire *effective* photocathode surface of a photodetector (S) has the form (Cummins and Swinney, 1970)

$$R_i(\tau) = \langle i \rangle^2 + e \langle i \rangle \delta(\tau) + \langle i \rangle^2 \begin{cases} 1; & S < S_{\text{coh}} \\ S_{\text{coh}}/S; & S > S_{\text{coh}} \end{cases} e^{-2\Gamma|\tau|} \quad (4.3.19)$$

where $\langle i \rangle = \langle j \rangle S$ and $S_{\text{coh}} [= \lambda^2/\Omega]$ is the coherence area with Ω as the solid angle which the source subtends at the detector. Benedek (1969) cites $S_{coh} = 2\lambda^2/\Omega$ for a three-dimensional source. Similarly, the corresponding power spectrum of the total photocurrent has the form (Cummins and Swinney, 1970)

$$S_i^+(\omega) = \frac{e\langle i \rangle}{\pi} + \langle i \rangle^2 \delta'(\omega) + 2\langle i \rangle^2 \begin{Bmatrix} 1; & S < S_{coh} \\ S_{coh}/S; & S > S_{coh} \end{Bmatrix} \frac{2\Gamma/\pi}{\omega^2 + (2\Gamma)^2}$$

$$(4.3.20)$$

Equations (4.3.19) and (4.3.20) demonstrate that the self-beating technique is capable of measuring the linewidth Γ from either the autocorrelation function or the power spectrum especially when there is only one linewidth Γ. In practice, the self-beating spectrum becomes too complex whenever we have more than two linewidths. For example, if $g^{(1)}(\tau)$ has the form

$$g^{(1)}(\tau) = \exp(-i\omega_0\tau)\{[\exp(-\Gamma_1|\tau|) + f\exp(-\Gamma_2|\tau|)]\} \quad (4.3.21)$$

then

$$|g^{(1)}(\tau)|^2 = \exp(-2\Gamma_1|\tau|) + 2f\exp[-(\Gamma_1 + \Gamma_2)|\tau|]$$

$$+ f^2\exp(-2\Gamma_2|\tau|) \quad (4.3.22)$$

and Eq. (4.3.9) changes to

$$R_j(\tau) = e\langle j \rangle \delta(\tau) + \langle j \rangle^2$$

$$\times \{1 + \exp(-2\Gamma_1|\tau|) + 2f\exp[-(\Gamma_1 + \Gamma_2)|\tau|]$$

$$+ f^2\exp(-2\Gamma_2|\tau|)\} \quad (4.3.23)$$

where f is the relative signal strength of Γ_2 with respect to Γ_1 at $\tau = 0$. Similarly, we can obtain the corresponding linewidth in the idealized power spectrum without regard to S_{coh}:

$$S_j(\omega) = \frac{e\langle j \rangle}{2\pi} + \langle j \rangle^2 \delta(\omega) + \langle j \rangle^2$$

$$\times \left(\frac{2\Gamma_1/\pi}{\omega^2 + (2\Gamma_1)^2} + 2f\frac{(\Gamma_1 + \Gamma_2)/\pi}{\omega^2 + [(\Gamma_1 + \Gamma_2)]^2} + f^2\frac{2\Gamma_2/\pi}{\omega^2 + (2\Gamma_2)^2} \right) \quad (4.3.24)$$

Equations (4.3.23) and (4.3.24) are complex spectra, each involving a dc term, a shot-noise term, and a superposition of signal terms consisting of three linewidths $2\Gamma_1$, $\Gamma_1 + \Gamma_2$, and $2\Gamma_2$. So, if the spectrum of the optical field is the sum of *two* Lorentzians, the photocurrent signal term in the self-beating power spectrum is the sum of *three* Lorentzians. These signal terms include not only the self-beating spectra of each of the two Lorentzians of linewidth $2\Gamma_1$ and $2\Gamma_2$ but also the cross-beating term of linewidth $\Gamma_1 + \Gamma_2$. Cross beating is a unique feature in optical mixing spectroscopy. With comparable Γ_1 and Γ_2, it is usually very difficult to resolve the measured signals into superpositions of many Lorentzians since superposition of Lorentzians of comparable linewidths can often be fitted with a single Lorentzian within the error limits of our experiments. On the other hand, we may utilize the unique feature of cross beating whenever Γ_1 and Γ_2 are very different. For example, if we have a dilute protein solution with an excessive amount of dust particles, then $f \ll 1$ at small scattering angles and $\Gamma_1 \ll \Gamma_2$, and Eq. (4.3.24) reduces to

$$S_j(\omega) \approx \frac{e\langle j \rangle}{2\pi} + \langle j \rangle^2 \delta(\omega) + \langle j \rangle^2$$

$$\times \left[\frac{2\Gamma_1/\pi}{\omega^2 + (2\Gamma_1)^2} + 2f\frac{(\Gamma_1 + \Gamma_2)/\pi}{\omega^2 + [(\Gamma_1 + \Gamma_2)]^2} \right] \quad (4.3.25)$$

The idealized power spectrum without regard to S_{coh} has mainly *two* linewidths, one (Γ_1) due to the translational motion of dust particles and the other (Γ_2) due to the translational motion of the protein molecules. Thus, when the solution is very "dusty," the *approximate* linewidth due to protein molecules comes from the cross-beat term $\Gamma_1 + \Gamma_2 \approx \Gamma_2$, which can be obtained by means of a simple three-parameter fit

$$S_j^+(\omega) \atop {\scriptstyle \omega > \Gamma_1} = C + \frac{B}{\omega^2 + (\Gamma)^2} \quad (4.3.26)$$

where C and B are related to the shot noise and the average power of the spectrum, respectively. In considering Eq. (4.3.25), we come to realize that the three-parameter fit [Eq. (4.3.26)] becomes better as $\Gamma_1 \to 0$. Thus, we want to use a local oscillator with $\Gamma_1 = 0$ and come to the heterodyne technique. Equation (4.3.25) will be discussed further in Section 7.7. The use of dust particles as a local oscillator is a bad practice which should be discouraged.

4.3.3 The Heterodyne Spectrometer

In heterodyne detection, the photomultiplier tube is illuminated simultaneously by the field under study, E_s, and by a *coherent* local-oscillator signal, $\mathbf{E}_{LO}(\mathbf{R}, t) = \mathbf{E}_{LO}^0 \exp(-i\omega_{LO}t)$. We recall

$$R_j(\tau) = e\langle j \rangle \delta(\tau) + e^2\alpha^2\langle E^*(t)E(t)E^*(t+\tau)E(t+\tau)\rangle \quad (4.3.9')$$

Now $E(t) = E_s(t) + E_{LO}^0 \exp(-i\omega_{LO}t)$, so Eq. (4.3.9) takes on a very complex form

$$R_j(\tau) = e[\langle j_s \rangle + j_{LO}]\,\delta(\tau) + j_{LO}{}^2 + 2j_{LO}\langle j_s \rangle$$
$$+ e^2\alpha^2 \langle E_s{}^*(t)E_s(t)E_s{}^*(t+\tau)E_s(t+\tau) \rangle$$
$$+ j_{LO}\exp(i\omega_{LO}\tau)e\alpha\langle E_s{}^*(t)E_s(t+\tau) \rangle$$
$$+ j_{LO}\exp(-\omega_{LO}\tau)e\alpha\langle E_s(t)E_s{}^*(t+\tau) \rangle$$
$$= e[\langle j_s \rangle + j_{LO}]\,\delta(\tau) + j_{LO}{}^2 + 2j_{LO}\langle j_s \rangle$$
$$+ e^2\alpha^2\langle E_s{}^*(t)E_s(t)E_s{}^*(t+\tau)E_s(t+\tau) \rangle$$
$$+ j_{LO}\langle j_s \rangle[\exp(i\omega_{LO}\tau)g_s{}^{(1)}(\tau) + \exp(-i\omega_{LO}\tau)g_s{}^{(1)*}(\tau)] \quad (4.3.27)$$

where

$$j_{LO} = \langle j_{LO} \rangle = e\alpha\langle E_{LO}{}^*(t)E_{LO}(t) \rangle$$

$$g_s{}^{(1)}(\tau) = \langle E_s{}^*(t)E_s(t+\tau) \rangle / \langle E_s{}^*(t)E_s(t) \rangle$$

and

$$g_s{}^{(1)*}(\tau) = \langle E_s(t)E_s{}^*(t+\tau) \rangle / \langle E_s(t)E_s{}^*(t) \rangle$$

However, if $j_{LO} \gg \langle j_s \rangle$,

$$R_j(\tau) \cong ej_{LO}\,\delta(\tau) + j_{LO}{}^2 + j_{LO}\langle j_s \rangle$$
$$\times [\exp(i\omega_{LO}\tau)g_s{}^{(1)}(\tau) + \exp(-i\omega_{LO}\tau)g_s{}^{(1)*}(\tau)] \quad (4.3.28)$$

and according to Eq. (4.3.2), the photocurrent power spectrum at a single point of the photocathode surface by means of heterodyne detection for $j_{LO} \gg \langle j_s \rangle$ has the form

$$S_j(\omega) \cong \frac{ej_{LO}}{2\pi} + j_{LO}{}^2\,\delta(\omega) + \frac{j_{LO}\langle j_s \rangle}{2\pi}\int_{-\infty}^{\infty}\exp(i\omega\tau)$$
$$\times [\exp(i\omega_{LO}\tau)g_s{}^{(1)}(\tau) + \exp(-i\omega_{LO}\tau)g_s{}^{(1)*}(\tau)]\,d\tau \quad (4.3.29)$$

which consists of a shot-noise term, a dc term, and the heterodyne light-beating spectrum. A very important factor comes into play in Eqs. (4.3.28) and (4.3.29), i.e., unlike the $g_s{}^{(2)}$ in Eq. (4.3.9), we need not assume Gaussian statistics for the signal field as expressed in Eq. (4.3.11). Substituting $g_s{}^{(1)}(\tau) = \exp(-i\omega_s\tau)\exp(-\Gamma|\tau|)$ into Eq. (4.3.29), we obtain

$$S_j{}^+(\omega) = \frac{ej_{LO}}{\pi} + j_{LO}{}^2\,\delta'(\omega) + j_{LO}\langle j_s \rangle \frac{2\Gamma/\pi}{(\omega - |\omega_s - \omega_{LO}|)^2 + \Gamma^2} \quad (4.3.30)$$

The heterodyne light-beating spectrum is a Lorentzian of half-width at half-maximum $\Delta\omega_{1/2} = \Gamma$, centered at $\omega = (\omega_s - \omega_{LO})$, with intensity proportional to j_{LO} and $\langle j_s \rangle$ $[\equiv \langle\langle j_s \rangle_{st}\rangle]$.

The *total* photocurrent autocorrelation function from the entire effective photocathode surface S again obeys Eq. (4.3.19) and for $j_{LO} \gg \langle j_s \rangle$, $R_i(\tau)$ has the form

$$R_i(\tau) \cong eS[j_{LO} + \langle j_s \rangle]\delta(\tau) + j_{LO}^2 S^2$$

$$+ j_{LO}\langle j_s \rangle S^2 \begin{Bmatrix} 1; & S < S_{coh} \\ S_{coh}/S; & S > S_{coh} \end{Bmatrix}$$

$$\cdot \{\exp[i(\omega_{LO} - \omega_s)\tau] \exp(-\Gamma \mid \tau \mid)$$

$$+ \exp[-i(\omega_{LO} - \omega_s)\tau] \exp(-\Gamma \mid \tau \mid)\} \quad (4.3.31)$$

where we have taken $g_s^{(1)}(\tau) = \exp(-i\omega_s\tau) \exp(-\Gamma \mid \tau \mid)$, and kept $\langle j_s \rangle$ in the shot-noise term. Similarly, the corresponding power spectrum of the total photocurrent fluctuations under the assumption that the scattered field is a Lorentzian of width Γ centered around the optical frequency ω_s has the form:

$$S_i^+(\omega) \approx j_{LO}^2 S^2 \delta'(\omega) + \frac{e(j_{LO} + \langle j_s \rangle)S}{\pi}$$

$$+ j_{LO}\langle j_s \rangle S^2 \begin{Bmatrix} 1; & S < S_{coh} \\ S_{coh}/S; & S > S_{coh} \end{Bmatrix} \frac{(2\Gamma/\pi)}{\Gamma^2 + (\omega - \mid \omega_s - \omega_{LO} \mid)^2}$$

$$(4.3.32)$$

Finally, we introduce a heterodyne mixing efficiency ϵ representing the degree to which the wave front of the scattered light and that of the local oscillator are matched over an area equal to a coherence area S_{coh} (Benedek, 1969):

$$S_i^+(\omega) \approx i_{LO}^2 \delta'(\omega) + e(i_{LO} + \langle i_s \rangle)/\pi$$

$$+ \epsilon i_{LO}\langle i_s \rangle \begin{Bmatrix} 1; & S < S_{coh} \\ S_{coh}/S; & S > S_{coh} \end{Bmatrix} \frac{2\Gamma/\pi}{\Gamma^2 + (\omega - \mid \omega_s - \omega_{LO} \mid)^2}$$

$$(4.3.33)$$

ϵ is equal to unity if the two wavefronts are perfectly matched in phase, and becomes very small when the relative phases of the two wavefronts fluctuate many times by $\pm 2\pi$ over the coherence area.

The geometrical approach on the spatial coherence area S_{coh} is qualitative in nature. Instead we should consider

$$\langle I(t_1)I(t_2) \rangle = \langle I \rangle^2[1 + f(S) \mid g^{(1)}(t_1 - t_2) \mid^2] \qquad (4.3.34)$$

where the spatial coherence factor $f(S)$ can be evaluated by means of the diffraction integral (see Section 6.5).

The heterodyne technique offers no specific advantage over the self-beating method for simple Lorentzians. It has the disadvantage of requiring optical matching equivalent to that of the alignment of a Michelson interferometer although in practice, ingenious ways have been devised to circumvent this problem. Furthermore, when the spectrum is a superposition of several linewidths, decomposition can sometimes be accomplished with the heterodyne technique if conditions are favorable. In the heterodyne scheme, the assumption of Gaussian statistics which may not hold for certain biological systems is *not* required.

We have summarized the theory of light-beating spectroscopy in terms of the classical coherence functions (Mandel and Wolf, 1965) according to Lastovka (1967) and to Cummins and Swinney (1970). The quantum-mechanical theory of optical coherence by Glauber (1963, 1964, 1965, 1969) provides an equivalent fundamental approach. However, the classical theory is adequate for the photocurrent spectrum. Both Cummins and Swinney (1970) and Benedek (1969) have also discussed the signal–to–noise problem in light-beating spectroscopy.

References

Alkemade, C. T. J. (1959). *Physica* **25**, 1145.

Arecchi, F. T. (1965). *Phys. Rev. Lett.* **15**, 912.

Arecchi, F. T. (1969). *In* "Enrico Fermi XLII Course, Varenna, 1967" (R. Glauber, ed.), pp. 57–110. Academic Press, New York and London.

Arecchi, F. T., Berne, A., and Sona, A. (1966). *Phys. Rev. Lett.* **17**, 260.

Arecchi, F. T., Giglio, M., and Tartari, U. (1967). *Phys. Rev.* **163**, 186.

Bedard, G. (1967). *Phys. Rev.* **161**, 1304.

Benedek, G. B. (1969). "Polarization Matiere et Rayonnement," Livre de Jubile en l'honneur du Professeur A. Kastler, pp. 49–84. Presses Universitaires de France, Paris.

Berge, P. (1967). *Bull. Soc. Fr. Mineral. Cristallogr.* **90**, 508.

Bertolotti, M., Crosignani, B., Di Porto, P., and Sette, D. (1967). *Phys. Rev.* **157**, 146.

Bertolotti, M., Crosignani, B., Di Porto, P., and Sette, D. (1969). J. Phys. A. **2**, 473.

Brown, R. H., and Twiss, R. Q. (1956). *Nature* **177**, 27.

Chen, S. H., and Polonsky-Ostrowsky, N. (1969a). *Opt. Commun.* **1**, 64.

Chen, S. H., and Polonsky-Ostrowsky, N. (1969b). *J. Phys. Soc. Japan* **26**, Suppl. 179.

Chu, B. (1970). *Annu. Rev. Phys. Chem.* **21**, 145.

Crosignani, B., Di Porto, P., and Engelmann, F. (1968). *Z. Naturforsch.* **23a**, 743; **23a**, 968.

Cummins, H. A., and Swinney, H. L. (1970). *Progr. Opt.* **8**, 135.

Davenport, W. B., Jr., and Root, W. L. (1958). "An Introduction to the Theory of Random Signals and Noise," p. 168, problem 2. McGraw-Hill, New York.

Forrester, A. T. (1961). *J. Opt. Soc. Am.* **51**, 253.

Forrester, A. T., Gudnumdsen, R. A., and Johnson, P. O. (1955). *Phys. Rev.* **99**, 1691.

Fox, R. F., and Uhlenbeck, G. E. (1970). *Phys. Fluids* **13**, 1893.

Freed, C., and Haus, H. A. (1965). *Phys. Rev. Lett.* **15**, 943.

French, M. J., Angus, J. C., and Walton, A. G. (1969). *Science* **163**, 345.

Glauber, R. J. (1963). *Phys. Rev.* **130**, 2529; **131**, 2766.

Glauber, R. J. (1964). "Quantum Electronics III," Proc. 3rd Conf., Paris, 1963 (N. Bloembergen and P. Grivet, eds.), p. 111. Columbia Univ. Press, New York.

Glauber, R. J. (1965). *In* "Quantum Optics and Electronics," Les Houche Summer School of Theoretical Physics, Grenoble, 1964 (C. Dewitt, A. Blandin, and C. Cohen-Tannoudji, eds.), p. 63. Gordon and Breach, New York.

Glauber, R. J. (1966). *In* "Physics of the Quantum Electronics" (P. L. Kelley, B. Lax, and P. E. Tannenwald, eds.), p. 788. McGraw-Hill, New York.

Glauber, R. J. (1969). *In* "Enrico Fermi XLII Course, Varenna, 1967" (R. Glauber, ed.), pp. 15–56. Academic Press, New York and London.

Jakeman, E., and Pike, E. R., (1968). *J. Phys. A.* **1**, 128; **1**, 625.

Jakeman, E., Oliver, C. J., and Pike, E. R. (1968). *J. Phys. A.* **1**, 406; **1**, 497.

Javan, A., Bennett, W. R., and Herriott, D. R. (1961). *Phys. Rev. Lett.* **6**, 106.

Kelley, P. L., and Kleiner, W. H. (1964). *Phys. Rev.* **136**, A316.

Korenman, V. (1967). *Phys. Rev.* **154**, 1233.

Lastovka, J. B. (1967). "Light Mixing Spectroscopy and the Spectrum of Light Scattered by Thermal Fluctuations in Liquids," Ph.D. thesis. MIT, Cambridge, Massachusetts

Landau, L. D. and Lifshitz, E. M. (1959). "Fluid Mechanics." Pergamon, New York.

Lehmberg, R. H. (1968). *Phys. Rev.* **167**, 1152.

Mandel, L. (1958). *Proc. Phys. Soc. London* **72**, 1037.

Mandel, L. (1959). *Proc. Phys. Soc. London* **74**, 233.

Mandel, L. (1963). *Prog. Opt.* **2**, 181. See also Davenport & Root (1958).

Mandel, L. (1964). *In* "Quantum Electronics III," Proc. 3rd Int. Conf., Paris, 1963 (N. Bloemberger and P. Grivet, eds.), p. 101. Columbia Univ. Press, New York.

Mandel, L. (1969). *Phys. Rev.* **181**, 75.

Mandel, L., and Wolf, E. (1965). *Rev. Mod. Phys.* **37**, 231.

Mandel, L., Sudarshan, E. C. G., and Wolf, E. (1964). *Proc. Phys. Soc. London* **84**, 435.

McLean, T. P., and Pike, E. R. (1965). *Phys. Lett.* **15A**, 318.

Mehta, C. L. (1970). *Progr. Opt.* **3**, 373.

Morgan, B. L., and Mandel, L. (1966). *Phys. Rev. Lett.* **16**, 1012.

Pusey, P. N., and Goldburg, W. I. (1968). *Appl. Phys. Lett.* **13**, 321.

Sudarshan, E. C. G. (1963a). *Phys. Rev. Lett.* **10**, 277.

Sudarshan, E. C. G. (1963b). "Proc. Symposium Optical Masers," p. 45. Wiley, New York.

Tartaglia, P., and Chen, S. H. (1973). *J. Chem. Phys.* **58**, 4389.

Wolf, E. (1966). *Opt. Acta* **13**, 281.

Zinman, J. M. (1964). "Principles of the Theory of Solids," pp. 23–25. Cambridge Univ. Press, London and New York.

Chapter V
‖ *INTERFEROMETRY*

5.1. General Consideration

5.1.1. Introduction

Although optical mixing spectroscopy is capable of extremely high resolutions where we have considered linewidths down to 1 Hz, the spectral range is limited to perhaps a few megahertz with present-day techniques. In quasielastic light scattering (or Brillouin scattering), whenever the linewidths (or the Doppler shifts) approach the megahertz range, it is advantageous to consider the more familiar form of interference spectroscopy even though few experiments (see Chapter VIII) thus far require its usage. There are several types of interferometers, with the Fabry–Perot interferometer being the most suitable one for our purposes. The theory and description of the Fabry–Perot etalon have been discussed in standard optics textbooks (Rossi, 1957; Born and Wolf, 1965; Klein, 1970). We shall review the essential aspects of theory which governs the Fabry–Perot interferometer as we have done for the Maxwell equations which govern the scattering theory since most chemists and biochemists are not familiar with the principles of optics. The purpose of this chapter is to try to provide sufficient background information so that the reader may feel reasonably comfortable when he is actually required to use the Fabry–Perot interferometer. It is advisable to consult the pertinent references for details.

5.1.2. Review on Sinusoidal and Exponential Waves

A plane sinusoidal wave traveling with velocity c in the positive x direction has the form

$$E(x, t) = E^0 \cos[\omega(t - x/c)] = E^0 \cos(\omega t - kx) \qquad (5.1.1)$$

where ω ($=2\pi\nu$) is the angular frequency. The wave number k ($=2\pi/\lambda$) obeys the relation $ck = \omega$ while the period $\tau = 2\pi/\omega$.

A wave AB in a medium with a refractive index n_1 incident upon the boundary surface between the two media with indices of refraction n_1 and n_2 splits into a reflected wave BD and a refracted wave BC, as shown in Fig. 5.1.1a. If we disregard phase changes at this interphase, the incident,

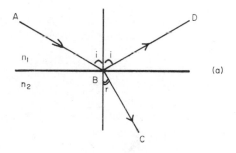

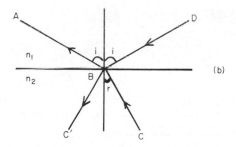

Fig. 5.1.1. Refraction and reflection at an interface.

reflected, and transmitted (refracted) waves are, respectively,

$$E_i = E^0 \cos[\omega(t + X_A/c_1)]$$

$$E_r = \varrho E^0 \cos[\omega(t - X_D/c_1)]$$

and

$$E_t = \tau E^0 \cos[\omega(t - X_C/c_2)]$$

where X_A, X_D, and X_C are the distances from B measured along the incident, reflected, and refracted rays, respectively while c_1 and c_2 are the velocities of light in media 1 and 2, respectively. ϱ is the ratio of the reflected to the incident amplitude at the boundary from medium 1 to medium 2. τ is the ratio of the transmitted to the incident amplitude at the boundary from

1 to 2.* Both ϱ and τ are positive if there is no phase change, and become negative if the phase is inverted.

We shall now apply the reversibility principle which implies that the wave equations remain valid in the absence of dissipation of energy when we change the sign of the time, i.e., from $t \rightarrow -t$. The electric field for the reversed reflected ray (DB), as shown in Fig. 5.1.1b, has the form:

$$E_r' = \varrho E^0 \cos[\omega(-t - X_D/c_1)] = \varrho E^0 \cos[\omega(t + X_D/c_1)]$$

which gives rise to a reflected wave (BA) and a refracted (transmitted) wave (BC'). Similarly, for the reversed refracted wave (CB)

$$E_t' = \tau E^0 \cos[\omega(t + X_C/c_2)]$$

we have a refracted wave (BA) and a reflected wave (BC').

The principle of optical reversibility assures us that the reversed beam in the direction of X_A must reproduce the *reversed* incident wave, and the two waves in the $X_{C'}$ direction must cancel. Thus, the equations (Rossi, 1957)

$$\varrho^2 E^0[\omega(t - X_A/c_1)] + \tau\tau' E^0 \cos[\omega(t - X_A/c_1)] = E^0 \cos[\omega(t - X_A/c_1)]$$

and

$$\varrho\tau E^0 \cos[\omega(t - X_{C'}/c_2)] + \tau\varrho' E^0 \cos[\omega(t - X_{C'}/c_2)] = 0$$

give

$$\varrho^2 + \tau\tau' = 1 \tag{5.1.2}$$

and

$$\varrho = -\varrho' \tag{5.1.3}$$

where ϱ' and τ' are the ratios of the reflected and transmitted amplitudes to the incident amplitude at the interface from medium 2 to medium 1. $\varrho^2 [= (-\varrho')^2]$ is the ratio of the reflected to the incident intensity and is known as reflectance. It should be noted that the principle of reversibility does not hold for half-silvered mirrors.

Equation (5.1.1) is a solution to the wave equation

$$\nabla^2 E - (1/c^2)(\partial^2 E/\partial t^2) = 0 \tag{5.1.4}$$

which has a complex solution of the form†

$$E = E^0 e^{i(\omega t - kx)} = E^0 e^{i\phi} e^{i(\omega t - kx)} \tag{5.1.5}$$

Since the electric field E is a real function of real variables, we retrieve

---

* The use of boldface for ϱ and τ does not indicate vector quantities, but is only meant to distinguish them from, e.g., ρ—density and τ—period.

† Strictly speaking, the symbol **E** should be used, e.g., see Eq. (3.1.5).

Eq. (5.1.1) by taking the real part of Eq. (5.1.5):

$$E = \mathrm{Re}(E^0 e^{i(\omega t - kx)}) = E^0 \cos(\omega t - kx) \qquad (5.1.1')$$

We shall now review the rules governing the addition of sinusoidal waves by considering the combination of two wave displacements $E_1(x, t)$ and $E_2(x, t)$:

$$E_1(x, t) = E_1{}^0 \cos(\omega t - kx + \phi_1) = \mathrm{Re}\{E_1{}^0 \exp[i(\omega t - kx + \phi_1)]\}$$

$$E_2(x, t) = E_2{}^0 \cos(\omega t - kx + \phi_2) = \mathrm{Re}\{E_2{}^0 \exp[i(\omega t - kx + \phi_2)]\}$$

where ϕ is the phase of the wave at $x = 0$. The resultant electric field has the form

$$\begin{aligned}
E(x, t) &= E_1(x, t) + E_2(x, t) \\
&= \mathrm{Re}\{[E_1{}^0 \exp(i\phi_1) + E_2{}^0 \exp(i\phi_2)] \exp[i(\omega t - kx)]\} \\
&= \mathrm{Re}\{E^0 \exp(i\phi) \exp[i(\omega t - kx)]\}
\end{aligned} \qquad (5.1.6)$$

where the relations of $E^0 \exp(i\phi)$, $E_1{}^0 \exp(i\phi_1)$, and $E_2{}^0 \exp(i\phi_2)$ are shown in Fig. 5.1.2.

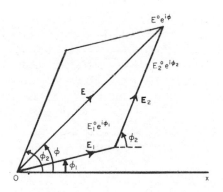

Fig. 5.1.2. Addition of two sinusoidal functions.

The magnitude E of the vectors $\mathbf{E}_1$ and $\mathbf{E}_2$ obeys the equation:

$$\begin{aligned}
E^{02} &= [E_1{}^0 \exp(i\phi_1) + E_2{}^0 \exp(i\phi_2)][E_1{}^0 \exp(-i\phi_1) + E_2{}^0 \exp(-i\phi_2)] \\
&= E_1{}^{02} + E_2{}^{02} + E_1{}^0 E_2{}^0 \{\exp[i(\phi_1 - \phi_2)] + \exp[-i(\phi_1 - \phi_2)]\} \\
&= E_1{}^{02} + E_2{}^{02} + 2E_1{}^0 E_2{}^0 \cos(\phi_2 - \phi_1)
\end{aligned} \qquad (5.1.7)$$

When $E_1{}^0 = E_2{}^0$, we have

$$E^{02} = 2E_1{}^{02}[1 + \cos(\phi_2 - \phi_1)]$$

To get ϕ, we take

$$E^0 e^{i\phi} = E_1{}^0 \exp(i\phi_1) + E_2{}^0 \exp(i\phi_2)$$

with

$$E^0 \cos \phi = E_1{}^0 \cos \phi_1 + E_2{}^0 \cos \phi_2$$

and

$$E^0 \sin \phi = E_1{}^0 \sin \phi_1 + E_2{}^0 \sin \phi_2$$

Thus,

$$\tan \phi = (E_1{}^0 \sin \phi_1 + E_2{}^0 \sin \phi_2)/(E_1{}^0 \cos \phi_1 + E_2{}^0 \cos \phi_2) \quad (5.1.8)$$

5.1.3. Interference in a Dielectric Slab

Consider a plane-parallel dielectric slab of refractive index n_2 and thickness d imbedded in a medium of refractive index n_1 as shown in Fig. 5.1.3.

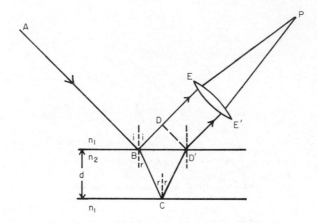

Fig. 5.1.3. Two-beam interference produced by reflection from a plane-parallel dielectric slab.

If we take the incident wave (AB) to be $E = E^0 \cos \omega t$, the reflected (BD) and transmitted (BC) waves are, respectively, $\varrho E^0 e^{i\omega t}$ and $\tau E^0 e^{i\omega t}$. The rays DE and D'E' are parallel. We first compute the optical path lengths of the rays BD and BCD' which are denoted by l_1 and l_2, respectively. With $l_1 = n_1 \overline{BD}$ and $l_2 = n_2(\overline{BC} + \overline{CD'})$, we get

$$l_2 - l_1 = n_2(\overline{BC} + \overline{CD'}) - n_1 \overline{BD}$$

From the geometry in Fig. 5.1.3 and Snell's law, we also get

$$n_1\overline{BD} = n_1\overline{BD}' \sin i = n_1(2d \tan r) \sin i$$

$$= \frac{n_2 \sin r}{\sin i} 2d \frac{\sin r}{\cos r} \sin i = 2n_2d \sin^2 r/\cos r \qquad (5.1.9)$$

and

$$n_2(\overline{BC} + \overline{CD}') = 2n_2d/\cos r$$

Thus,

$$l_2 - l_1 = 2n_2d(1/\cos r - \sin^2 r/\cos r) = 2n_2d \cos r \qquad (5.1.10)$$

The phase difference due to the optical-path-length difference is $2\pi(l_2 - l_1)/\lambda_0$, where λ_0 is the wavelength in vacuum. However, reflection at B for the ray ABD has a reflection coefficient ϱ, while reflection at C for the ray ABCD' has a reflection coefficient ϱ' which is equal to $-\varrho$. Thus, the phase difference due to both optical-path-length difference and reflection at upper and lower boundaries is

$$\phi = 2\pi(l_2 - l_1)/\lambda_0 - \pi = 2\pi(2n_2d \cos r/\lambda_0 - \tfrac{1}{2}) \qquad (5.1.11)$$

Interference of the two rays at P will produce a maximum intensity at $\phi = 2\pi m$ and a minimum intensity at $\phi = \pi m$ with $m = 0, 1, 2, \ldots$. If $\cos r \approx 1$, we then have

$$d = \begin{cases} (2m + 1)\tfrac{1}{4}\lambda & \text{interference maxima} \qquad (5.1.12) \\ m(\tfrac{1}{2}\lambda) & \text{interference minima} \qquad (5.1.13) \end{cases}$$

where $\lambda = \lambda_0/n_2$.

The first (DE) and second (D'E') reflected waves can be represented in terms of the complex exponential notation by

$$\varrho E^0 e^{i\omega t}$$

and

$$\tau\tau'\varrho' E^0 e^{i\omega t}e^{-i\phi} = \tau\tau'\varrho E^0 e^{i\omega t}e^{-i\alpha}e^{\pi i}(-1)$$

$$= \tau\tau'\varrho E^0 e^{i\omega t}e^{-i\alpha}$$

respectively, where $e^{\pi i} = -1$ and $\alpha = 2\pi(l_2 - l_1)/\lambda_0$.

5.1.4. Interference by Multiple Reflection

We shall consider the case where Eqs. (5.1.2) and (5.1.3) holds. The pertinent geometrical and physical relationships can be derived with the aid of Fig. 5.1.4. For the transmitted waves, we first compute the optical path

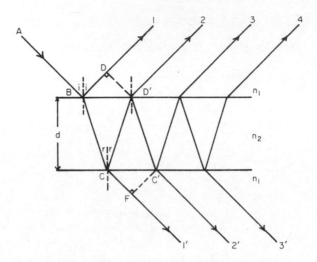

Fig. 5.1.4. Multiple wave interference.

length from B to F and from B to C' which are, respectively,

$$l_1' = n_1\overline{CF} + n_2\overline{BC} = n_1\overline{CC'}\sin i + n_2\overline{BC}$$

$$= n_1 2d\tan r\sin i + n_2\overline{BC}$$

$$l_2' = n_2\overline{BC} + n_2(\overline{CD'} + \overline{D'C'}) = n_2\overline{BC} + n_2(2d/\cos r)$$

Thus,

$$l_2' - l_1' = 2n_2(d/\cos r) - n_1 2d\tan r\sin i = 2dn_2\cos r \quad (5.1.10')$$

and the phase difference due to the optical-path-length difference between neighboring waves is

$$\alpha = 2\pi(l_2 - l_1)/\lambda_0 = 2\pi(2d\cos r/\lambda) = k(2d\cos r) \quad (5.1.14)$$

where $\lambda = \lambda_0/n_2$ and $k = 2\pi/\lambda$.

The optical disturbance of the various transmitted waves at the point of interference can be listed as follows:

$$E_{t1'} = \tau\tau' E^0 e^{i\omega t}$$

$$E_{t2'} = \tau\tau' \varrho^2 E^0 e^{i(\omega t - \alpha)}$$

$$\vdots$$

$$E_{tm'} = \tau\tau' \varrho^{2(m-1)} E^0 e^{i[\omega t - (m-1)\alpha]}$$

$$= \tau\tau' E^0 e^{i\omega t}(\varrho^2 e^{-i\alpha})^{m-1}$$

The total transmitted electric field E_t is

$$E_t = E_{t1'} + E_{t2'} + \cdots + E_{tm'} + \cdots$$

$$= \tau\tau' E^0 e^{i\omega t} \sum_{m=1}^{\infty} (\varrho^2 e^{-i\alpha})^{m-1} = \tau\tau' E^0 e^{i\omega t}/(1 - \varrho^2 e^{-i\alpha}) \quad (5.1.15)$$

The energy transmission coefficient T will be given by

$$T = |E_t|^2/|E^0|^2 = |\tau\tau'|^2/[(1 - \varrho^2 e^{-i\alpha})(1 - \varrho^2 e^{+i\alpha})]$$

or

$$\boxed{T = |\tau\tau'|^2/(1 + \varrho^4 - 2\varrho^2 \cos \alpha)} \quad (5.1.16)$$

Similarly, we can compute the reflected intensity. Various reflected waves at the point of interference can be represented by

$$E_{r0} = \varrho^2 E^0 e^{i\omega t}$$

$$E_{r1} = \tau\tau' \varrho E^0 e^{i(\omega t - \alpha)}$$

$$E_{r2} = \tau\tau' \varrho^3 E^0 e^{i(\omega t - 2\alpha)}$$

$$\vdots$$

$$E_{rm} = \tau\tau' \varrho^{2m-1} E^0 e^{i(\omega t - m\alpha)}$$

$$\vdots$$

The total reflected electric field E_r is

$$E_r = E_{r0} + E_{r1} + E_{r2} + \cdots + E_{rm} + \cdots$$

$$= E^0 e^{i\omega t} [\varrho' + \tau\tau' \varrho e^{-i\alpha} \sum_{m=1}^{\infty} (\varrho^2 e^{-i\alpha})^{m-1}]$$

$$= [\varrho' + \tau\tau' \varrho e^{-i\alpha}/(1 - \varrho^2 e^{-i\alpha})] E^0 e^{i\omega t}$$

$$= \varrho(e^{-i\alpha} - 1) E^0 e^{i\omega t}/[1 - \varrho^2 e^{-i\alpha}] \quad (5.1.17)$$

Thus, the energy reflection coefficient R is

$$R \left[= \frac{|E_r|^2}{|E^0|^2} \right] = \frac{2\varrho^2(1 - \cos \alpha)}{1 + \varrho^4 - 2\varrho^2 \cos \alpha} \quad (5.1.18)$$

Equations (5.1.16) and (5.1.18) are the fundamental equations for the Fabry–Perot interferometer. With $\cos \alpha = 1 - 2\sin^2(\tfrac{1}{2}\alpha)$, we can also express the two equations in somewhat different but equivalent forms:

$$T = (1 - \varrho^2)^2/[(1 - \varrho^2)^2 + 4\varrho^2 \sin^2(\tfrac{1}{2}\alpha)] \quad (5.1.16a)$$

$$R = 4\varrho^2 \sin^2(\tfrac{1}{2}\alpha)/[(1 - \varrho^2)^2 + 4\varrho^2 \sin^2(\tfrac{1}{2}\alpha)] \quad (5.1.18a)$$

where $T + R = 1$.

It should be noted that in deriving Eqs. (5.1.16) and (5.1.18), we have assumed that Eqs. (5.1.2) and (5.1.3) are valid. With metallic films, such as half-silvered mirrors, owing to absorption, Eqs. (5.1.16) and (5.1.18) may no longer hold. In other words, $\varrho^2 + \tau\tau' \neq 1$ and $\varrho \neq -\varrho'$.

For mirrors with absorption we define the change of phase on reflection as ϵ (Ditchburn, 1963). The phase difference between two neighboring waves is

$$\Delta = (2\pi n_2 2d \cos r/\lambda_0) + 2\epsilon \qquad (5.1.19)$$

which differs from Eq. (5.1.14) by 2ϵ. The resultant total transmitted electric field is

$$E_t = E^0 e^{i\omega t}\tau\tau'[1 + \varrho^2 e^{-i\Delta} + \cdots + \varrho^{2(m-1)}e^{-i(m-1)\Delta} + \cdots]$$

$$= \tau\tau' E^0 e^{i\omega t}/(1 - \varrho^2 e^{-i\Delta}) \qquad (5.1.20)$$

Thus, the corresponding energy transmission and reflection coefficients are the same as Eqs. (5.1.16) and (5.1.18) except that α is replaced by Δ:

$$T = (\tau\tau')^2/[(1 - \varrho^2)^2 + 4\varrho^2 \sin^2(\tfrac{1}{2}\Delta)] \qquad (5.1.21)$$

$$R = 4\varrho^2 \sin^2(\tfrac{1}{2}\Delta)/[(1 - \varrho^2)^2 + 4\varrho^2 \sin^2(\tfrac{1}{2}\Delta)] \qquad (5.1.22)$$

Maxima occur when $\cos \Delta = 1$ (i.e., when $\Delta = 2\pi m$) and the minima are halfway between the maxima (i.e., when $\Delta = m\pi$) as we have discussed in Eqs. (5.1.12) and (5.1.13).

5.2. Fabry–Perot Interferometer: General Characteristics

The Fabry–Perot interferometer utilizes interference by multiple reflection. Figure 5.2.1 shows the basic elements for such an etalon or interferometer where the slab is really an air gap between two partially silvered mirrors, M_1 and M_2, spaced at a distance d apart. For convenience, the Fabry–Perot etalon mirrors usually come in pairs with $\varrho_1^2 = \varrho_2^2 = \varrho^2$ and $\tau_1^2 = \tau_2^2 = \tau^2$. In addition, the approximation $\varrho^2 + \tau\tau' = 1$ holds.

The transmission coefficient T can be characterized by α with

$$T = [1 + F \sin^2(\tfrac{1}{2}\alpha)]^{-1} \qquad (5.2.1)$$

where $F \ [= 4\varrho^2/(1 - \varrho^2)^2]$ is called the contrast, and

$$\alpha = (2\pi/\lambda)(2d \cos r) = k_2(2d \cos r).$$

$T_{\max} = 1$ when $\sin(\tfrac{1}{2}\alpha) = 0$ or $\alpha = 2\pi m$ with $m = 0, 1, 2, \ldots$; $T_{\min}$ when $\sin(\tfrac{1}{2}\alpha) = 1$ or $\alpha = m\pi$ with $m = 0, 1, 2, \ldots$. Thus,

$$T_{\min} = [(1 - \varrho^2)/(1 + \varrho^2)]^2 \qquad (5.2.2)$$

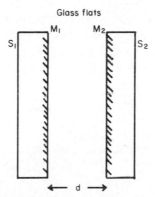

Fig. 5.2.1. Basic elements of a Fabry–Perot interferometer. M_1, M_2: high reflection mirrors; d: spacing between the two flats; glass flats with wedges $(S_1 \not\parallel M_1; S_2 \not\parallel M_2)$ so that $S_1 \not\parallel S_2$ when $M_1 \parallel M_2$.

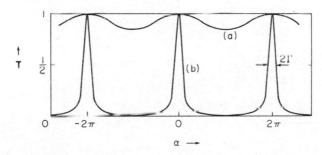

Fig. 5.2.2. Intensity transmission coefficient T in the interference fringes using two plane-parallel plates (a) $\varrho^2 \ll 1$ and (b) $\varrho^2 \simeq 1$ with negligible absorption effects with 2Γ given by Eq. (5.2.8).

Figure 5.2.2 shows a plot of T vs α for (a) $\varrho^2 \ll 1$ and (b) $\varrho^2 \approx 1$. Large values of ϱ^2 are obtained either with metallic layers or dielectric coatings. In real situations, $T_{\max}$ is not likely to be equal to one. Then, by means of Eq. (5.1.21), we have

$$T_{\max} = |\, \tau\tau' \,|^2 / (1 - \varrho^2)^2 \qquad (5.2.3)$$

and

$$T_{\min} = T_{\max}[(1 - \varrho^2)/(1 + \varrho^2)]^2 \qquad (5.2.4)$$

By combining Eq. (5.2.3) with Eq. (5.1.21), we obtain

$$T = \frac{T_{\max}}{1 + [4\varrho^2/(1 - \varrho^2)^2] \sin^2(\tfrac{1}{2}\Delta)}$$

$$= \frac{T_{\max}}{1 + F \sin^2(\tfrac{1}{2}\Delta)} \qquad (5.2.5)$$

which is known as the Airy formula (Klein, 1970). In Fig. 5.2.2, we note that T_{min} is very small when $\varrho^2 \approx 1$. In other words, when the mirrors are good reflectors, T remains small unless Δ is close to $\pm 2\pi m$. If we neglect the effects of absorption, Δ is replaced by α. When $\alpha = \pi + 2m\pi$, $\sin(\frac{1}{2}\alpha) = \pm 1$ and $T = T_{min}$. Then,

$$T_{max}/T_{min} = 1 + F \tag{5.2.6}$$

If we take $\varrho^2 = 0.8$, $F = 3.2/(1 - 0.8)^2 = 80$. Thus, when $\varrho^2 \approx 1$, F can be a very large number. If F is very large, Eq. (5.2.5) without the absorption effects where we simply replace Δ by α is a Lorentzian in α for α close to $2\pi m$. Then,

$$T = \frac{T_{max}}{1 + F \sin^2(\frac{1}{2}\alpha)} = \frac{T_{max}}{1 + F(\frac{1}{2}\alpha - m\pi)^2}$$

$$= T_{max} \frac{1/F}{1/F + (\frac{1}{2}\alpha - m\pi)^2} \tag{5.2.7}$$

where $\sin^2(\frac{1}{2}\alpha) \approx \sin^2(\frac{1}{2}\alpha - m\pi) \simeq (\frac{1}{2}\alpha - m\pi)^2$ and $|\frac{1}{2}\alpha - m\pi| \ll 1$. The half-width at half-maximum Γ is the value of $\frac{1}{2}\alpha - m\pi$ at which $T = \frac{1}{2}T_{max}$. Thus,

$$\tfrac{1}{2}T_{max} = T_{max}[1 + F(\tfrac{1}{2}\alpha - m\pi)^2]^{-1}$$

which gives

$$\Gamma = 2/\sqrt{F} = (1 - \varrho^2)/\varrho \tag{5.2.8}$$

as shown in Fig. 5.2.2. The full linewidth at half-maximum is 2Γ.

The order of a fringe in a Fabry–Perot interferometer obeys Eq. (5.1.14) where the bright fringes correspond to

$$m = 2n_2 d \cos r/\lambda_0 \tag{5.2.9}$$

with $m_{max} = 2n_2 d/\lambda_0$ which needs not be an integer.

The free spectral range is the spectral separation of adjacent transmission maxima (bright fringes) which can be observed without overlap, as shown in Fig. 5.2.3. For two wavelengths λ_a and λ if λ_a exceeds λ by $\Delta\lambda$, defined as the free spectral range, the mth-order fringe for λ_a will coincide with the $(m + 1)$th-order fringe for λ:

$$(m + 1)\lambda = m\lambda_a = m(\lambda + \Delta\lambda)$$

With Eq. (5.2.9), we then have

$$\Delta\lambda = \lambda/m = \lambda^2/2d \cos r \tag{5.2.10}$$

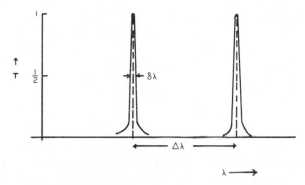

Fig. 5.2.3. A schematic plot of T vs wavelength λ. $\Delta\lambda$: free spectral range in wavelength; $\delta\lambda$: instrumental bandwidth in wavelength.

If $\cos r = 1$ or $r \ll \frac{1}{2}\pi$

$$\Delta\lambda \simeq \lambda^2/2d \qquad (5.2.11)$$

which is the usual free spectral range expressed in wavelength. Since the wave number $\tilde{\nu} = 1/\lambda$ and $d\tilde{\nu} = -d\lambda/\lambda^2$, the corresponding free spectral range expressed in $\tilde{\nu}$ is

$$\Delta\tilde{\nu} = 1/2d \qquad (5.2.11a)$$

Similarly, with $\lambda\nu = c$ and $d\nu = -(c/\lambda^2)\,d\lambda$, we get

$$\Delta\nu = c/2d \qquad (5.2.11b)$$

Equation (5.2.8) gives us the instrumental bandwidth (2Γ) when T is plotted against α. In terms of λ, we have

$$\delta\lambda = 2\Gamma\,\frac{\lambda}{2\pi m} = \frac{4}{\sqrt{F}}\,\frac{\lambda}{2\pi m} \qquad (5.2.12)$$

The resolving power $\mathcal{R}^\dagger$, defined as $\lambda/\delta\lambda$, is thus given by

$$\mathcal{R}^\dagger = \frac{\lambda}{\delta\lambda} = \frac{\sqrt{F}}{2}\,\pi m = \frac{\pi m \varrho}{1 - \varrho^2} \qquad (5.2.13)$$

The ratio of the free spectral range to the instrumental bandwidth is called the finesse $\mathcal{F}$. By Eqs. (5.2.10) and (5.2.12), we get

$$\mathcal{F} = \frac{\Delta\lambda}{\delta\lambda} = \frac{\lambda}{m}\,\frac{\sqrt{F}}{4}\,\frac{2\pi m}{\lambda} = \frac{\pi\sqrt{F}}{2} = \frac{\pi\varrho}{1 - \varrho^2} \qquad (5.2.14)$$

The finesse $\mathcal{F}$ can also be defined as $\Delta\tilde{\nu}/\delta\tilde{\nu}$ or $\Delta\nu/\delta\nu$ and is a very important characteristic of the Fabry–Perot interferometer. With modern-day multilayer dielectric coatings a finesse of greater than 100 can be achieved.

For example, if we take $\varrho^2 = 0.99$, $F = 3.96/(10^{-2})^2 = 3.96 \times 10^4$ and $\mathfrak{F} = (3.96 \times 10^4)^{1/2} (3.14)/2 = 3.13 \times 10^2$. In practice, the finesse is usually degraded by other factors, such as irregularities in the surfaces of the mirrors. Thus, Eq. (5.2.14) represents the instrumental finesse as limited by reflectance alone but in the absence of other losses.

For $\varrho \simeq 1$, Eq. (5.2.14) can be reduced to

$$\mathfrak{F}_R = \pi/(1 - \varrho^2) \tag{5.2.14a}$$

which is the reflectivity limited finesse, valid for most of the present-day plane-parallel Fabry–Perot etalons. By substituting Eq. (5.2.14a) into Eq. (5.1.21), we can express the transmission coefficient T in terms of finesse $\mathfrak{F}$ and the parameter Δ.

$$T = (\tau\tau'\mathfrak{F}/\pi)^2\{1 + [(2\mathfrak{F}/\pi) \sin(\tfrac{1}{2}\Delta)]^2\}^{-1} \tag{5.1.21a}$$

where we have taken $\mathfrak{F}$ as the instrumental finesse. When other loss mechanisms are present, the total net finesse is related to the individual contributions $\mathfrak{F}_i$ by

$$\mathfrak{F}^{-1} = \sum_i \mathfrak{F}_i^{-1} \tag{5.2.15}$$

In addition to the reflectivity limited finesse, the major factors which tend to degrade the instrumental finesse are irregularities in the mirror surface, mirror misalignment, diffraction at the mirror aperture, and absorption.

We shall first consider the effect of irregularities in the mirror surfaces on the finesse. If the irregularity is smooth, and is of the order of λ/m across the effective aperture, then the plane-figure limited finesse $\mathfrak{F}_f$ is approximately

$$\mathfrak{F}_f \approx \lambda/2f \approx \tfrac{1}{2}m \tag{5.2.16}$$

where f ($=\lambda/m$) is the mean surface deformation. It should be noted that an angular misalignment of the plates is equivalent to a corresponding plate deformation

$$\mathfrak{F}_\beta \approx \lambda/2d\beta \tag{5.2.17}$$

where β is the tilt angle in radians and d is the plate separation distance. The instrumental finesse due to plate irregularities may be reduced by decreasing the effective aperture. However, in practice, the reduction of etalon aperture significantly increases diffraction losses. On the other hand, a spherical Fabry–Perot etalon does not have this defect, nor does it require such careful angular alignment since our angular misalignment in a spherical Fabry–Perot etalon merely redefines the optical axis of the system.

For a plane-parallel Fabry–Perot etalon, the diffraction limited finesse is approximately equal to

$$\mathfrak{F}_D \approx D^2/2\lambda d \qquad (5.2.18)$$

where D is the aperture diameter.

If a small fraction L of the radiation incident on the mirror is lost in making a single transit, then by analogy to Eq. (5.2.14a), the resultant contribution to the finesse is

$$\mathfrak{F}_L \approx \pi/L \qquad (5.2.19)$$

Table 5.2.1 shows a comparison of $\mathfrak{F}_i$ for the plane-parallel and the spherical Fabry–Perot etalons. The listings clearly indicate that we require high reflectivity and smoothness of the mirrors.

Table 5.2.1

A comparison of finesse in plane-parallel and spherical-mirror Fabry–Perot etalons

Finesse	Factor	Plane parallel	Spherical[a]
$\mathfrak{F}_R$	Reflectivity	$\pi/(1 - \varrho^2)$	$\pi\varrho^2/[1 - (\varrho^2)^2] \approx \pi/2(1 - \varrho^2)$
$\mathfrak{F}_f$	Surface deformation	$\tfrac{1}{2}m$	$\tfrac{1}{2}m$
$\mathfrak{F}_\beta$	Plate-tilt	$\lambda/(2\,d\beta)$	Only redefines optical axis
$\mathfrak{F}_D$	Mirror aperture	$D^2/2\lambda d$	Negligible
$\mathfrak{F}_L$	Absorption	π/L	$\pi/2L$

[a] Hercher (1968).

For plane-parallel Fabry–Perot etalons, we also need to make more careful alignment of the mirrors and cannot try to increase $\mathfrak{F}_f$ by reducing the etalon aperture because of $\mathfrak{F}_D$. It appears that the spherical-mirror Fabry–Perot etalon has unique advantages. However, the plane-parallel Fabry–Perot etalon requires relatively low tolerance in determining the mirror separation distance and it can vary its free spectral range according to Eq. (5.2.11), while in the confocal arrangement, a precise mirror separation distance fixes the free spectral range for each set of mirrors of a spherical Fabry–Perot etalon. The spherical-mirror Fabry–Perot interferometer may be mode matched to the laser for cavity resonance at frequencies satisfying the condition:

$$\nu_0 = (c/2d)[q + \pi^{-1}(1 + m + n) \cos^{-1}(1 - d/R)] \qquad (5.2.20)$$

Mode matching can double free spectral range as well as the instrumental

Table 5.2.2

Pertinent formulas for plane-parallel and spherical-mirror Fabry–Perot etalons with high reflectivity

	Plane parallel	Spherical[a] (mode degenerate)
Resonance condition ν_0	$mc/2d$	$(c/2dl)(lq + 1 + m + n)$
Airy formula I/I_0 ($\varrho^2 \simeq 1$)	$\left[\left(1 + \dfrac{A}{\tau^2}\right)^2\right]^{-1}$ $\times \left[1 + \left(\dfrac{4\pi d}{c(1 - \varrho^2)}\right)^2\right.$ $\times (\nu - \nu_0)^2\Big]^{-1}$	$\left[l\left(1 + \dfrac{A}{\tau^2}\right)^2\right]^{-1}$ $\times \left[1 + \left(\dfrac{4\pi d}{c(1 - \varrho^2)}\right)^2\right.$ $\times (\nu - \nu_0)^2\Big]^{-1}$
Free spectral range $\Delta\nu$	$c/2d$	$c/2ld$
Instrumental bandwidth $\delta\nu$	$c(1 - \varrho^2)/2\pi d$	$c(1 - \varrho^2)/2\pi d$
Finesse $\mathfrak{F}_R$	$\pi/(1 - \varrho^2)$	$\pi/l(1 - \varrho^2)$
Resolving power $\mathfrak{R}$[†] (or quality factor Q)	$2\pi\nu d/c(1 - \varrho^2)$	$2\pi\nu d/c(1 - \varrho^2)$

[a] Notation: A is the dissipative loss of the mirrors; q and m, n are integers denoting the longitudinal- and transverse-mode numbers; l is an integer satisfying the condition $\cos^{-1}(1 - d/R) = \pi/l$, where R is the radius of curvature. In the confocal arrangement, $l = 2$ (and $d = R$).

transmission. However, the angular tolerance on this alignment using a TEM$_{00}$ mode laser is extremely critical. The confocal spherical-mirror interferometer, being one of the best-known mode-degenerate interferometers, is more useful for practical applications. The theory, design, and use of the confocal spherical-mirror Fabry–Perot interferometer has been described in detail (Hercher, 1968). Table 5.2.2 lists a comparison of the pertinent formula for plane-parallel and spherical-mirror Fabry–Perot interferometers with high reflectivity ($\varrho^2 \simeq 1$).

References

Born, M., and Wolf, E. (1965). "Principles of Optics," 3rd revised ed. Pergamon, Oxford.

Ditchburn, R. W. (1963). "Light," p. 143. Wiley (Interscience), New York.

Hercher, M. (1968). *Appl. Opt.* **7**, 951.

Klein, M. (1970). "Optics." Wiley, New York.

Rossi, B. (1967). "Optics." Addison-Wesley, Reading, Massachusetts.

Chapter VI

PHOTON-COUNTING FLUCTUATIONS

6.1. Photocount Autocorrelation

In optical mixing spectroscopy as we have discussed in the previous chapters, the bulk of the experimental work to date has utilized a wave (or spectrum) analyzer in which a scanning electrical filter is used to analyze the spectrum of photocurrent fluctuations from a square-law detector, such as a photomultiplier tube. The equivalent information, namely the photo-current correlation function which is the Fourier transform of the power spectrum, has been measured using a signal correlator. Unfortunately, most commercial signal correlators take only analog signals even though internal processes of those correlators are often "digital." The most promising technique which recognizes and takes advantages of the digital nature of photon statistics of scattered laser light (Pike, 1969) is that of photocount autocorrelation. Pike and his co-workers have done pioneering work in this field (Jakeman *et al.*, 1968; Jakeman and Pike, 1968, 1969a, b; Jakeman, 1970).

In digital intensity correlation, the autocorrelation function of photo-counting fluctuations which, for stationary processes, may be written as $\langle n(0, T)n(\tau, T) \rangle$, is related to the autocorrelation function of the short-time integrated-intensity fluctuations [Eq. (4.3.1)] by the formula

$$\langle n(0, T)n(\tau, T) \rangle = (aT)^2 \langle I(0)I(\tau) \rangle \qquad (6.1.1)$$

where $n(\tau, T)$ is the number of photocounts (i.e., photoelectron counts) during the time interval τ to $\tau + T$ with T as the sample time and $T \ll \tau_{coh}$; $I(t) \; [\equiv \langle I(t) \rangle_{st}]$ represents the short-time averaged intensity of light incident on the unit (point) photocathode at time t; a is the quantum

121

efficiency of the photodetector; and τ_{coh} ($\equiv 1/\Gamma$) is the correlation (or coherence) time of the intensity fluctuations. For an optical field which obeys Gaussian statistics, we have, according to Eq. (4.3.9),

$$\langle I(0)I(\tau)\rangle = \langle I\rangle^2[1 + \exp(-2\Gamma_s\tau)] \qquad (6.1.2)$$

where $2\Gamma_s = \Gamma_m$ is the Lorentzian half-linewidth at half-maximum of the intensity fluctuations. We shall henceforth drop the subscript s in describing the linewidth of the self-beating spectrum but keep in mind that the coherence time is reciprocal of the *measured* linewidth (Γ_m). In Eq. (6.1.2), the δ-function shot-noise term has been neglected. By combining Eqs. (6.1.1) and (6.1.2), we get

$$\langle n(0, T)n(\tau, T)\rangle = (aT)^2\langle I\rangle^2[1 + \exp(-2\Gamma\tau)]$$

$$= \langle n\rangle^2[1 + \exp(-2\Gamma\tau)] \qquad (6.1.3)$$

with $\langle n\rangle = \bar{n} = \langle n(0)\rangle = \langle n(\tau)\rangle = \langle aTI\rangle$. If $n(t, T)$ is a random process, the photocount autocorrelation function has the form

$$\langle n(t_1, T)n(t_2, T)\rangle = \sum_{n_1=0}^{\infty} \sum_{n_2=0}^{\infty} n_1 n_2 p(n_2, t_2, T; n_1, t_1, T) \qquad (6.1.4)$$

where $p(n_2, t_2, T; n_1, t_1, T)$, or more simply $p(n_1, n_2)$ is the joint photocount distribution function denoting the probability of having n_1 photoelectron pulses at time t_1 in the time interval T and n_2 photoelectron pulses at time t_2 in the time interval T.

An alternative but more general approach is to consider the photocount autocorrelation function in terms of Eq. (4.3.17), whereby

$$\langle n(t_1, T)n(t_2, T)\rangle = (aT)^2\langle I(t_1)I(t_2)\rangle$$

$$= (aT)^2\lambda^4\langle A^*(t_1)A(t_1)A^*(t_2)A(t_2)\rangle \qquad (4.3.17a)$$

Here we can compute the photocount autocorrelation function directly from $A(t)$ which can be related to hydrodynamic fluctuations [Eq. (4.3.15)], including even the critical region in second-order phase transitions, or to independent particles due to Brownian motion, bacteria mobility, etc. (Chapter 8). In this more general approach we do not have to use the Gaussian property of $E(t)$ which has been shown not to be a Gaussian random variable with a realistic incident laser beam even though $A(t)$ obeys the Gaussian statistics (Mandel, 1969). However, the result [Eq. (4.3.16)], with the exception of weaker assumptions, is equivalent to calculate $\langle n(t_1, T)n(t_2, T)\rangle$ by the joint photocount distribution function

$p(n_1, n_2)$. Therefore, we shall use the more "established" but less general approach.

In practice, computation of Eq. (6.1.4) requires an excess amount of digital electronics for data acquisition and multiplication processes. So, Jakeman and Pike (1969b) introduced the method of "clipping" a fluctuating signal before correlation which permitted considerable simplification of the instrumentation. The idea was analogous to those more sophisticated techniques for the experimental determination of autocorrelation functions in radar applications. The principle is as follows.

We shall assume that T is relatively small and drop it from our notation. From Eqs. (4.3.8) and (6.1.3) we can write

$$\langle n(0)n(\tau) \rangle / \langle n \rangle^2 = g^{(2)}(\tau)$$

except when $\tau = 0$. Let us introduce a binary random variable $n_k(t)$ for the clipped photocount:

$$n_k(t) = 1 \quad \text{if } n(t) > k$$
$$= 0 \quad \text{if } n(t) \leq k \quad (6.1.5)$$

where k is an integer or zero. The functions of interest are $\langle n_k(0)n(\tau) \rangle$ and $\langle n_k(0)n_k(\tau) \rangle$, the single-clipped and double-clipped photocount autocorrelation functions. Experimentally $n_k(t)$ can be measured with simpler instrumentation than $n(t)$. With the delayed channel clipped, the past history of the system can be stored in shift registers as a linear chain of zeros and ones. Multiplication processes in computing the time correlation function are simplified when one (single clipping) or both (double clipping) of those numbers is always a one or a zero. We now need to relate correlations involving $n_k(t)$ and $g^{(2)}(\tau)$.

The two-dimensional generating function for the joint probability distribution involving counting over two discrete intervals is

$$Q(\lambda_1, \lambda_2) = \langle (1 - \lambda_1)^{n(0)}(1 - \lambda_2)^{n(\tau)} \rangle$$

$$= \sum_{n(0)=0}^{\infty} \sum_{n(\tau)=0}^{\infty} (1 - \lambda_1)^{n(0)}(1 - \lambda_2)^{n(\tau)}p[n(0), n(\tau)] \quad (6.1.6)$$

Thus, by definition, we get

$$\langle n(0)n(\tau) \rangle = \sum_{n(0)=0}^{\infty} \sum_{n(\tau)=0}^{\infty} n(0)n(\tau)p[n(0), n(\tau)]$$

$$= \frac{\partial^2}{\partial \lambda_1 \, \partial \lambda_2} Q(\lambda_1, \lambda_2) \bigg|_{\lambda_1 = \lambda_2 = 0} \quad (6.1.7)$$

$$\langle n_k(0)n(\tau)\rangle = \sum_{n(0)=k+1}^{\infty} \sum_{n(\tau)=0}^{\infty} n(\tau)p[n(0), n(\tau)]$$

$$= \sum_{n(0)=k+1}^{\infty} \frac{(-1)^{n(0)+1}}{n(0)!} \frac{\partial^{n(0)+1}}{\partial^{n(0)}\lambda_1 \partial\lambda_2} Q(\lambda_1, \lambda_2)\bigg|_{\lambda_1=1,\lambda_2=0} \qquad (6.1.8)$$

and

$$\langle n_0(0)n_0(\tau)\rangle = 1 - p[n(0) = 0] - p[n(\tau) = 0]$$

$$+ p[n(0) = 0, n(\tau) = 0]$$

$$= 1 - Q(\lambda_1, \lambda_2)\big|_{\lambda_1=1,\lambda_2=0}$$

$$- Q(\lambda_1, \lambda_2)\big|_{\lambda_1=0,\lambda_2=1} + Q(\lambda_1, \lambda_2)\big|_{\lambda_1=\lambda_2=1} \qquad (6.1.9)$$

where $\langle n_0(0)n_0(\tau)\rangle$ represents the correlation function for double clipping at zero photocount number. Double clipping at photocount levels other than zero produces more complex expressions.

Our next step is to evaluate the generating function $Q(\lambda_1, \lambda_2)$ for the joint probability distribution of intensity fluctuations. Equation (6.1.6) permits connection of the field to the photocount distribution by means of the relation (Arecchi *et al.*, 1966)

$$p[n(0), n(\tau)] = \frac{(-1)^{n(0)}(-1)^{n(\tau)}}{n(0)!n(\tau)!} \left(\frac{d^{n(0)}}{d\lambda_1^{n(0)}} \frac{d^{n(\tau)}}{d\lambda_2^{n(\tau)}} Q(\lambda_1, \lambda_2)\right)_{\lambda_1=\lambda_2=1}$$

$$(6.1.10)$$

The result has been generalized by Bedard (1967) for N-fold joint photocount distributions of a Gaussian (thermal) light of arbitrary spectral profile. The basic formula

$$p(n, t, T) = \frac{1}{n!} \int_0^{\infty} e^{-aW}(aW)^n P(W)\, dW \qquad (4.2.23)$$

relates the statistical photocount distribution $p(n, t, T)$ registered with a single detector in a sample time interval T to the probability density distribution $P(W)$ for the quantity

$$W = \int_t^{t+\tau} \langle I(\delta T')\rangle_{st}\, dT' \qquad (4.2.22)$$

Alternatively, we can write Eq. (4.2.23) in a more compact form

$$p(n, t, T) = \langle ((aW)^n/n!)e^{-aW}\rangle \qquad (6.1.11)$$

with the angular brackets denoting the appropriate averaging process over the phase–space functional. The results can be extended to a twofold photocount distribution whereby

$$p(n_1, n_2) \sim \left\langle \prod_{i=1}^{2} \frac{(aW)_i^{n_i}}{n_i!} \exp[-(aW)_i] \right\rangle \qquad (6.1.12)$$

Therefore, we can introduce a generating function

$$Q(\lambda_1, \lambda_2) = \langle \exp(-\lambda_1 U_1) \exp(-\lambda_2 U_2) \rangle \qquad (6.1.13)$$

where $U = aW$, or in terms of the joint probability density distribution, $p_2(E_1, E_2)$:

$$Q(\lambda_1, \lambda_2) = \iint p_2(E_1, E_2) \exp(-\lambda_1 |E_1|^2 T)$$

$$\times \exp[-\lambda_2 |E_2|^2 T] \, d^2E_1 \, d^2E_2 \qquad (6.1.14)$$

For a stationary Gaussian–Markovian field, the result is

$$Q(\lambda_1, \lambda_2) = \{\langle n \rangle^2 [1 - |g^{(1)}(\tau)|^2]\lambda_1\lambda_2 + \langle n \rangle(\lambda_1 + \lambda_2) + 1\}^{-1} \qquad (6.1.15)$$

which represents the degenerate form of a two-detector arrangement ($N = 2$) with (Bedard, 1967)

$$Q(\lambda_1, \lambda_2) = [1 + \langle n_1 \rangle\lambda_1 + \langle n_2 \rangle\lambda_2 + \langle n_1 \rangle\langle n_2 \rangle\lambda_1\lambda_2(1 - |\gamma_{12}|^2)]^{-1}$$

Here γ_{12} is the second-order complex degree of coherence for the radiation field at detector 1 located at the space–time point R_1, t_1 and detector 2 located at R_2, t_2. In our case, we have $R_1 = R_2$ signifying light falling at a single space point on the photocathode, and $\tau = t_2 - t_1$. Thus, Eq. (6.1.15) is retrieved. By substituting Eq. (6.1.15) into Eqs. (6.1.7)–(6.1.9), we obtain

$$\langle n(0)n(\tau) \rangle = \langle n \rangle^2 [1 + |g^{(1)}(\tau)|^2] \qquad (6.1.16)$$

$$\langle n_k(0)n(\tau) \rangle = \langle n \rangle \left(\frac{\langle n \rangle}{1 + \langle n \rangle} \right)^{k+1} \left(1 + \frac{1+k}{1 + \langle n \rangle} |g^{(1)}(\tau)|^2 \right) \qquad (6.1.17)$$

and

$$\langle n_0(0)n_0(\tau) \rangle = \left(\frac{\langle n \rangle}{1 + \langle n \rangle} \right)^2 \left(1 + \frac{|g^{(1)}(\tau)|^2}{(1 + \langle n \rangle)^2 - \langle n \rangle^2 |g^{(1)}(\tau)|^2} \right) \qquad (6.1.18)$$

In expressing Eqs. (6.1.17) and (6.1.18) we have computed $\langle n_k(0) \rangle$

according to the Bose–Einstein distribution of Eq. (4.2.27):

$$\langle n_k(0) \rangle = \sum_{n(0)=k+1}^{\infty} p[n(0)] = \frac{1}{1+\langle n \rangle} \sum_{n=k+1}^{\infty} \left(\frac{\langle n \rangle}{1+\langle n \rangle} \right)^n$$

$$= \frac{1}{1+\langle n \rangle} \left[\sum_{n=0}^{\infty} \left(\frac{\langle n \rangle}{1+\langle n \rangle} \right)^n - \sum_{n=0}^{k} \left(\frac{\langle n \rangle}{1+\langle n \rangle} \right)^n \right]$$

$$= \frac{1}{1+\langle n \rangle} \left[\sum_{n=0}^{\infty} X^n - \sum_{n=0}^{k} X^n \right]$$

where $X = \langle n \rangle / (1 + \langle n \rangle)$. The second term is a geometrical progression. We then have

$$\langle n_k(0) \rangle = \frac{1}{1+\langle n \rangle} \left(\frac{1}{1-X} - \frac{1-X^{k+1}}{1-X} \right) = \left(\frac{\langle n \rangle}{1+\langle n \rangle} \right)^{k+1} \qquad (6.1.19)$$

The same information may be obtained easily by using the generating function for the single photon probability distribution of intensity fluctuations $(1 + \langle n \rangle \lambda)^{-1}$. Equation (6.1.19) permits a direct comparison of the correlation functions Eqs. (6.1.17) and (6.1.18) with Eq. (6.1.16a) which has the form

$$\langle n(0) n(\tau) \rangle / \langle n \rangle^2 = 1 + |g^{(1)}(\tau)|^2 \qquad (6.1.16a)$$

Now the normalized single- and double-clipped photocount autocorrelation functions are given by

$$\langle n_k(0) n(\tau) \rangle / \langle n_k(0) \rangle \langle n(\tau) \rangle$$

$$= 1 + [(1+k)/(1+\langle n \rangle)] |g^{(1)}(\tau)|^2 \qquad (6.1.17a)$$

and

$$\langle n_0(0) n_0(\tau) \rangle / \langle n_0 \rangle^2$$

$$= 1 + |g^{(1)}(\tau)|^2 / [(1+\langle n \rangle)^2 - \langle n \rangle^2 |g^{(1)}(\tau)|^2] \qquad (6.1.18a)$$

It should be interesting to note that the expression [Eq. (6) of Jakeman and Pike (1969b)]

$$\frac{\langle n_0(0) n_0(\tau) \rangle}{\langle n_0 \rangle^2} = \frac{1 + [(1-\langle n \rangle)/(1+\langle n \rangle)] |g^{(1)}(\tau)|^2}{1 - [\langle n \rangle/(1+\langle n \rangle)]^2 |g^{(1)}(\tau)|^2}$$

is identical to Eq. (6.1.18a). If $\langle n \rangle \ll 1$, Eq. (6.1.18a) is reduced to Eq. (6.1.16a), while, if $\langle n \rangle \gg 1$, Eq. (6.1.18a) approaches a constant value of unity whereby the spectral information is lost from this extreme form of clipping. On the other hand, in single clipping, little spectral information is lost. In fact, if $k = \langle n \rangle$, Eq. (6.1.17a) reduces exactly to Eq. (6.1.16a).

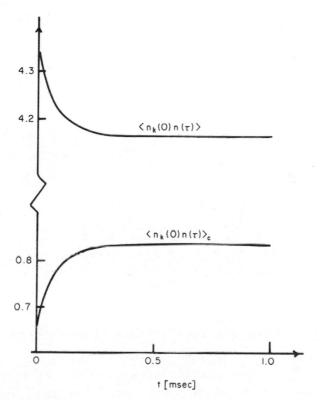

Fig. 6.2.1. $\langle n_k(0)n(\tau)\rangle$ and $\langle n_k(0)n(\tau)\rangle_c$ as a function of time for $k = 0$, $\langle n\rangle = 5$ and $\tau_{\mathrm{coh}} = 150$ μsec (Chen *et al.*, 1973).

6.2. Complementary Clipped Autocorrelation Function

Equations (6.1.8) and (6.1.17) are fundamental for the digital photon correlation technique. By rewriting Eq. (6.1.8),

$$\langle n_k(0)n(\tau)\rangle = \sum_{n(0)=k+1}^{\infty} \sum_{n(\tau)=0}^{\infty} n(\tau)p[n(0), n(\tau)]$$

$$= \sum_{n(\tau)=0}^{\infty} \left\{ \sum_{n(0)=0}^{\infty} n(\tau)p[n(0), n(\tau)] - \sum_{n(0)=0}^{k} n(\tau)p[n(0), n(\tau)] \right\}$$

$$= \sum_{n(\tau)=0}^{\infty} n(\tau)p[n(\tau)] - \sum_{n(\tau)=0}^{\infty} \sum_{n(0)=0}^{k} n(\tau)p[n(0), n(\tau)]$$

$$= \langle n\rangle - \langle n_k(0)n(\tau)\rangle_c \tag{6.2.1}$$

Chen *et al.* (1972) first introduced a complementary clipped autocorrelation function $\langle n_k(0) n(\tau) \rangle_c$, where the subscript c denotes complementary clipping. By combining Eqs. (6.1.17) and (6.2.1), we get

$$\langle n_k(0) n(\tau) \rangle_c = \sum_{n(0)=0}^{k} \sum_{n(\tau)=0}^{\infty} n(\tau) p[n(0), n(\tau)]$$

$$= \langle n \rangle - \langle n_k(0) n(\tau) \rangle$$

$$= \langle n \rangle \left[1 - \left(\frac{\langle n \rangle}{1 + \langle n \rangle} \right)^{k+1} \right]$$

$$- \langle n \rangle \left(\frac{\langle n \rangle}{1 + \langle n \rangle} \right)^{k+1} \left(\frac{1+k}{1 + \langle n \rangle} \right) \mid g^{(1)}(\tau) \mid^2 \quad (6.2.2)$$

which gives an alternative approach for measuring $\mid g^{(1)}(\tau) \mid^2$. Figure 6.2.1 shows the two quantities $\langle n_k(0) n(\tau) \rangle$ and $\langle n_k(0) n(\tau) \rangle_c$ as a function of time for $k = 0$, $\langle n \rangle = 5$, and $\tau_{\text{coh}} = 150$ μsec.

6.3. Sampling Scheme of a Clipped Digital Correlator

The essence of the clipped sampling scheme used in digital autocorrelation of photon-counting fluctuations can be shown schematically in Figs. 6.3.1 and 6.3.2. This method makes use of the fact that zero crossings of a Gaussian signal contain most of the spectral information of the original unclipped correlation function. The present emphasis has been on single-clipped digital correlators.

In single clipping, the *l*th channel receives counts of $n_k n(t_l = lT)$ for each sampling. After N samplings, the content of the *l*th channel is

$$\hat{S}(t_l) = \sum_{r=1}^{N} n_k(t_r) n(t_{r+l}) \qquad \text{single clipping} \qquad (6.3.1)$$

while the total photocounts during N samplings are

$$\hat{n} = \sum_{r=1}^{N} n(t_r) = N \langle n \rangle \qquad (6.3.2)$$

In complementary single clipping, the *l*th channel receives counts of

$$(1 - n_k) n(t_l = lT)$$

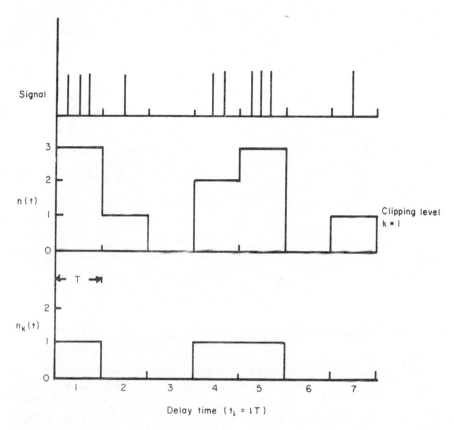

Fig. 6.3.1. A schematic representation of the clipped photocount number $n_k(t)$. The sampling time T is the period of the shift clock in Fig. 6.3.2.

for each sampling. After N samplings, the content of the lth channel is

$$\hat{S}_c(t_l) = \sum_{r=1}^{N} [1 - n_k(t_r)]n(t_{r+l}) \quad \text{complementary single clipping} \quad (6.3.3)$$

Thus, $\hat{S}(t_l)$ and $\hat{S}_c(t_l)$ contain the same information.

In practice, the digital correlator often has a buffer storage of finite bits. Then, complementary clipping offers an advantage whenever $\langle n \rangle$ is large. For example, if we take $k = 0$, we obtain from Eq. (6.1.17) that, on the average, the maximum counts in a channel per sample time T for single clipping is about $\langle n \rangle \langle n_0 \rangle = \langle n \rangle \langle n \rangle / (1 + \langle n \rangle)$ which approaches $\langle n \rangle$ for

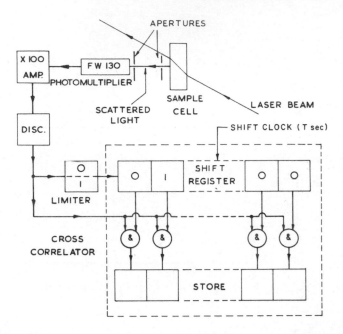

Fig. 6.3.2. A block diagram of the single-clipped digital autocorrelator (Pike, 1969).

large $\langle n \rangle$, while for complementary single clipping, the averaged maximum counts in a channel per sample time T is $\langle n \rangle[1 - \langle n \rangle/(1 + \langle n \rangle)] = \langle n \rangle/(1 + \langle n \rangle)$ which is always less than 1. Thus, complementary clipping alleviates the overflow problem. For example, Nossal and Chen (1972) used a four-bit buffer storage counter after the coincident gate at each channel as shown schematically in Fig. 6.3.3. The multichannel scaler mode of their multichannel analyzer has a serial transfer rate of 10 μsec/channel. For a 130-channel correlator, the output, which has been divided by 16, can be read into the memory of the multichannel scaler every $130 \times 10 = 1300$ μsec or 1.3 msec. Thus, the coincident output per channel must be less than 16 during the 1.3 msec. If the total counting rate is 3×10^4 counts/sec and the sampling time is $T = 200$ μsec, the average photocount per channel $\langle n \rangle = 3 \times 10^4 \times 2 \times 10^{-4} = 6$, and in 1.3 msec, there are about $1.3/.2 \simeq 6$ samplings. In the normal-clipping mode, the buffer storage must exceed 36 while in complementary clipping the needed buffer storage corresponds roughly to only the number of samplings during the transfer into the memory of a multichannel analyzer. Complementary clipping is especially useful in heterodyne measurements where optical mixing of the signal with a strong local-oscillator beam is required.

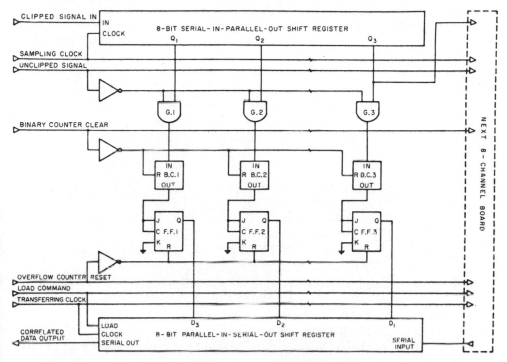

Fig. 6.3.3. Schematic circuit diagram of 8 channels of the digital autocorrelator. G1···G8 = coincidence gates; FF1···FF8 = flip-flop overflow counters. The output of the flip-flops are read every 1.31 msec into the lower shift register, and then transferred serially into the memory of a multichannel analyzer. Thus, the data are accumulated continuously and displayed as the experiment progresses (Nossal and Chen, 1972).

In double clipping, we can also reformulate Eq. (6.1.9):

$$\langle n_0(0)\,n_0(\tau)\rangle = \sum_{n(0)=0}^{\infty}\sum_{n(\tau)=0}^{\infty} p[n(0), n(\tau)]$$

$$= 1 - p[n(0) = 0] - p[n(\tau) = 0]$$
$$+ p[n(0) = 0, n(\tau) = 0]$$
$$= 1 - 2p(0) + p(0,0) \tag{6.3.4}$$

or with the generating function (Eq. 6.1.15), we have

$$\langle n_0(0)\,n_0(\tau)\rangle = \frac{\langle n\rangle - 1}{\langle n\rangle + 1} + \frac{1}{(1 + \langle n\rangle)^2 - \langle n\rangle^2 \mid g^{(1)}(\tau)\mid^2}$$

$$= \frac{\langle n\rangle - 1}{\langle n\rangle + 1} + p(0,0) \tag{6.3.5}$$

where $p(0, 0) \equiv \langle n_0(0)n_0(\tau) \rangle_c$ represents the complementary double clipping at zero photocount number. The method of complementary double clipping is very useful whenever dust particles in the sample become a problem. At small scattering angles, the scattering by dust particles is usually very strong. As dust particles enter the effective scattering volume, the sudden increase in the scattered intensity essentially shuts off the correlator in the complementary double-clipping mode.

In an actual experiment, the content of the lth channel for N delays after M sweeps is

$$M\widehat{S}(t_l) = M \sum_{r=1}^{N} n_k(t_r)n(t_{r+l}) = MN\langle n_k(t_r)n(t_{r+l}) \rangle \quad (6.3.6)$$

while the total photocounts during M sweeps with N channels are

$$M\hat{n} = M \sum_{r=1}^{N} n(t_r) = MN\langle n \rangle \quad (6.3.7)$$

with $\langle n \rangle$ being the average number of photocounts per channel with sample period T. Thus, MN gets canceled out since n_k is a number and is unimportant in the equations we have discussed in this chapter. However, Eqs. (6.3.6) and (6.3.7) do tell us that the counting capacity of the lth correlator channel must be more than $M\widehat{S}(t_l)$ and that of the scaler for total photocounts more than $MN\langle n \rangle$.

6.4. Statistical Accuracy in the Digital Autocorrelation of Photon-Counting Fluctuations†

Following the introduction of light-beating spectroscopy by Benedek and clipped photocount autocorrelation by Jakeman and Pike (1969b), several extensive studies on the statistical accuracy of spectral linewidth in optical mixing spectroscopy have been reported. Special cases of the problem corresponding experimentally to using a detector area much larger than a coherence area of the light have been discussed by Benedek (1968), Haus (1969), and Cummins and Swinney (1970). Degiorgio and Lastovka (1971) have presented the statistical errors inherent in intensity correlation spectroscopy owing to the stochastic nature of both the scattering and the photoemission processes. They have determined the variance of the intensity autocorrelation function of Gaussian–Lorentzian light for arbitrary delay times and have computed the uncertainty on the measured correlation time (line-width) by means of a generalized three-parameter

† Jakeman et al., 1971b; Pike, 1972.

least-mean-squares fitting procedure. Independently, Jakeman *et al.* (1971b, c) have investigated the statistical errors (caused by the finite duration of experiments) in the intensity autocorrelation function and in the spectral linewidth of Gaussian–Lorentzian light. Analysis of Gaussian light by clipped photocount autocorrelation has also been extended to include the effects of finite duration sampling intervals and incomplete spatial coherence by Koppel (1971). The details of these lengthy developments can best be obtained by reading the original papers, especially the work of Degiorgio and Lastovka (1971) on intensity correlation spectroscopy and of Jakeman *et al.* (1971b) on statistical accuracy in the digital autocorrelation of photon-counting fluctuations. While the analysis of data using three variables generally leads to larger errors, and the one-parameter fit of Kelly (1971) is more restrictive, the two-parameter approach of Pike and his co-workers for single exponential decays represents a more realistic treatment of this complex problem. Pike (1972) has summarized some of the pertinent guidelines.

1. Given a fixed number of channels C for the correlator, the ratio of the sample time T to the coherence time r_{coh} ($=1/\Gamma_m$, although we shall drop the subscript m denoting the measured value from now on) has an optimum value $CT\Gamma \simeq 2$–3. Figure 6.4.1 (Pike, 1972) shows the dependence of linewidth accuracy on the sample-time/coherence-time ratio (ΓT) and on photocounts per coherence time for fixed values of the number of channels ($C = 20$), detector area (0.01 coherence area; $A/A_{coh} = 0.01$), experiment duration (10^4 coherence times), and single clipping at zero ($k = 0$). In this chapter, we have denoted the effective photocathode area by A instead of S and the spatial coherence area by A_{coh} instead of S_{coh} (Chapter 4).

2. Increase in the effective scattering area will increase the light flux but decrease the correlation coefficients (Scarl, 1968; Jakeman *et al.*, 1970a). The effects compensate asymptotically (Jakeman *et al.*, 1971a) so that there is no advantage in using more than one coherence area. With high light flux the area can be reduced to well below a coherence area. Figure 6.4.2 (Pike, 1972) shows the percentage error in linewidth as a function of A/A_{coh} for fixed values of the number of channels ($C = 20$), sample-time/coherence-time ratio ($\Gamma T = 0.1$), experiment duration (10^4 coherence times), and single clipping at zero ($k = 0$). A decrease in the A/A_{coh} decreases the averaging effects of the signal statistics without losing accuracy from photon statistics; but the count rate also decreases. The break-even point which depends also on the clipping level and number of channels is about 10 photocounts per coherence time.

3. Clipping levels should be set between one-half and two times the

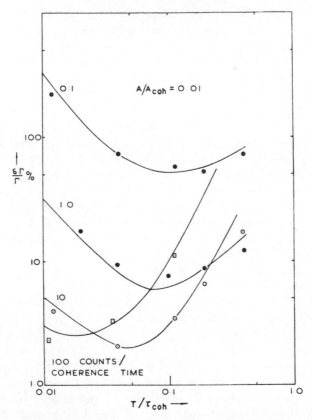

Fig. 6.4.1. The linewidth accuracy for 20 channels, single-clipped at zero, obtained with an experimental duration of 10^4 coherence times, as a function of sample-time/coherence-time ratio and counts per coherence time. The solid lines are the theory for a point detector. The points are experimental values using a detector area 0.01 times a coherence area. The ordinate scales as the square root of the number of coherence times in the duration of an experiment (Pike, 1972).

mean counting rate $\langle n \rangle$. Figure 6.4.3 (Pike, 1972) shows the percentage error in linewidth as a function of single-clipping level and photocounts per coherence time for fixed number of channels ($C = 20$), sample-time/co-herence-time ratio ($\Gamma T = 0.1$), detector area ($A/A_{\mathrm{coh}} = 0.01$), and experiment duration (10^4 coherence time). Using an appropriate clipping level, the accuracy improves with increasing photocounts per coherence time. However, the improvements quickly saturate, depending on the number of channels, as the number of photocounts per coherence time exceeds about 10.

In summary, we learn that for *single* exponential decay curves there is

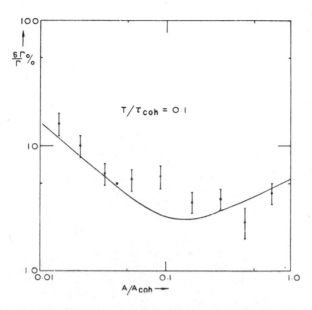

Fig. 6.4.2. The linewidth accuracy for 20 channels single-clipped at zero, obtained with an experimental duration of 10^4 coherence times, as a function of detector-area/coherence-area ratio. The solid line shows the theory for a point detector with equivalent count rates. The points are experimental values using a sample time 0.1 times a coherence time. The number of photodetections per coherence time ranged from 0.5 to 23. The accuracy increases with area until the count rate becomes too high for clipping at zero when it reduces again (Pike, 1972).

no special advantage in having a correlator with an excessive number of channels, such as 400. Rather it is essential (a) to set up the clipping level to be the mean counting rate per delay time, (b) to have $A/A_{\text{coh}} < 1$ with 10–100 photoelectrons per coherence time, and (c) to adjust the total delay to 2 optical correlation (or coherence) times, which for a 20-channel correlator corresponds to $\Gamma T \leq 0.1$. Alternatively, use with $A/A_{\text{coh}} = 1$ is near optimum for a very wide range of scattering cross sections. When the number of photocounts per coherence time is reduced to 0.1–1, the total delay times should be increased to 2–3 coherence times which for a 20-channel correlator corresponds to $\Gamma T \geq 0.1$. As we increase the number of channels, say to 400 from 20, the mean counting rate per channel will be reduced by a factor of 20. At very low light flux levels, the efficiency at even single-zero-clipping decreases. The dependence of the percentage error in linewidth on the number of channels is more complex as shown in Fig. 6.4.4 (Jakeman *et al.*, 1971b). In Fig. 6.4.4 a comparison has also been made between the unclipped and the single-clipped-at-zero correlations where r represents the number of photocounts per coherence time. When $r = 0.1$

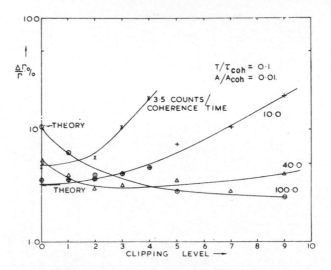

Fig. 6.4.3. The linewidth accuracy for 20 channels obtained with an experimental duration of 10^4 coherence times, as a function of single-clipping level, and counts per coherence time. The points are experimental values using a sample time 0.1 times the coherence time and a detector area 0.01 times a coherence area. The maximum accuracy obtainable does not improve significantly with count rate above about 10 counts per coherence time. Theoretical values are shown at zero clipping level only, the behavior at higher values has been confirmed by computer simulations (Pike, 1972).

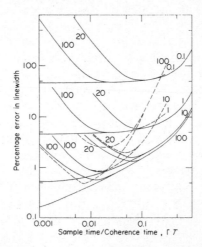

Fig. 6.4.4. The percentage error in linewidth as a function of sample time for the photon flux and number of channels shown on the right-hand and left-hand side of the graph, respectively: solid line unclipped; dashed line clipped at zero. When $r = 0.1$ and 1 the clipped and unclipped results coincide for $\Gamma T < 0.1$. $N\Gamma T = 10^4$ (Jakeman et al., 1971b).

and 1, the clipped and unclipped results coincide for $\Gamma T \leq 0.1$. Unexpectedly, for $r = 100$, the clipped results actually provide less error in linewidth than the unclipped ones at small values of ΓT. For fixed maximum delay time and fixed experiment time, the error in linewidth cannot be reduced significantly by improving the resolution of the instrument, i.e., by using more channels. Figure 6.4.5 (Jakeman *et al.*, 1971b) shows the percentage

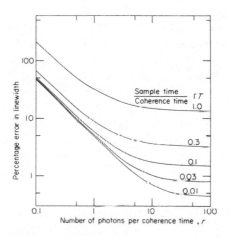

Fig. 6.4.5. The percentage error in linewidth as a function of photon flux for values of ΓT shown and an infinite number of channels in the unclipped case. $N\Gamma T = 10^4$ (Jakeman, *et al.*, 1971b).

error in linewidth as a function of r at various values of ΓT using $N\Gamma T = 10^4$ and an infinite number of channels in the unclipped case. However, the argument breaks down for more complex correlation functions which are not single exponentials. Again, the error in linewidth cannot be reduced by indefinitely increasing r. The important point is to try to get $r \geq 10$. Finally, each run should be normalized independently against its own total counts since this gives greater accuracy than subsequent normalization against a long-term mean value. The best approach is to use an on-line computer to normalize a large number of short runs independently. The length of the runs can be reduced until the bias, of order $1/N$, affects the results measurably, i.e., for $N \simeq 10^3$, where N is the total number of samples. A more detailed discussion has been presented elsewhere (Hughes *et al.*, 1973).

Under the assumption that the counting time of incremental samples is much smaller than the light coherence time, Saleh (1973) has considered statistical errors which arise in estimating parameters of the spatial coherence function by photon-counting techniques for a Gaussian stationary and cross-spectrally pure light field.

6.5. Non-Gaussian Signal Statistics

Experiments such as laser light near threshold (Jakeman et al., 1970b), motions of particles in turbulent fluids (DiPorto et al., 1969; Bourke et al., 1970), and light scattering from small numbers of particles undergoing Brownian motions (Schaefer and Berne, 1972; Schaefer and Pusey, 1972; Adrian, 1972), follow non-Gaussian statistics.

Schaefer and Berne (1972) show that non-Gaussian concentration fluctuations arise at low concentrations because the particles in the scattering volume have a Poisson distribution. In this case, the homodyne intensity autocorrelation function decays on two widely different time scales. The fast process is the usual Brownian motion of the individual particles, while the slow process is related to the time dependence of the fluctuations in the total number of particles in the scattering volume. This slow process does not appear in the heterodyne correlation function. Thus, the homodyne technique can be used to probe fundamental properties of colloid statistics.

The scattered field amplitude for a system of M identical spheres in a scattering volume v has the following form:

$$E_{\mathrm{s}}(t) = \lambda^* \sum_{i=1}^{M} b_i(t) \, \exp[i\mathbf{K}\cdot\mathbf{r}_i(t)] \qquad (6.5.1)$$

where the scattering amplitude λ^* of each particle depends upon the polarizability and the wavelength of the incident light, $b_i(t)$ is a random variable with

$$b_i(t) = 1 \qquad \text{if particle } i \text{ is in the scattering volume } v$$

$$= 0 \qquad \text{if it is not} \qquad (6.5.2)$$

In heterodyne studies, $R_E(\tau) = \langle E_{\mathrm{s}}{}^*(\mathbf{K}, 0) E_{\mathrm{s}}(\mathbf{K}, \tau) \rangle$, while in homodyne studies, $R_I(\tau) = \langle | E_{\mathrm{s}}(\mathbf{K}, 0) |^2 | E_{\mathrm{s}}(\mathbf{K}, \tau) |^2 \rangle$ where we have neglected the constants in Eq. (3.3.7) and identified I with E^*E.

For N particles in total volume V, the average number of particles in the scattering volume v, $\langle M \rangle$, is

$$\langle M(t) \rangle = N(v/V) \qquad (6.5.3)$$

and the instantaneous number of particles in v is

$$M(t) = \sum_{i=1}^{N} b_i(t) \qquad (6.5.4)$$

Then,

$$\langle M(t) \rangle = \sum_{i=1}^{N} \langle b_i(t) \rangle = N \langle b_i(t) \rangle \qquad (6.5.5)$$

By comparing Eq. (6.5.3) with Eq. (6.5.5), we get

$$\langle b_i(t) \rangle = v/V \qquad (6.5.6)$$

and obtain for independent particles in a homogeneous solution:

$$R_E(\mathbf{K}, \tau) = \lambda^{*2} \sum_{j=1}^{M} \langle b_j(0) b_j(\tau) \rangle F(\mathbf{K}, \tau) \qquad (6.5.7)$$

and

$$R_I(\mathbf{K}, \tau) = \lambda^{*4} \sum_{l,j=1}^{M} \langle b_j{}^2(0) b_l{}^2(\tau) \rangle$$

$$+ \lambda^{*4} \sum_{l \neq m=1}^{M} \langle b_l(0) b_l(\tau) b_m(0) b_m(\tau) \rangle \mid F(\mathbf{K}, \tau) \mid^2 \qquad (6.5.8)$$

where $F(\mathbf{K}, t)$ is the self-intermediate-scattering function and $F(\mathbf{K}, \tau) = \exp(-DK^2\tau)$ for dilute macromolecular solutions. In Eq. (6.5.8), the first term is related to the correlation function of occupation number fluctuations, $\langle \delta M(0) \, \delta M(\tau) \rangle$, where $\delta M(t) \; [\equiv M(t) - \langle M(t) \rangle]$ is the fluctuation of the total number of particles in the scattering volume v. The factorization of averages in Eq. (6.5.8) follows from the fact that the time scale of fluctuations in occupation numbers is several orders of magnitude slower, i.e., $\tau_M = L^2/24D \gg (DK^2)^{-1}$ where L is a typical dimension of the scattering volume. If we take $\langle M(M-1) \rangle = \langle M \rangle^2$ for a Poisson process, Eq. (6.5.8) can be expressed in terms of the occupation numbers:

$$R_I(\mathbf{K}, \tau) = \lambda^{*4}\{ \langle \delta M(0) \, \delta M(\tau) \rangle + \langle M \rangle^2 [1 + \mid F(\mathbf{K}, \tau) \mid^2] \} \qquad (6.5.9)$$

Schaefer and Berne used a 20-channel digital correlator in combination with a scaling technique (Pusey and Goldburg, 1971). The scaled photocount autocorrelation function for $\langle n^{(s)} \rangle \ll 1$, takes the form

$$\langle n^{(s)}(0) n(\tau) \rangle = \alpha^2 [\langle M \rangle + \langle M \rangle^2 (1 + \beta e^{-2\Gamma\tau})]/s \qquad (6.5.10)$$

where $n^{(s)}(t)$ is the number of scaled-by-s photocounts observed in a sampling time interval T at time t and β is a constant ≤ 1 (Koppel, 1971). The decay rate and $\langle M \rangle$ can be analyzed from

$$C(\tau) = \langle n^{(s)}(0) n(\tau) \rangle s / \langle n \rangle^2 = \langle M \rangle^{-1} + 1 + \beta e^{-2\Gamma\tau} \qquad (6.5.11)$$

A non-Gaussian correction to the clipped photocount correlation function to the order $1/\langle M \rangle^2$ has been derived by Chen and Tartaglia (1972). They obtained the zeroth-clipped and the average-clipped photocount up to the order $\langle M \rangle^{-2}$ and in the limit of total spatial coherence (or an ideal point detector) they are as follows:

$$\langle n_0 \rangle = \frac{\langle n \rangle}{1 + \langle n \rangle} \left(1 + \frac{\langle n \rangle}{2(1 + \langle n \rangle)^2} \frac{1}{\langle M \rangle} + \frac{8\langle n \rangle^2 - \langle n \rangle^3}{12(1 + \langle n \rangle)^4} \frac{1}{\langle M \rangle^2} \right) \quad (6.5.12)$$

and

$$\frac{\langle n_0(0) n(\tau) \rangle}{\langle n_0(0) \rangle \langle n(\tau) \rangle} = 1 + \frac{g_{12}^2}{1 + \langle n \rangle} \left(1 - \frac{\langle n \rangle^2 + \langle n \rangle + 2}{2(1 + \langle n \rangle)^2} \frac{1}{\langle M \rangle} \right.$$

$$\left. + \frac{\langle n \rangle^4 - 4\langle n \rangle^3 + 7\langle n \rangle^2 - 18\langle n \rangle}{12(1 + \langle n \rangle)^4} \frac{1}{\langle M \rangle^2} \right) \quad (6.5.13)$$

where $g_{12} \equiv \langle \exp[+i\mathbf{K} \cdot \mathbf{r}_i(0)] \exp[-i\mathbf{K} \cdot \mathbf{r}_i(\tau)] \rangle \equiv g^{(1)}(\tau) \equiv F(\mathbf{K}, \tau)$. The first term in Eq. (6.5.13) gives the well-known Gaussian result of Eq. (6.1.17a) for a normalized single-clipped-at-zero photocount autocorrelation function

$$\langle n_0(0) n(\tau) \rangle (\langle n_0 \rangle \langle n \rangle)^{-1} = 1 + (1 + \langle n \rangle)^{-1} |g^{(1)}(\tau)|^2 \quad (6.1.17b)$$

when $\langle M \rangle \to \infty$. The non-Gaussian correction appears as powers of $\langle M \rangle^{-1}$ and is contained in both $\langle n_0 \rangle$ and the factor multiplying g_{12}^2. Equation (6.5.13) has the following limits:

$$\lim_{\tau \to \infty} \frac{\langle n_0(0) n(\tau) \rangle}{\langle n_0 \rangle \langle n \rangle} = 1 \quad (6.5.14)$$

$$\lim_{\langle M \rangle \to \infty} \frac{\langle n_0(0) n(\tau) \rangle}{\langle n_0 \rangle \langle n \rangle} = 1 + \frac{1}{1 + \langle n \rangle} |g^{(1)}(\tau)|^2 \quad (6.5.15)$$

$$\lim_{\langle n \rangle \to 0} \frac{\langle n_0(0) n(\tau) \rangle}{\langle n_0 \rangle \langle n \rangle} = 1 + g_{12}^2 \left(1 - \frac{1}{\langle M \rangle} \right) \quad (6.5.16)$$

Equation (6.5.14) simply implies that for very long times, the photocounts are not correlated and that it is an exact limit for any two-time correlation function. Equation (6.5.15) retrieves Eq. (6.1.17b). The reader is advised to read the detailed derivation of Eqs. (6.5.12) and (6.5.13) from the article by Chen and Tartaglia (1972).

Bendjaballah (1973) has extended the clipped photocount autocorrelation function at zero photon number to non-Gaussian optical fields, to sinusoidal and Gaussian modulation of ideal laser light, and to Gaussian modulation of thermal light.

Tartaglia and Chen (1973) have extended the derivation of Eq. (6.5.13) to a more realistic case where the photodetector has an effective finite circular area A and obtained a spatial coherence factor as obtained by Jakeman et al. (1970a) and Scarl (1968) without invoking the stricter Gaussian assumption.

The correlation of the photocurrent output from a photomultiplier tube has the form

$$R_{i,N}(\tau) = \int_A d^2R_1 \int_A d^2R_2 \int_{t_1}^{t_1+T} \frac{dt_1'}{T} \int_{t_2}^{t_2+T} \frac{dt_2'}{T}$$

$$\times \frac{\langle j(\mathbf{R}_2, t+\tau) j(\mathbf{R}_1, t) \rangle_{\text{st}}}{\langle j(\mathbf{R}_2, t) j(\mathbf{R}_1, t) \rangle_{\text{st}}} \quad (6.5.17)$$

where $\mathbf{R}_1$ and $\mathbf{R}_2$ are any two points on the photocathode. The average current is

$$\langle i \rangle = \int_A d^2R \int_0^T e\alpha E_{\text{s}}^*(\mathbf{R}, t) E_{\text{s}}(\mathbf{R}, t) \, dt/T \quad (6.5.18)$$

where the scattered electric field for M particles in scattering volume v is given by

$$E_{\text{s}}(\mathbf{R}, t) = \lambda^\dagger(\mathbf{R}, t) \sum_{i=1}^M \exp(i\mathbf{K}\cdot\mathbf{r}_i) \quad (6.5.19)$$

with $\mathbf{K} = \mathbf{k}_{\text{s}} - \mathbf{k}_{\text{I}}$.

For the intensity–intensity correlation we can write

$$\langle j(\mathbf{R}_1, t_1) j(\mathbf{R}_2, t_2) \rangle$$

$$= e^2\alpha^2 \langle E_{\text{s}}^*(\mathbf{R}_1, t_1) E_{\text{s}}(\mathbf{R}_1, t_1) E_{\text{s}}^*(\mathbf{R}_2, t_2) E_{\text{s}}(\mathbf{R}_2, t_2) \rangle$$

$$= e^2\alpha^2\lambda^{\dagger 4} \sum_{ijkl}^M \langle \exp[-i\mathbf{K}_1\cdot\mathbf{r}_i(t_1)] \exp[i\mathbf{K}_1\cdot\mathbf{r}_j(t_1)]$$

$$\times \exp[-i\mathbf{K}_2\cdot\mathbf{r}_k(t_2)] \exp[i\mathbf{K}_2\cdot\mathbf{r}_l(t_2)] \rangle$$

$$= e^2\alpha^2\lambda^{\dagger 4}\{M^2 + M(M-1) \mid \langle \exp[-i\mathbf{K}_1\cdot\mathbf{r}(t_1)] \exp[i\mathbf{K}_2\cdot\mathbf{r}(t_2)] \rangle \mid^2\}$$

$$(6.5.20)$$

since the nonzero contributions come from terms where $i = j$, $k = l$, and $i = l \neq j = k$. Thus,

$$\frac{\langle j(\mathbf{R}_1, t_1) j(\mathbf{R}_2, t_2) \rangle}{\langle j \rangle^2} = 1 + \left(1 - \frac{1}{M}\right) \left| \frac{\langle E_{\text{s}}^*(\mathbf{R}_1, t_1) E_{\text{s}}(\mathbf{R}_2, t_2) \rangle}{\langle \mid E_{\text{s}}(\mathbf{R}, t) \mid^2 \rangle} \right|^2 \quad (6.5.21)$$

which is equivalent to Eq. (6.5.16).

In amplitude correlation, we can write

$$\langle E_{\mathrm{s}}{}^{*}(\mathbf{R}_1, t_1) E_{\mathrm{s}}(\mathbf{R}_2, t_2) \rangle$$

$$= \lambda^{\dagger *}(\mathbf{R}_1, t_1) \lambda^{\dagger}(\mathbf{R}_2, t_2) \sum_{i=1}^{M} \sum_{j=1}^{M} \langle \exp[-i\mathbf{K}_1\cdot\mathbf{r}_i(t_1)] \exp[i\mathbf{K}_2\cdot\mathbf{r}_j(t_2)]\rangle$$

$$= \lambda^{\dagger *}(\mathbf{R}_1, t_1) \lambda^{\dagger}(\mathbf{R}_2, t_2) \int_{v} d\mathbf{r}_1 \int_{v} d\mathbf{r}_2 \, \langle \rho(\mathbf{r}_1, t_1)\rho(\mathbf{r}_2, t_2) \rangle$$

$$\times \exp(-i\mathbf{K}_1\cdot\mathbf{r}_1 + i\mathbf{K}_2\cdot\mathbf{r}_2)$$

$$= \tfrac{1}{4}\lambda^{\dagger *}(\mathbf{R}_1, t_1) \lambda^{\dagger}(\mathbf{R}_2, t_2) \int_{v} d\mathbf{r} \exp[-i(\mathbf{K}_1 + \mathbf{K}_2)\cdot\mathbf{r}/2]\langle\rho(0, 0)\rho(\mathbf{r}, \tau) \rangle$$

$$\times \int_{v'} d\mathbf{r}' \exp[i(\mathbf{K}_2 - \mathbf{K}_1)\cdot\mathbf{r}'/2] \qquad (6.5.22)$$

where $\mathbf{r} = \mathbf{r}_1 - \mathbf{r}_2$, $\mathbf{r}' = \mathbf{r}_1 + \mathbf{r}_2$, and the number density and its Fourier transform are defined by

$$\rho(\mathbf{r}, t) = \sum_{i=1}^{M} \delta[\mathbf{r} - \mathbf{r}_i(t)] \qquad (6.5.23)$$

$$\rho(\mathbf{K}, t) = \sum_{i=1}^{M} \exp[i\mathbf{K}\cdot\mathbf{r}_i(t)] \qquad (6.5.24)$$

The last integral in Eq. (6.5.22) gives rise to the spatial coherence factor. Since the distance from the scattering volume to the photocathode surface, r_0, is much greater than $|\mathbf{R}_2 - \mathbf{R}_1|$,

$$|\mathbf{K}_2 - \mathbf{K}_1| = |\mathbf{k}_{\mathrm{s}2} - \mathbf{k}_{\mathrm{s}1}| \simeq (k_{\mathrm{I}}/r_0) |\mathbf{R}_2 - \mathbf{R}_1| \qquad (6.5.25)$$

Therefore, the integral depends on the transverse dimension of the effective scattering volume as seen by the photocathode. With circular pinhole and photocathode of radius s:

$$\int_{v'} d\mathbf{r}' \exp[\tfrac{1}{2}i(\mathbf{K}_2 - \mathbf{K}_1)\cdot\mathbf{r}'] = (2J(x)/x) \exp[i(\mathbf{K}_2 - \mathbf{K}_1)\cdot\mathbf{r}_0] \qquad (6.5.26)$$

where

$$x = s \,|\mathbf{K}_2 - \mathbf{K}_1|$$

By substituting Eqs. (6.5.21), (6.5.22), and (6.5.26) into (6.5.17), we finally get

$$R_{i,N}(\tau) = 1 + \frac{1}{T^2} \int_{t_1}^{t_1+T} dt_1' \int_{t_2}^{t_2+T} dt_2' \left| \frac{\langle \rho(0,0)\rho(\mathbf{r},\tau) \rangle}{\langle | \rho(0,0) |^2 \rangle} \right|^2$$

$$\times \left[\frac{1}{A^2} \int_A d^2R_1 \int_A d^2R_2 \left(\frac{2J_1(x)}{x} \right)^2 \right] \quad (6.5.27)$$

where the last factor is the socalled spatial coherence factor

$$f(A) = \frac{1}{A^2} \int_A d^2R_1 \int_A d^2R_2 \left(\frac{2J_1(x)}{x} \right)^2 \quad (6.5.28)$$

with $A = \pi s^2$.

6.6. Correlation of Scaled Photon-Counting Fluctuations†

Scaling, like clipping, is a one-bit technique. It approximates uniform random clipping and provides an estimate of the time intensity correlation function, regardless of signal statistics. The electronic circuitry for scaling is considerably simpler than that required for uniform random clipping and full correlation. Thus, it is important to establish a relationship between single-scaled and single-clipped correlation functions of photon arrivals.

Suppose we take a correlation system consisting of two channels separated by a delay time τ. Channel 1 records the actual signal counts detected in a sample time interval T and channel 2 records only the clipping-at-zero counts of the scaled-by-s photopulses, as shown schematically in Fig. 6.6.1. After a period of time τ,

$$n(\tau, T) = ms + r \quad \text{and} \quad n^{(s)}(\tau, T) = m \quad (6.6.1)$$

where $r \le s - 1$; r is the remainder, and s is the scaling; m is the number of scaled photopulses in time period T before clipping-at-zero. If $q(r)$ is the probability distribution of the remainder, the probability of recording one or more counts in the sample interval T following the sample period τ in the scaled channel is

$$\sum_{r=0}^{s-1} q(r) \sum_{n=s-r}^{\infty} p(n, T) \quad (6.6.2)$$

† Jakeman et al., 1972.

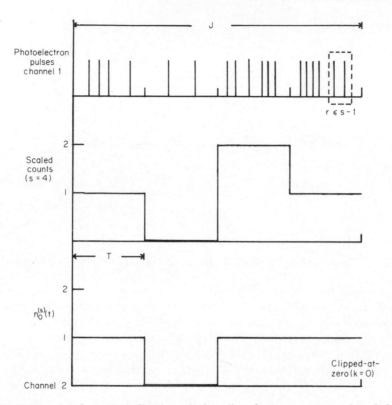

Fig. 6.6.1. A schematic indication of the clipped-at-zero counts of scaled-by-s photocount number $n_0^{(s)}(t)$. $\tau \equiv$ a period of time; $T \equiv$ sample time; $s(\equiv$ scale$) = 4$. The condition: $r \leq s - 1$ is satisfied.

where $p(n, T)$ is the probability of having n photoelectron pulses in the time interval T. The joint probability of having one or more counts in the scaled channel and $n(\tau)$ counts in the other channel is

$$\sum_{r=0}^{s-1} q(r) \sum_{n(0)=s-r}^{\infty} p[n(0), n(\tau)] \qquad (6.6.3)$$

where $p[n(0), n(\tau)]$ $[\equiv p(n_2, T, t_2; n_1, T, t_1)]$ is the joint probability of having n_1 $[\equiv n(0)]$ photoelectron pulses at time t_1 $(\equiv 0)$ in the time interval T and n_2 $[\equiv n(\tau)]$ photoelectron pulses at time t_2 $(\equiv \tau)$ in the time interval T. The correlation function of photocounts scaled in one channel has the form

$$G_s^{(2)}(\tau) \equiv \langle n_k^{(s)}(0) n(\tau) \rangle = \sum_{k=0}^{s-1} q(s - k - 1) G_k^{(2)}(\tau) \qquad (6.6.4)$$

where

$$G_k^{(2)}(\tau) = \langle n_k(0)n(\tau) \rangle = \sum_{n(0)=k+1}^{\infty} \sum_{n(\tau)=0}^{\infty} n(\tau)p[n(0), n(\tau)] \quad (6.6.5)$$

Equation (6.6.4) reveals that scaling in one channel averages the single-clipped correlation function over a finite distribution of clipping level. If $q(r)$ is uniform, scaling represents uniform random clipping over the same distribution of clipping levels. Then, Eq. (6.6.4) is reduced to

$$G_s^{(2)}(\tau) = (1/s) \sum_{n(0)=0}^{s} \sum_{n(\tau)=0}^{\infty} n(0)n(\tau)p[n(0), n(\tau)]$$

$$+ [G_k^{(2)}(\tau)]_{k=s} \quad (6.6.6)$$

If s is chosen so that $G_s^{(2)}(\tau) \gg [G_k^{(2)}(\tau)]_{k=0}$. Then, a measure of $G_s^{(2)}(\tau)$ becomes a measure of the full photocount autocorrelation function. Jakeman *et al.* (1972) have shown that $q(r)$ is uniform by the following analysis.

For $\tau \gg$ the coherence time of the light τ_{coh} the number of counts arriving within τ follows a Poisson distribution:

$$q(r) = \exp(-\bar{N}) \sum_{l=0}^{\infty} \bar{N}^{ls+r}/(ls+r)! \quad (6.6.7)$$

where $\bar{N} = \bar{n}\tau/T$ and $\bar{n}$ is the mean photoelectron pulses per sample time T. Then

$$q(r) = \frac{1}{s}\left[1 + \exp(-\bar{N}) \sum_{k=1}^{s-1} \exp\left(\bar{N} \cos\frac{2\pi k}{s} \right) \right.$$

$$\times \left. \cos\left(\frac{2\pi k(s-r)}{s} + \bar{N}\sin\frac{2\pi k}{s} \right) \right] \quad \text{for } s > 1 \quad (6.6.8)$$

and

$$q(r) \simeq \frac{1}{s}\left\{ 1 + 2\exp\left[-\bar{N}\left(1 - \cos\frac{2\pi}{s} \right) \right] \cos\left(\frac{2\pi r}{s} - \bar{N}\sin\frac{2\pi}{s} \right) \right\}$$

$$\text{for } s > 2 \quad (6.6.9)$$

Equation (6.6.9) is uniform to better than 1 % for $s \le 4$, $\bar{N} > 5$. For larger s, this degree of uniformity can be obtained when $\bar{N} > 5s^2/2\pi^2$. For Gaussian light, Eq. (6.6.4) becomes

$$G_s^{(2)}(\tau) = \frac{\langle n \rangle^2}{s}\left\{ 1 - \left(\frac{\langle n \rangle}{1 + \langle n \rangle} \right)^2 + |g^{(1)}(\tau)|^2 \right.$$

$$\times \left. \left[1 + \frac{1 + \langle n \rangle + s}{1 + \langle n \rangle}\left(\frac{\langle n \rangle}{1 + \langle n \rangle} \right)^s \right] \right\} \quad (6.6.10)$$

which differs from the true autocorrelation function by $<1\%$ owing to cutoff at $s-1$ in the sum of Eq. (6.6.4) if we choose $\bar{n} \gtrsim 1$, $s > 10\bar{n}$, and $\tau \simeq 25\bar{n}T$.

Jakeman *et al.* (1972) found that at least for Gaussian light, scaling at relatively small s is essentially as accurate as clipping, which is comparable in accuracy to full correlation. They also suggested a method for quick selection of the optimum scaling level in any experiment by picking a s such that the correlation counting rate is much greater for scaled–clipped-at-zero correlation, than for scaled–clipped-at-one correlation. The scaled–clipped-at-zero correlation function is then a good approximation to the full correlation function.

6.7. Uniform and Sequential Clipping

Correlation of *scaled* photon-counting fluctuations which we have discussed in Section 6.6 (Jakeman *et al.*, 1972; Koppel and Schaefer, 1973) provides a method for measuring the full photocount correlation function by means of a clipped correlator. An alternative technique is to use uniform and sequential clipping (USC) of incoming photocounts (Tartaglia *et al.*, 1973) instead of single-channel scaling (SCS). The idea is applicable because the infinite sum in the definition which relates the full photocount correlation function $\langle n(0)n(\tau) \rangle$ and the single-clipped photocount correlation function $\langle n_k(0)n(\tau) \rangle$,

$$\langle n(0)n(\tau) \rangle = \sum_{k=0}^{\infty} \langle n_k(0)n(\tau) \rangle \qquad (6.7.1)$$

can be replaced by a finite sum. For example, Tartaglia *et al.* (1973) have pointed out that for $\langle n \rangle = 1$, a finite sum over all the clipping levels $k \le 6$ will represent the full photocount correlation function within an accuracy of 1% for Gaussian light. Experimentally, the finite summing is achieved by uniformly and sequentially clipping the incoming photocounts with $k = l$ during each of $l+1$ sampling periods, and then starting over again at $k = l$. In other words, Eq. (6.7.1) is reduced to

$$\langle G \rangle = \frac{N}{l+1} \sum_{k=0}^{l} \langle n_k(0)n(\tau) \rangle \simeq \frac{N}{l+1} \langle n(0)n(\tau) \rangle \qquad (6.7.2)$$

where N is the total number of samplings, and we have taken

$$\sum_{k=l+1}^{\infty} \langle n_k(0) n(\tau) \rangle$$

to be negligible for sufficiently large l. For Gaussian light, we need

$$[\langle n \rangle / (1 + \langle n \rangle)]^{l+1} \ll 1 \tag{6.7.3}$$

to set the level of l for uniform and sequential clipping. The two schemes (USC and SCS) are equivalent. However, Jakeman *et al.* (1973) claim that SCS is a more useful method for general application because it does not have a deficiency with respect to synchronous signals.

Blake and Barakat (1973) have developed a numerical scheme for evaluating the double generating function from which the joint probabilities, the photoelectron correlation function, and the clipped photoelectron correlation function can be evaluated. Further developments in photo-detection counting statistics will undoubtedly come forth.

A brief survey of the literature shows that in *J. Phys. A, Math., Nucl. Gen.* **6,** under the titles of optics and quantum optics, the following papers and letters to the editor related to photon correlation and statistics have been published in 1973:

1. Kelly, H. C., "Multiple scattering in light scattering spectroscopy," A353.
2. Chen, S. H., Tartaglia, P., and Pusey, P. N., "Light scattering from independent particles—non-Gaussian correction to the clipped intensity correlation function," A490.
3. Bendjaballah, C., "Analysis of clipped photocount autocorrelation formula for non-Gaussian light," A837.
4. Saleh, B. E. A., "Statistical accuracy in estimating parameters of the spatial coherence function by photon-counting techniques," A980.
5. Blake, J., and Barakat, R., "Twofold photoelectron counting statistics: the clipped correlation function," A1196.
6. Hughes, A. J., Jakeman, E., Oliver, C. J., and Pike, E. R., "Photon-correlation spectroscopy: dependence of linewidth error on normalization, clip level, detector area, sample time, and count rate," A1327.
7. Saleh, B. E. A., and Cardoso, M. F., "The effect of channel correlation on the accuracy of photon-counting digital autocorrelators," A1897.
8. Srinivasan, S. K., Sukavanam, S., and Sudarshan, E. C. G., "Many-time photocount distributions," A1910.
9. Tartaglia, P., Postol, T. A., and Chen, S. H., "Comment on the letter by Jakeman, E., Oliver, C. J., Pike, E. R., and Pusey, P. N. (1972), *J. Phys. A: Gen. Phys.* **5,** L93–6, 'Correlation of scaled photon-counting fluctuations,'" AL-35; author's reply, AL-36.
10. Jakeman, E., and Pusey, P. N., "The statistics of light scattered by a random phase screen," AL88.

11. Saleh, B. E. A., "Photon time of arrival, time between consecutive photons, and the moment generating function," AL161.
12. Saleh, B. E. A., and Minkowski, J. M., "Spatial properties of quasi-stationary Gaussian optical fields," AL165.

Every (1973) has extended photon statistics to electron counting. The field is obviously being expanded rapidly and new approaches involving time-dependence of non-Gaussian intensity fluctuations and spatial cross-correlation functions obtained by multiple-detector experiments (Cantrell, 1968; Swift, 1973) carry more information than second-order correlation functions in the Gaussian limit. Thus, the main aim in this chapter is to introduce the reader to photon statistics and correlation and to emphasize the fundamental and practical aspects that give us the essential equations and various forms of clipping as necessary tools in laser light scattering. The interested reader should study the references for specific details.

6.8. Design of an Ideal Digital Correlator†

In an ideal correlator, Eq. (6.3.1) changes to

$$\hat{S}(t_l) = \sum_{r=1}^{N} n(t_r) n(t_{r+l}) \tag{6.8.1}$$

where $\hat{S}(t_l)$ is the content of the lth-channel storage counter, and $n(t_r)$ is the number of pulses during sampling time T at time t_r. In laser light scattering, $\hat{S}(t_l)$ is proportional to the time-dependent correlation function of the scattered light at delay time lT. One essential feature of a full correlator is that a real time multiplication is performed in each channel [for each value of $\hat{S}(t_l)$] during each sample time interval.

Asch and Ford (1973) have constructed a correlator approaching ideality by increasing the bit multiplication capacity of each channel. Figure 6.8.1 shows a logic diagram of a single channel of a three-bit digital correlator. Its relation to the "ideal" multichannel digital correlator is shown in Fig. 6.8.2. In principle, the method can be extended to an arbitrary number of bits. A three-bit number corresponding to the number of counts obtained in a single sample time interval (T) is passed down a shift register with a single stage associated with each channel. Each pulse arriving at the correlator causes the number stored in each stage of the shift register to be

† Asch and Ford, 1973.

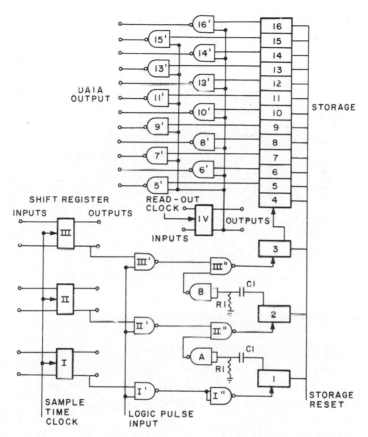

Fig. 6.8.1. Logic diagram of a single channel of a three-bit digital correlator. JK flip–flops I, II, III, 1, 2, 3. NAND Gates I', II', III', I'', II'', III''. Two delaying circuits each consisting of a RC circuit and a gate (A and B, respectively). 1–16 counter storage including flip–flops 1, 2, and 3 (Asch and Ford, 1973).

added to the storage counter of that corresponding channel. Thus, multiplication is accomplished by successive additions. Asch and Ford (1973) have also provided a short description of their circuit components.

The advantages of the correlator by Asch and Ford over the single-clipped correlator are twofold. First, the collection of information is more efficient leading to a reduction in the time required to perform an experiment. The second advantage arises for non-Gaussian signals. The only disadvantage is that such correlators are relatively slow, e.g., a SAICOR (4 bit × 4 bit) digital correlator runs with delay times as short as 10 μsec while the fastest single-clipped correlator using TTL integrated circuit

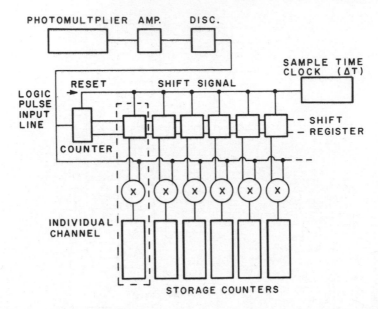

Fig. 6.8.2. Block diagram of an "ideal" digital correlator (Asch and Ford, 1973).

can have delay times as short as 50 nsec. The SAICOR digital correlator changes over to a relatively inefficient "batch" process at shorter delay times, even though in principle full digital correlators with very short delay times are technically within reach.

References

Adrian, R. J. (1972). *J. Phys. E.* **5**, 91.
Arecchi, F. T., Berne, A., and Sona, A. (1966). *Phys. Rev. Lett.* **17**, 260.
Asch, R., and Ford, N. C. (1973). *Rev. Sci. Instr.* **44**, 506.
Bédard, G. (1967). *Phys. Rev.* **161**, 1304.
Bendjaballah, C. (1973). *J. Phys. A.* **6**, 837.
Benedek, B., (1968). "Polarisation, Matière et Rayonnement," pp. 49–84. Presses Universitaires de France, Paris.
Blake, J. and Barakat, R. (1973). *J. Phys. A.* **6**, 1196.
Bourke, P. J., Butterworth, J., Drain, L. E., Egelstaff, P. A., Hughes, A. J., Hutchinson, P., Jackson, D. A., Jakeman, E., Moss, B., O'Shaughnessy, J., Pike, E. R., and Schofield, P. (1970) *J. Phys. A.* **3**, 216.
Cantrell, C. D. (1968). Ph.D. Thesis, Princeton Univ., Princeton, New Jersey.
Chen, S. H., and Tartaglia, P. (1972). *Opt. Commun.* **6**, 119.
Chen, S. H., Tartaglia, P., and Pusey, P. (1973). *J. Phys. A.* **6**, 490.
Chen, S. H., Tartaglia, P., and Polonsky-Ostrowsky, N. (1972). *J. Phys. A.* **5**, 1619.

Cummins, H. Z., and Swinney, H. L. (1970). *Progr. Opt.* **8**, 135 (E. Wolf, ed.). North-Holland, Amsterdam.

Degiorgio, V., and Lastovka, J. B. (1971). *Phys. Rev. A.* **4**, 2033.

DiPorto, P., Crosignani, B., and Bertolotti, M. (1969). *J. Appl. Phys.* **40**, 5083.

Every, I. M. (1973). *J. Phys. A* **6**, 1375.

Haus, H. A. (1969). *In* "Proc. Int. School of Physics Enrico Fermi, Course XLII," p. 111. Academic Press, New York.

Hughes, A. J., Jakeman, E., Oliver, C. J., and Pike, E. R. (1973). *J. Phys. A.* **6**, 1327.

Jakeman, E. (1970). *J. Phys. A* **3**, 201.

Jakeman, E., and Pike, E. R. (1968). *J. Phys. A* **1**, 128.

Jakeman, E., and Pike, E. R. (1969a). *J. Phys. A* **2**, 115.

Jakeman, E., and Pike, E. R. (1969b). *J. Phys. A* **2**, 411.

Jakeman, E., Oliver, C. J., and Pike, E. R. (1968). *J. Phys. A* **1**, 406.

Jakeman, E., Oliver, C. J., and Pike, E. R. (1970a) *J. Phys. A* **3**, L45.

Jakeman, E., Oliver, C. J., and Pike, E. R. (1971a). *J. Phys. A* **4**, 827.

Jakeman, E., Pike, E. R., and Swain, S. (1971b). *J. Phys. A* **4**, 517.

Jakeman, E., Pike, E. R., and Swain, S. (1971c). *J. Phys. A* **3**, L55.

Jakeman, E., Pike, E. R., and Swain, S. (1973). *J. Phys. A* **6**, L36.

Jakeman, E., Oliver, C. J., Pike, E. R., Lax, M., and Zwanziger, M. (1970b). *J. Phys. A* **3**, L52.

Jakeman, E., Oliver, C. J., Pike, E. R., and Pusey, P. N. (1972). *J. Phys. A* **5**, L03.

Kelly, H. C. (1971). *IEEE J. Quantum Electron.* QE-7, 541.

Koppel, D. E. (1971). *J. Appl. Phys.* **42**, 3216.

Koppel, D. E., and Schaefer, D. W. (1973). *Appl. Phys. Lett.* **22**, 36.

Mandel (1969). *Phys. Rev.* **181**, 75.

Nossal, R., and Chen, S. H. (1972). *J. Phys. (Paris) Suppl.* **33**, C1-172.

Pike, E. R. (1969). *Riv. Nuovo Cimento, Ser. 1* **1**, Numero Speciale 277–314.

Pike, E. R. (1972). *J. Phys. (Paris) Suppl.* **33**, C1-177.

Pike, E. R., and Schofield, P. (1970). *J. Phys. A* **3**, 216.

Pusey, P. N., and Goldburg, W. I. (1971). *Phys. Rev. A* **3**, 766.

Saleh, B. A. (1973). *J. Phys. A* **6**, 980.

Scarl, D. B. (1968). *Phys. Rev.* **175**, 1661.

Schaefer, D. W., and Berne, B. J. (1972). *Phys. Rev. Lett.* **28**, 475.

Schaefer, D. W., and Pusey, P. N. (1972). Proc. 3rd Conf. on Coherence and Quantum Optics, Rochester (to be published).

Swift, J. (1973). *Ann. Phys. NY* **75**, 1–8.

Tartaglia, P. and Chen, S. H. (1973). *Opt. Commun.* **7**, 379.

Tartaglia, P., Postol, T. A., and Chen, S. H. (1973). *J. Phys. A* **6**, L35.

Chapter VII
EXPERIMENTAL METHODS

7.1. Introduction

This chapter describes the pertinent features dealing with the experimental aspects of optical mixing spectroscopy. Particular attention is paid to the photon-counting technique as well as optical setups. The discussion of the experimental methods can be divided into three major sections.

The first section deals with the physical and operational characteristics of the laser which is our light source and also acts as the optical local oscillator in heterodyne spectroscopy. The second section analyzes the several optical setups which have been used in laser light scattering for studying phase transitions, liquids, and macromolecules in solution. The third section presents the photon-counting technique for intensity and digital correlation measurements, although power spectral analysis by means of a wave (or spectrum) analyzer will be discussed briefly.

The purpose of this chapter is to try to provide sufficient background information so that a person who wants to utilize optical mixing spectroscopy will learn how to proceed without too much fear of performing the wrong measurements. It is advisable to consult the references for details. This is especially true for biologists and chemists who are not familiar with lasers, optics, and electronics. As a chemist, the author is aware of the difficulties which one encounters in trying to understand a technique of this type. We shall emphasize the many experimental difficulties that we have encountered and hope that the same mistakes will not be repeated.

7.2. The Laser

7.2.1. General Features

Helium–neon and argon ion lasers have been so well developed during the past few years that most good commercial systems are suitable for use as light sources in optical mixing spectroscopy. Our experience has been such that we always use a TEM_{00q} laser where TEM means that the normal mode disturbance is a transverse electromagnetic wave. The subscripts 00 stand for $m = 0$, $n = 0$ which correspond to the uniphase wave front while the integral q tells us the number of half-wavelengths (or axial modes) which are contained in the resonator. Figure 7.2.1 shows the

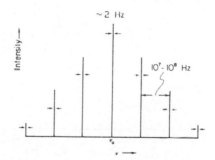

Fig. 7.2.1. Spectral width of a uniphase wave front helium–neon laser with several longitudinal modes $\lambda_0 = 632.8$ nm (Chu, 1968).

spectral width of a uniphase wave front He–Ne laser with several longitudinal modes. Each spectral line can act as a local oscillator. Superposition of line broadening centered at the zero frequency in light-beating spectroscopy permit the presence of many axial modes. However, when the linewidth of interest becomes very broad and is of the order of the spacings between the axial modes, then it is more appropriate for us to use optical interferometry and a single-mode single-frequency laser. These types of lasers are also available on the market. Most such lasers are not frequency stabilized but use an intracavity Fabry–Perot etalon (sometimes thermally compensated) in order to isolate the axial mode of interest. Then, mode hopping is usually a problem if long-term stability is required.

The uniphase modes have several advantages which we can utilize in quasielastic light-scattering experiments.

The intensity has a Gaussian profile given by

$$I = I_0 \exp(-2r^2/r_0^2) \tag{7.2.1}$$

where I is the intensity at a radial distance r from the cavity axis, I_0 is the peak intensity on the cavity axis $(r = 0)$, and r_0 represents the beam radius where the intensity falls to $1/e^2$ or 0.135 of the peak on-axis value, as shown schematically in Fig. 7.2.2. Integrating Eq. (7.2.1) from the cavity

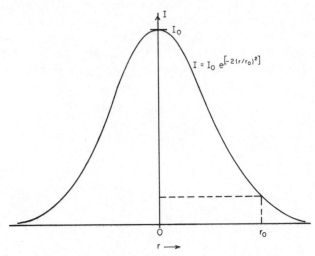

Fig. 7.2.2. Intensity cross section of a uniphase wave front Gaussian beam.

axis $(r = 0)$ to r determines the power $P(r)$ in a Gaussian beam passing through an aperture of radius r:

$$P(r) = \int_0^r 2\pi r I(r) \, dr = \tfrac{1}{2}\pi I_0 r_0^2 [1 - \exp(-2r^2/r_0^2)] \tag{7.2.2}$$

or

$$P(r)/P_\infty(r) = 1 - \exp(-2r^2/r_0^2) \tag{7.2.3}$$

where the total power $P_\infty(r) = \tfrac{1}{2}\pi I_0 r_0^2$. Thus, 86.5 % of the power is contained within the spot diameter $2r_0$. Figure 7.2.3 shows a collimated laser beam of diameter D, focused by a lens of focal length f to a spot diameter $d_0 \; (= 2r_0)$. The equation

$$d_0 = (4/\pi)\lambda f/D \tag{7.2.4}$$

is a useful linear far-field relationship which shows that the focused spot

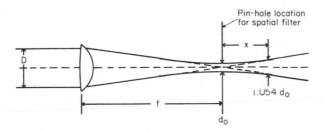

Fig. 7.2.3. Collimated beam focused by a lens. D: laser beam diameter; f: focal length; d_0: spot diameter. $d_0 = (1/\pi)(\lambda f/D)$.

size d_0 is proportional to the wavelength of the laser λ and focal length of the focusing lens and inversely proportional to the diameter of the laser beam. Equation (7.2.4) is almost precisely the relation between the lens aperture diameter D_f and the diameter of the first Airy disk d in the image formed by a thin lens of focal length f (Klein, 1970):

$$d = 1.22(\lambda f/D_f) \qquad (7.2.5)$$

The intensity profile along the (cavity) optical axis of the beam can best be described by defining a distance x such that the power density is reduced to say 90 % that at d_0 where $x = 0$, or $d_x = (1/0.9)^{1/2}d_0 = 1.054d_0$. If we take $r = r_0[1 + (\lambda x/\pi r_0^2)^2]^{1/2}$ (Kogelnik and Li, 1966), then

$$d/d_0 = 1.054 = [1 + (4\lambda x/\pi d_0^2)^2]^{1/2}$$

or

$$x = 0.333\pi d_0^2/4\lambda = (\pi/12)d_0^2/\lambda \qquad (7.2.6)$$

Now if we redefine the depth of focus as the distance from the focus over which the intensity is reduced to 50% that at d_0, then $d = (2)^{1/2}d_0$ and x becomes three times the 90% intensity depth of focus (Marshall, 1971). The uncertainty in the divergence angle $\delta\theta$ has the form

$$\delta\theta = d_0/f \qquad (7.2.7)$$

It is very important to remember $\delta\theta$ when we design instruments for small-angle light-scattering work, as $\delta\theta$ represents one of the uncertainties in momentum transfer which often influences indirectly the spectral distribution of scattered laser light. $\delta\theta$ also plays an important role in estimating the effective coherence area [Eq. (4.3.19)].

Equation (7.2.4) also determines the pinhole size of a spatial filter for diffraction-limited operation by inserting the pinhole at f in Fig. 7.2.3. Usually, a short focal lens with pinholes of the order of 10–50 μm in diam but computed according to the relation $d > (4/\pi)\lambda f/D$ is used. The

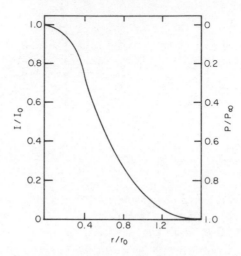

Fig. 7.2.4. Relative integrated power as a function of relative radius (r/r_0) in a Gaussian beam $I/I_0 = \exp[-2(r/r_0)^2]$, $P/P_\infty = 1 - \exp[-2(r/r_0)^2]$.

inequality is introduced to account for imperfections and eccentricity of the pinhole. In a truncated Gaussian beam, it is worthwhile to remember Eqs. (7.2.1) and (7.2.3) for choosing beam apertures. Figure 7.2.4 shows the relative integrated power (P/P_∞) as a function of relative radius r/r_0. For example $P/P_\infty = 0.956$ when $r/r_0 = 1.25$. Spatial filtering of the laser light is very helpful for small-angle light-scattering work where stray light due to laser imperfections cannot be easily taken out by means of baffles, pinholes, and slits.

7.2.2. Helium–Neon Continuous Wave Gas Laser

The design of optical and detection systems should be such that the efficiency of the instruments has been maximized for the particular problem of interest. Then, a laser of the lowest appropriate power may be utilized. For systems that scatter light strongly, the internal mirror cold aluminum cathode He–Ne plasma tubes with output powers of about 3–5 mW in the TEM_{00} mode have worked very satisfactorily in our laboratory. By mounting the laser tube on a granite table the mechanical instability is virtually nonexistent especially if the temperature changes in the plasma tube while in operation are taken into account. There are several advantages for using such He–Ne plasma tubes. (1) They are very reasonably priced. (2) They need no adjustments in mirror alignment. (3) They are usually very short so that spacings between the axial modes $(\Delta\nu)_{axial}$ are relatively far apart. For example, if the mirror spacing l in a hemispherical system is 33 cm,

$\Delta\nu_{\text{axial}} = c/2l = 450$ MHz. Thus, it is possible to use such a laser for line-broadening studies of the central Rayleigh component close to the 100-MHz region by means of optical interferometry. Finally, (4) they have an average lifetime of over 7500 hr.

The stability of the laser also depends upon the power supply. We have obtained good results by using high-voltage power supplies normally reserved for photomultiplier tubes. Figure 7.2.5 shows a typical starting

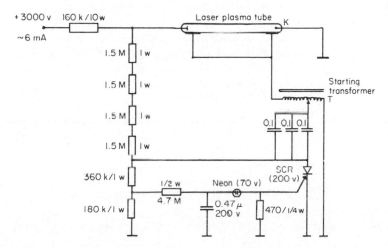

Fig. 7.2.5. A typical starting circuit for a He–Ne plasma tube (Spectra Physics model No. 076-4) as designed by W. Tscharnuter.

circuit that has operated successfully in our laboratory for a Spectra Physics model 076-4 plasma tube with the following characteristics: 4-mW TEM$_{00}$ output power at 632.8 nm; $\Delta\nu_{\text{axial}} = 460$ MHz; beam diameter at $1/e^2 (2r_0) = 0.8$ mm; beam divergence = 1.0 mrad; starting voltage = 8500 V; operating voltage (dc, across tube only) = 2050 V; operating current = 6.0 ± 1.0 mA; and ballast resistance within 5 in. of anode = 90 KΩ.

For high-powered He–Ne lasers with adjustable mirror spacings, it is essential that the lasers themselves be checked for amplitude modulation effects. Although "mode locking" tends to take place naturally in sufficiently long cavities, operation in the locked condition reduces the noise modulation. The lasers work best when they are tuned to the maximum output power. Long-term stability is not needed in signal correlation or spectrum analysis. However, if a wave analyzer is used, slow variation in the laser output power can be compensated for by monitoring the dc current of the scattered light.

7.2.3. Argon Laser

The argon laser has a higher output power, and in the blue–green region, offers an increased detection efficiency because of the frequency dependence of the sensitivity of the photomultiplier tubes. However, many argon lasers have plasma and mode instabilities which will degrade the signal-to-noise ratio as well as produce false homodyne spectra. The use of an argon laser as a light source for optical mixing spectroscopy must be carefully assessed.

Jackson and Paul (1969) considered several argon lasers as a light source for low-frequency heterodyne anemometry experiments. Table 7.2.1 lists

Table 7.2.1
Tube construction and running condition of argon lasers [a]

Tube construction	Silica	Beryllia	Segmented carbon disk
Source	Univ. St. Andrews	SERL, Baldock	Coherent radiation
Capillary diam. (mm)	3	3	3
Cavity length (m)	1.5	0.65	1.2
Power output (w)	1	>3	3
Discharge current (A)	20	35	25
Magnetic field (G)	0–1000	0–1000	850

[a] Jackson and Paul (1969).

the tube construction and appropriate tuning conditions of the argon lasers which were all operated at the TEM_{00q} mode and tuned to the 488-nm line by an intracavity prism. They reported that both silica and beryllia tubes had the defect of a heavily modulated spectrum while the carbon disk laser showed no observed modulation even at its maximum power level. The modulated spectrum of the silica tube could be suppressed by increasing the magnetic field. On the other hand, the modulation in the Beryllia tube increased with increasing magnetic field. It should be noted that the lasers they tested were not commercial models.

The main criterion is that the laser must have a noise-free low-frequency homodyne spectrum. Our experience tells us that the modulation spectrum depends upon the gas pressure in the (carbon) plasma tube of our Coherent

Radiation model 54 argon laser. We examine the low-frequency components of laser light by monitoring the scattering from a ground glass plate. When operating at low plasma pressures, the carbon disk laser produces a noise spectrum which presumably comes from plasma oscillations. The noise spectrum disappears on raising the gas pressure to its optimum condition, e.g., the optimum plasma pressure is 325 mtorr for our argon laser. The new BeO tubes seem to show no detectable noise spectrum.

Many commercial argon ion lasers (Spectra Physics 165, Coherent Radiation 52, 54) are capable of single-frequency operation which greatly increases the coherence length and suppresses the noise spectrum because of multimode instabilities. Jackson and Paul (1969) also suggested that the intracavity etalon for single-frequency operation should not be aligned normal to the laser beam as the unstable multicavity configuration could produce a noise spectrum due to mode hopping.

In conclusion, commercial lasers are quite suitable for optical mixing spectroscopy even though a careful assessment of the light source is strongly advised. The argon ion laser should be operated with an intracavity etalon for single-frequency output. When using the carbon disk plasma tube, the pressure must be maintained at its optimum value in order to ensure the absence of a low-frequency noise spectrum. Operation under the optimum condition tends to reduce the noise spectrum.

Finally, Maes and Moore (1973) have designed a simple and inexpensive intensity stabilizing circuit for use with a (Coherent Radiation 52A) continuous wave (cw) argon laser. Using their circuit, they claimed a reduction in the noise level from 1 % to <0.002 % and a stability of <1 % change over periods of days.

7.3. The Optical System

Optical systems in laser light scattering have been designed mainly for either the angular distribution of scattered light or its spectral distribution. Optimization is often achieved at the expense of other needs. Ideally, it would be wonderful to have an optical system capable of (a) measuring the intensity as well as the spectral distribution of scattered light over the largest possible angular range ($0° < \theta < 180°$), (b) studying polarized and depolarized scattering, and (c) using cells of different designs suitable for studies of macromolecules in solution or phase transitions. In practice, it is difficult to achieve optimum conditions satisfying all the requirements in one system, since the cell design influences the optics required.

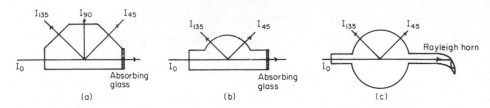

Fig. 7.3.1. Cylindrical-type cells (a) hemioctagonal cell, (b) cell with flat entrance and exit windows, (c) cell with flat entrance window and Rayleigh horn at the exit.

7.3.1. Cylindrical-Type Cells

Figure 7.3.1 shows several cylindrical-type cells which require virtually no angular corrections for refraction since the entrance and emergent beams are always at right angles to the faces of the scattering cell. The absorbing glass in Figs. 7.3.1a and 7.3.1b at the exit walls reduce the back reflection. Simple cylindrical cells with diameters as small as 6 mm have been used successfully in light-scattering experiments where refraction and reflection difficulties are alleviated by immersing the scattering cell in an immersion fluid which matches the refractive index of the scattering cell. Figure 7.3.2

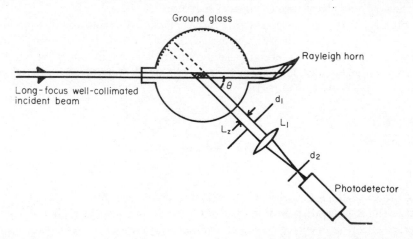

Fig. 7.3.2. A schematic representation of the detection optics for cylindrical-type cells.

shows a schematic representation of the detection optics. In a cylindrical cell $L_z \sin \theta$ is limited to the diameter of the cell; d_1 determines the effective scattering volume L_z while d_2 determines the angular uncertainty $\delta\theta$ of the collecting system. Such a setup is very good for the angular distribution of scattered intensity and for linewidth measurements of strongly opalescent systems, but is not suitable for quasielastic scattering at low-scattering angles ($\theta < 20°$) and for weak-scattering systems.

7.3.2. Rectangular Cells

Good spectroscopic rectangular cells are cheaper than cylindrical-type cells of similar quality. The flat entrance and exit windows tend to reduce stray light scattering in the system. However, the scattering angle θ has to be corrected for refraction of the light as it passes from the scattering medium to the outside. Thus, the refractive index of the solution must be measured in order to determine θ and $K \left[= (4\pi/\lambda) \sin (\tfrac{1}{2}\theta) \right]$. Figure 7.3.3a shows a schematic representation of the detection optics for a rec-

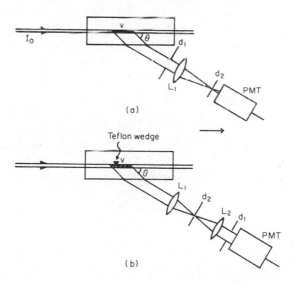

Fig. 7.3.3. Schematic representations of the detection optics for a rectangular cell. d_2 is an adjustable aperture which determines $\delta\theta$. In (b) the variable aperture d_1 which determines the effective scattering volume is transferred near the face of the photocathode. The Teflon wedge is introduced for the heterodyne configuration by Cummins *et al.* (1969). The (b) scheme requires a large effective photocathode.

tangular cell. The rectangular cell offers several advantages: (1) a long light-path cell may be used in order to increase the effective scattering volume (or L_z); (2) high-optical-quality cells are easily available so that stray light due to cell imperfections may be minimized; and (3) very low scattering angles are accessible, dependent upon the optical design of the system.

Occasionally, a short-light-path cell (0.1–1 mm thick) has been used for very strongly scattered systems in order to avoid multiple scattering. Furthermore, for systems which scatter light strongly, L_z can be reduced to a very small size so that the collimating lens L_1 is no longer needed. Figure 7.3.4 shows the scattering geometry for measurements at two fixed scattering angles using a flat cell (Lai and Chen, 1972).

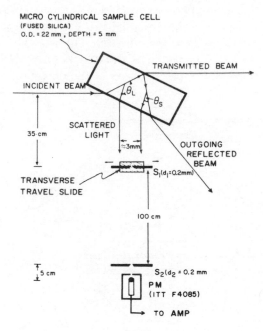

Fig. 7.3.4. Scattering geometry for measurement at two fixed scattering angles (Lai and Chen, 1972).

In a heterodyne spectrometer, several techniques have been developed to use the laser source as an optical local oscillator. The important requirement is to be able to combine the scattered radiation with the local-oscillator signal at the photocathode of the photomultiplier tube so that the fields are spatially coherent. The local-oscillator signal is usually a portion of the unshifted incident radiation ($\omega_{LO} = \omega_0$), such as a small portion of the transmitted beam (Lastovka and Benedek, 1966a), the scattering from "dust" or imperfections on the cell windows (Lastovka and Benedek, 1966b), the scattering from a plate of appropriately cut smoky quartz (Berge, 1967), the scattering from a thin layer of fixed scatterers (Uzgiris, 1972), or

the scattering from a Teflon prism in the scattering cell with its edge partially intersecting the incident beam (Cummins et al., 1969), as shown in
Fig. 7.3.3b. An alternative approach for the local-optical oscillator in
heterodyne detection is to use a portion of the incident radiation which has
been shifted to some other frequency ($\omega_{LO} \neq \omega_0$) (Cummins et al., 1964).
The frequency-shifted local oscillator imposes many difficulties, mainly
because any optical imperfection will tend to reduce the mixing efficiency,
while the scattered field and the unshifted local-oscillator field can be made
to traverse identical optical paths and thus have very high mixing effi-
ciencies (Adam et al., 1969). Cummins et al. (1969) found that the milky
quartz plate did not scatter sufficiently uniformly at all angles to make it
generally useful. A small Teflon prism of triangular cross section seemed to
work very well. The prism in Fig. 7.3.3b should be held rigidly relative to
the scatterers. Movement of the prism produces another source of modulation signals that will contribute to the power spectrum, especially at low
frequencies.

Thus, mechanical disturbances, such as building vibrations, are more
crucial in a heterodyne experiment than a homodyne one. Wada et al.
(1972) presented a simple modification by utilizing a cylindrical collimating
lens for his optical heterodyne system in order to reduce the sensitivity
of mechanical vibrations to the local oscillator.

7.3.3. Conical Cells

The scattering cells with conical optics have been used successfully by
Ford and Benedek (1965) in their observation of the spectrum of light
scattered from a pure fluid near its critical point and by Benedek and
Greytak (1965) in Brillouin scattering of water and toluene. Figures 7.3.5

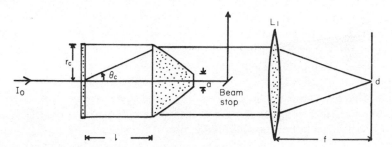

Fig. 7.3.5. Scattering cell with conical optics. The diameter of the flat exit window,
a, should be slightly greater than the incident beam diameter. The maximum light
path thickness of the cell *l* is related to the diameter of the conical lens [$\tan \theta_c = r_c/l$].
The pinhole diameter *d* controls the angular spread $\delta\theta$.

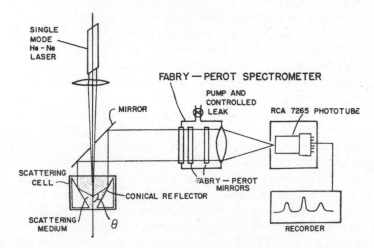

Fig. 7.3.6. Scattering cell with a conical reflector (Benedek and Greytak, 1965).

and 7.3.6 show the scattering cells with conical optics. In Fig. 7.3.5, light scattered through an angle θ is collected over an azimuth of 2π by a conical lens and emerges parallel to the cone axis. The spherical lens L_1 with focal length f then focuses the scattered light at the center of a pinhole aperture d which controls $\delta\theta$ of the scattering angle θ_c, accepted by the spectrometer. Conical optics is a very efficient light-collection system, because it collects light over the full length of the illuminated region (l), and it collects an azimuth of 2π. Its disadvantages are as follows: (1) each conical lens permits scattering at a predesigned *fixed* angle θ_c, (2) the conical lens has to be specially made and is expensive, and (3) the advantage of an azimuth of 2π disappears if the polarized and the depolarized spectrum are appreciably different. Figure 7.3.6 shows a scattering cell with a conical reflector (Benedek and Greytak, 1965). If ϕ is the full apex angle of the conical reflector, the light scattered at an angle $\theta_c = 180° - \phi$ will be collected by the cone and emerges parallel to the axis of the reflector. Benedek and Greytak (1965) have pointed out that if the direction of the incident beam is reversed, one collects light scattered through an angle $\phi = 180° - \theta_c$. Thus, a single conical reflector (or lens) enables a study of scattering at two fixed angles, even though reversing the incident beam direction or the sample cell is usually more involved than it appears.

7.3.4. Refraction Correction to the Scattering Angle of Rectangular Cells

Refraction at the cell windows could have the following effects: (1) it may change the cross section of the incident beam; (2) it may displace the

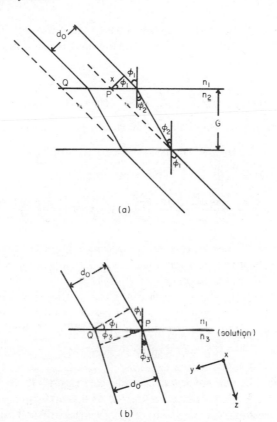

Fig. 7.3.7. (a) Displacement of a parallel incident beam due to cell window of thickness G. (b) Change in dimension of a parallel incident beam due to refraction through a flat surface as measured in the yz plane of the scattering volume.

incident beam; and (3) it changes the effective scattering angle θ as well as its divergence $\delta\theta$. Figure 7.3.7 shows displacement of the incident beam (a) and the change in dimension of the cross section of the displaced incident beam (b). The basic rule is to use Snell's law ($n_1 \sin \phi_1 = n_2 \sin \phi_2$). If ϕ_1 is the entrance angle from medium 1 with refractive index n_1 and G is the thickness of the cell window glass with refractive index n_2, the parallel incident beam will be displaced by an amount x corresponding to

$$x = G \cos \phi_1 [\tan \phi_1 - \tan \phi_2] \qquad (7.3.1)$$

For simplicity in our discussion, we shall henceforth set the beam displacement aside. Figure 7.3.7b shows the change in cross section of the parallel incident beam. We get

$$\cos \phi_1 / \cos \phi_3 = d_0' / d_0 \qquad (7.3.2)$$

where ϕ_3 represents the angle between the normal of the cell window and the scattering medium, and d_0' and d_0 are the incident beam diameters in media 1 and 3, respectively.

If the cell is oriented at Brewster's angle, where

$$\tan \phi_1 = n_{13} = n_3/n_1 \qquad \text{(Brewster angle)} \qquad (7.3.3)$$

or in combination with Snell's law $(\sin \phi_1/\sin \phi_3 = n_3/n_1)$, we have

$$\cos \phi_1 = \sin \phi_3 \qquad \text{(Brewster angle)} \qquad (7.3.4)$$

Thus, Eq. (7.3.2) is reduced to (Brewster angle)

$$\frac{d_0'}{d_0} = \frac{\cos \phi_1}{\cos \phi_3} = \frac{\sin \phi_3}{\cos \phi_3} = \tan \phi_3 = \frac{1}{n_{13}} = \frac{n_1}{n_3} \qquad (7.3.5)$$

The change in the cross section of the parallel incident beam is proportional to the ratio of the refractive indices inside and outside the scattering medium $[d_0 = (n_3/n_1)d_0'$ at Brewster angle$]$.

Owing to refraction, the scattering angle θ in the scattering medium is changed to θ'. If the scattering cell is oriented perpendicular to the incident beam, as shown in Fig. 7.3.8, a simple application of Snell's law tells us

$$\sin \theta/\sin \theta' = n_1/n_3 \qquad (7.3.6)$$

and the changes in the divergence angle correspond to $\delta\theta = (n_1/n_3)\,\delta\theta'$. However, perpendicular orientation has a back-scattering problem which could become serious. Orientation of the scattering cell at an angle ϕ_1 changes the apparent scattering angle θ' as follows.

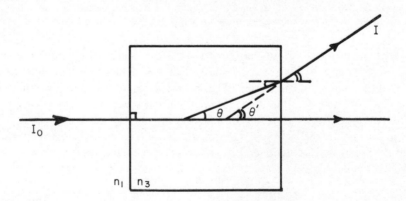

Fig. 7.3.8. Relationship between the true scattering angle θ and the apparent scattering angle θ' for a flat rectangular cell oriented perpendicular to the incident beam. Note: Back scattering could become a serious problem.

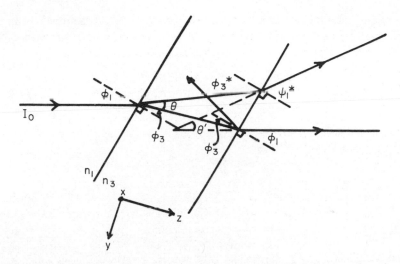

Fig. 7.3.9. Relationship between the true scattering angle θ and the apparent scattering angle θ' for a flat cell oriented at an angle ϕ_1 between the normal of the cell window and the incident beam direction. Note: In this figure, the reflected beam imposes a back-scattering problem. The scattering should be viewed on the other side as shown in Fig. 7.3.10.

From Fig. 7.3.9, we see that

$$\theta = \phi_3{}^* - \phi_3 \tag{7.3.7}$$

and

$$\theta' = \phi_1{}^* - \phi_1 \tag{7.3.8}$$

With Snell's law, we have

$$\sin \phi_1 = (n_3/n_1) \sin \phi_3 \tag{7.3.9}$$

By substituting Eqs. (7.3.7) and (7.3.8) into (7.3.9), we get

$$\sin(\phi_1{}^* - \theta') = (n_3/n_1) \sin(\phi_3{}^* - \theta) \tag{7.3.10}$$

Since $\sin(x - y) = \sin x \cos y - \cos x \sin y$, Eq. (7.3.10) can be changed to $\sin \phi_1{}^* \cos \theta' - \cos \phi_1{}^* \sin \theta' = (n_3/n_1)(\sin \phi_3{}^* \cos \theta - \cos \phi_3{}^* \sin \theta)$.

With Eq. (7.3.9), we get

$$(n_3/n_1) \sin \phi_3{}^*(\cos \theta - \cos \theta') = (n_3/n_1) \cos \phi_3{}^* \sin \theta - \cos \phi_1{}^* \sin \theta'$$

or

$$(n_3/n_1)[\cos \theta - \cos \theta'] = (n_3/n_1) \cot \phi_3{}^* \sin \theta$$
$$- (\cos \phi_1{}^*/\sin \phi_3{}^*) \sin \theta' \tag{7.3.11}$$

The angle θ can be determined by knowing n_3, n_1, $\phi_1{}^*$, $\phi_3{}^*$, and θ'. At Brewster's angle, $\sin \phi_1{}^* = (n_3/n_1) \cos \phi_1{}^*$, $\sin \phi_3{}^*/\cos \phi_3{}^* = n_1/n_3$, and $\cos \phi_1{}^* = \sin \phi_3{}^*$. Then, with $n_{13} = n_3/n_1$, Eq. (7.3.11) is reduced to

$$n_{13}(\cos \theta - \cos \theta') = n_{13}{}^2 \sin \theta - \sin \theta'$$

or   (7.3.12)

$$n \cos \theta - n^2 \sin \theta = n \cos \theta' - \sin \theta'$$

with the subscript 13 deleted. For small θ, $\cos \theta \simeq \cos \theta' \simeq 1$, $\sin \theta \simeq \theta$, and $\sin \theta' \simeq \theta'$, we then have

$$\theta' = n^2\theta \qquad\qquad (7.3.13)$$

whose divergence angles have the relationship $\delta\theta' = n^2\,\delta\theta$. It should be noted that if the spectrum of scattered light is explicitly dependent upon **K**, the effect of the finite momentum window on the spectral function should be considered (Yeh, 1969).

Figure 7.3.10 shows the relationship between the scattering angle θ and its apparent scattering angle θ' for the three situations using a rectangular cell oriented at Brewster's angle with respect to the incident beam. Equations (7.3.12) and (7.3.13) correspond to the exit at face a.

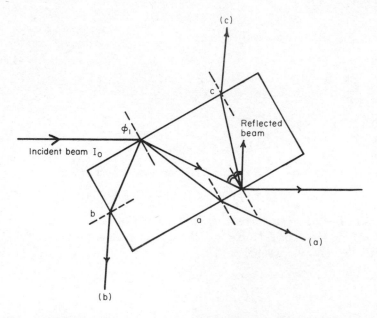

Fig. 7.3.10. Relationship between the true scattering angle θ and its apparent scattering angle θ' using the three exit windows of a rectangular scattering cell oriented at Brewster's angle with respect to the incident beam.

From faces b and c we get

$$n^2 \cos \theta + n \sin \theta = n \sin \theta' + \cos \theta' \qquad (7.3.14)$$

and

$$n \cos \theta + n^2 \sin \theta = n \cos \theta' + \sin \theta' \qquad (7.3.15)$$

respectively. There are varous situations to which we can orient our scattering cell. We have tried to describe only a few of the many possibilities. The answers can always be obtained through the use of Snell's and Brewster's laws.

For a rectangular cell at normal incidence with the incoming beam, as shown in Fig. 7.3.8, the incident electric (and magnetic) field(s) $\mathbf{E}$ (and $\mathbf{H}$) are parallel to the interface between air and medium. Then, the distinction between σ ($\mathbf{E}$ perpendicular plane of incidence) and π ($\mathbf{E}$ in the plane of incidence) cases is lost. With $n_3/n_1 = 1.5$, the reflectivity R is

$$| (n_3 - n_1)/(n_3 + n_1) |^2 = 0.04$$

and the transmissivity is $1 - R = 0.96$. However, for an oblique incidence onto a less dense medium, such as the case for the exit beam, we have n_3 (medium) $> n_1$ (air). In fact, we should take n_2 (glass) $> n_1$. There we have a critical angle θ_c which, according to Snell's law, is $\sin \theta_c = n_1/n_3$. For $n_3/n_1 = 1.5$, $\theta_c = 41.8°$. At angles greater than θ_c, the light is totally reflected. At angles smaller than θ_c, the reflectivity starts at 0.04 for $\theta = 0$, and approaches 1 as $\theta \to \theta_c$. Since $\mathbf{E}$ is no longer parallel to the interface, R_σ and R_π behave differently for $0 < \theta < \theta_c$. Nevertheless, the important point here is that we have to correct for transmissivity, which depends upon θ in addition to geometrical considerations, if we want to use such optical arrangements for angular distribution of the (integrated) scattered intensity. Furthermore, the efficiency of the setup for quasielastic light scattering decreases rapidly as θ approaches θ_c. Thus, it is advisable to use the configuration of Fig. 7.3.10 if we want several scattering angles covering a wide angular range. The reader should consult the optics book by Klein (1970) for a detailed discussion on reflection and transmission of light at an interface.

The other point to which we should pay attention is that the center of rotation of the detector moves inside the rectangular cell because of refraction. It is very convenient to mount the cell on a translational stage (parallel to the incident beam). Such an arrangement permits observation of the scattering in a region with only scattered light for self-beating or with scattered light and "controlled" strong interfacial scattering acting as a local oscillator for heterodyning.

7.3.5. Optical Arrangements for Depolarized Spectra

Wada *et al.* (1969, 1970) have studied rotary diffusion broadening of Rayleigh lines scattered from optically anisotropic macromolecules in solution. Figure 7.3.11 shows a schematic diagram of the filtering arrange-

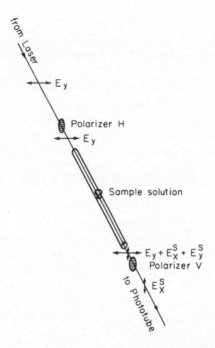

Fig. 7.3.11. Schematic diagram of the filtering arrangement of depolarized scattered light. **E**: electric vector of light. Superscript s denotes scattered light (Wada *et al.*, 1969).

ment for the depolarized scattered light. The polarized incident beam is focused by a lens system into the middle of a long solution cell (150 mm). The incident light must contain polarizations in only one direction. The laser beam first passes through a Glan–Thompson polarizer H before entering the scattering cell as shown in Fig. 7.3.11, in order to remove the remaining other component of polarization and to fix the sense of polarization in space. The light transmitted from the cell contains mainly the very strong incident beam, scattered light polarized in the same direction as the incident beam, and scattered light *depolarized* perpendicular to the incident beam. The last component is filtered out by passing the transmitted light through a second Glan–Thompson polarizer V whose optical axis has been carefully adjusted to be perpendicular to the first (polarizer H). In such a setup, a small portion of the incident beam leaks through the depolarization filter even in the absence of the solution cell. The leakage is found to be *elliptically polarized*, is about 100–1000 times as intense as the depolarized scattered light, and can act as the optical local oscillator. Thus, only a heterodyne spectrum can be observed.

It is not essential that depolarized light scattering be limited by the heterodyne technique, even though chances for heterodyning are usually very great, because the depolarized scattered light is much weaker than the polarized scattered light. Figure 7.3.12 shows a schematic diagram for

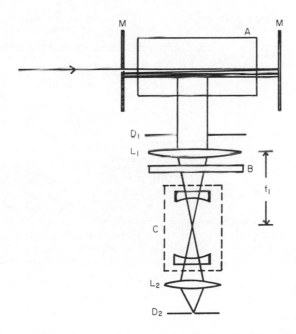

Fig. 7.3.12. A schematic arrangement for depolarized light scattering using a spherical Fabry–Perot interferometer (c) (Dubin *et al.*, 1971). Lens L_1 has a focal length f_1, pinhole D_2 has a diameter D_2, A is the scattering cell, and B is the Glan–Thompson prism.

depolarized light scattering using a spherical Fabry–Perot interferometer (Dubin *et al.*, 1971). A single-frequency He–Ne laser is used. The effective light path has been increased by passing the incident beam several times through the scattering cell with a pair of high-reflectivity dielectric coated mirrors. An increase in the collected scattered light by a factor of about 5 was reported. In a multiple-path cell, scattering is restricted to $\theta = 90°$.

The diaphragm D_1 again determines the effective scattering volume, while the pinhole D_2 determines the angular resolution $\delta\theta$. The Glan–Thompson analyzer permits measurements of the polarized as well as the depolarized scattered light. Removal of the spherical Fabry–Perot interferometer corresponds to changing over the apparatus for intensity fluctuation spectroscopy. Then, L_2 can be avoided if we place D_2 at position C and use a photomultiplier tube with a sufficiently large photocathode area immediately after D_2. There, $\delta\theta \approx D_2/f_1$.

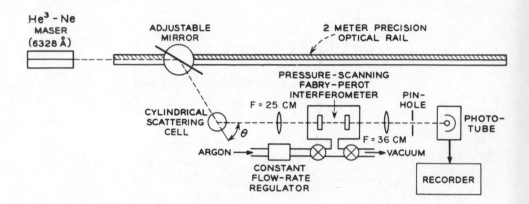

Fig. 7.3.13. Apparatus for observing normal Brillouin scattering as a function of angle. The scattering angle θ is varied by a combination of the adjustable mirror and translation along the precision optical rail. The mirror is mounted on a spectroscopic table with a vernier angular scale for measuring θ (Fleury and Chiao, 1966).

The optical arrangements are such that both the laser and the interferometer system are fixed in space. Occasionally, measurements at different scattering angles are required. Figure 7.3.13 shows one approach to the problem by Fleury and Chiao (1966), when they studied the spectrum of light scattered from thermal sound waves in liquids.

Lastovka and Benedek (1966a) have devised a rather ingenious method for studying the spectrum of light scattered from toluene using a Brewster's angle sample cell located inside the laser cavity, as shown in Fig. 7.3.14. An even more demanding optical system was set up for the detection of Brillouin scattered light by optical superheterodyning, as shown in Fig.

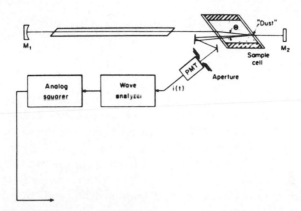

Fig. 7.3.14. A schematic representation of the optical heterodyne spectrometer used to study the spectrum of light scattered from toluene. The Brewster's angle sample cell is located inside the laser cavity formed by mirrors M_1 and M_2 (Lastovka and Benedek, 1966a, b).

7.3.15 (Lastovka and Benedek, 1966b). The detail design of this optical system, which is based on the optical schemes of a Mach–Zehnder interferometer (Born and Wolf, 1964), can best be appreciated by reading the comprehensive and monumental Ph.D. thesis of Lastovka (1967).

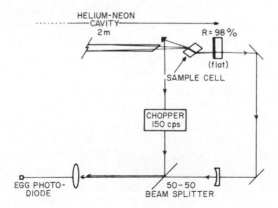

Fig. 7.3.15. Optical system used in the detection of Brillouin scattered light by optical superheterodyning (Lastovka and Benedek, 1966b).

7.4. Photon-Counting Technique

7.4.1. Introduction

In laser light scattering the techniques of optical mixing spectroscopy and of optical interferometry require us to pay particular attention in selecting photomultiplier (PM) tubes and their housing designs. Furthermore, the same system can be used, in a similar manner, for measuring the integrated intensity of scattered light by means of photon counting. Using photomultiplier tubes of an advanced type as well as fast low-noise electronic devices capable of wide-band amplification and high-speed digital processing, the photon-counting technique covers a dynamic range for the integrated intensity extending from very low statistically or quantum limited light levels to high light levels where the PM-tube linearity becomes marginal. In our studies, we are interested in photon counting and photon correlation. Thus, the selection of an appropriate detector and its housing is the first crucial step in achieving good instrumentation in laser light scattering. Beginning chemists or biologists are usually not familiar with the use of photomultiplier tubes. In this chapter, we shall attempt to outline some of the pertinent features of good housing design and the tube-selection criteria for application to photon counting and correlation.

When light falls on the photocathode of the PM tube, single photoelectrons are ejected. These photoelectrons are then multiplied by a cascaded secondary-emission process to produce pulses of charge at the anode. At high light levels, the pulses will overlap and the light intensity is measured by the anode current. At low light levels, the pulses no longer overlap and the light intensity is proportional to the number of those pulses. Aside from photon correlation the principal modes of operation in detecting the integrated intensity are dc current or voltage measurement, charge integration, synchronous detection, pulse counting, and the shot-noise method of Pao *et al.* (1966) and Pao and Griffiths (1967). Young (1969) noted that dc and charge integration detections are equivalent. Chopping, followed by phase-sensitive (i.e., synchronous) detection, is similar to dc measurement, except that (a) chopping throws away half of the incident signal power, and (b) the final bandpass is shifted from dc (zero frequency) to the chopping frequency. Thus, the signal-to-noise ratio for phase-sensitive detection is $\frac{1}{2}^{1/2}$ that of dc method if the noise is *independent* of frequency. There are then three basic schemes: dc, pulse counting, and the shot-noise-power method of Pao and Griffith (1967).

The three basic methods of detection correspond to utilizing three different weighting functions of the signal pulse height. In pulse counting, all pulses between two pulse heights are counted equally (weight 1) and all others are ignored (weight 0). The discrete single photoelectron pulses with random amplitudes on a wandering baseline are first amplified and put on a stable baseline. The single-channel analyzer (or discriminator) selects the pulses with heights E to $E + \Delta E$, and all the pulses between those two heights are counted with equal weight. In dc or charge integration, each pulse is weighted by its height (charge), while in shot-power detection, each pulse is weighted by the square of its height, as shown schematically by Young (1969) in Fig. 7.4.1.

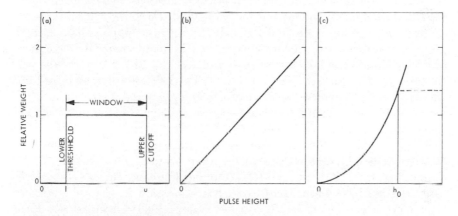

Fig. 7.4.1. Weighting functions for (a) pulse counting, (b) dc detection, and (c) shot-power detection. The dashed line in (c) indicates the effect of clipping at height h_0 (Young, 1969).

7.4.2. Photomultiplier Tube Selection
(Noise and Time-Dependent Statistical Properties)

The noise in photomultipliers influences the sensitivity with which the photoelectrons can be detected. Various sources of noise are present (Eberhardt, 1967), the main ones being (Akins et al., 1968): (a) noise from thermionic emission at the cathode, (b) temperature-independent dark noise, (c) gain noise of the multiplier chain, and (d) statistical noise in the signal (shot noise).

The primary source of noise in an uncooled photomultiplier is due to thermionic emission from the cathode, based on the quasiexponential dependence of anode dark current on temperature. Cooling the photomultiplier tube will greatly reduce the thermal electrons but may not necessarily enhance the signal-to-noise ratio (S/N) because the overall quantum counting efficiency (counts out per photon in) of the tube depends, in general, upon temperature as well as wavelength. Harker *et al.* (1969) have shown that for a (nonselected) ITT FW 130 (S-20) photomultiplier tube, a larger S/N is obtained with the tube cooled to 205°K if the counting rate is less than about 8000 photons/sec, while for counting rates greater than 8000 photons/sec room-temperature operation gives the larger S/N. Thus, the optimum tube temperature in photon-counting systems depends upon the counting rate and the tube characteristics. In other words, optimum performance is achieved at a specific tube temperature, and it is not true that cooling the PM tube will always improve its performance. In fact, performance in the far red for most photocathodes will be impaired by excessive cooling (Cole and Ryer, 1972). In some applications, a small photocathode area tube should be selected. The requirement for coherence-area consideration in signal correlation makes the ITT FW 130 tube particularly suitable for laser light scattering. The FW 130 tube can be ordered with an effective photocathode area of about 0.1 mm², which reduces the dark count rate to about a few counts per sec even with the tube operated at room temperatures.

When the dark pulses are reduced to a few counts per sec, the bulk of those nonthermal dark pulses have other origins. The residual pulses originating in the PM tube, not the amplifier noise or Johnson noise in the load resistor, have been ascribed to photoemission in the tube window from light generated by cosmic rays (Young, 1966; Chodil *et al.*, 1965; Jerde *et al.*, 1967) and to radioactivity in the tube (Krall, 1967; Dressler and Sptizer, 1967). Electroluminescence of the glass and dynode glow are, at most, only weakly temperature dependent and are usually made worse by cooling the tube. After applying voltage to a PM tube, the dark count rate will gradually decrease to an equilibrium value over a period of several hours or days. Phosphorescence is partially responsible for the temporary increase in dark count rates after the PM tube has been exposed to light. The glass envelopes of PM tubes contain enough potassium 40 to produce one or more dark counts per sec. Tubes with pure silica windows are less radioactive but are more sensitive to cosmic rays. For some tubes, there is an additional component of the dark current which is due to the ionization of gases by energetic electrons (Young, 1969).

The temperature dependence of the dark count rate has been extensively studied (Morton, 1968; Oliver and Pike, 1968; Gadsden, 1965; Rodman and Smith, 1963). The dark count rate of most photocathodes, with the exception of S-1 type, asymptotically approaches a minimum at about -30 to $-40°C$ with the higher-temperature region obeying the Richardson–Dushman equation for thermionic emission (ln count rate/$T^2 \propto 1/T$; Kittel, 1968). The S-1 type photocathode requires cooling to less than

− 100°C in order to reduce the temperature-dependent component of the dark count rate.

In photon correlation, it is particularly important to select a PM tube whose dark counts exhibit Poisson photon-counting statistics, i.e., the dark pulses are randomly distributed in time. Oliver and Pike (1968) have shown that the dark counts of an ITT FW 130 PM tube have Poisson statistics both at room temperature and cooled, while a Mullard 56 TVP PM tube has about two standard deviations from the correct value at room temperature and major correlations when the tube is cooled.

The variation of photon-counting correlations with discriminator dead time for the ITT FW 130 tube, when the cathode is illuminated with coherent light, is shown in Fig. 7.4.2 (Foord *et al.*, 1969). The measurements

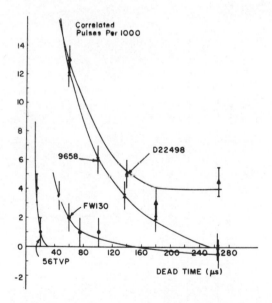

Fig. 7.4.2. Variation of the photon-counting correlations with discriminator dead time for the ITT FW 130 PM tube (Foord *et al.*, 1969).

show that the ITT FW 130 tube can be used for photon correlation studies with a discriminator dead time of 75 nsec. The shorter the dead time, the higher the permissible repetition rate. So tubes with very short dead times permit measurements of very short correlation times. The RCA C70045C gives good photon-counting performance with a dead time of only 10 nsec, while the EMI 9558 tube has a dead time of 200 nsec. Table 7.4.1 shows a summary of photomultiplier photon counting and dark count properties

Table 7.4.1

Summary of photomultiplier photon counting and dark count properties[a]

Photomultiplier	External amplification	Tube voltage (kV)	Dead time (nsec)	Quantum-counting efficiency α (%)	Correlated pulses[b] per 10³	Dark count rate at 0°C (counts per sec)	Dark count rate (0°C) per 1% quantum efficiency (QE)	Cathode area (cm²)	Dark count rate (0°C) per unit QE per unit area	Lowest dark count rate/1% QE (counts/sec)
EMI 9558	×100	1.525	200	0.55	<1	1999	3636	13.5	269	45[c]
EMI 9658	×100	1.4	200	1.1	<1	3623	3294	13.5	244	—
EMI D22498	×100	1.13	>200	0.50	5	86	96	0.29	331	—
Mullard 56 TVP	×10	2.1	20	0.63	<1	1785	2833	13.5	210	71
ITT FW 130[d]	×100	2.15	75	0.46	<1	6	13	0.05	260	1.1
RCA 7265	×10	3.0	>16	1.6	25	—	—	—	—	—
RCA C70045C	×8	6.0	10	1.2	<1	—	—	—	—	—

[a] Foord et al. (1969).
[b] May be underestimated. See A. T. Young (1971); R. Foord et al. (1971).
[c] Rodman and Smith (1963).
[d] This tube may be purchased with effective photocathode areas down to 10^{-5} cm² with consequently lower dark count rates ($\sim$1/sec at room temperature).

(Foord *et al.*, 1969). For a more detailed discussion on the use of photo-multiplier tubes for photon counting, the reader is advised to read the excellent article by Foord *et al.* (1969). We shall restate the pertinent properties of the PM tube suitable for laser light scattering as summarized by Foord *et al.* (1969):

(a)   There must be few correlated pulses for coherent illumination. This requirement is satisfied by the EMI 9558, 9658, the Mullard 56 TVP, the ITT FW 130, and the RCA C70045C but not by the EMI D22498 and the RCA 7265.

(b)   The anode pulses must be as narrow as possible for the tube to take high pulse-counting rates without pulse pileup, and there should be no correlated after-pulsing. The most suitable tubes, in order of merit, are C70045C with a 10-nsec discriminator dead time, the 56 TVP with a 20-nsec discriminator dead time, the FW 130 with a 75-nsec discriminator dead time, the 9558 and 9658 with a 200-nsec discriminator dead time.

(c)   For low-light-level detection, the dark count rate per unit quantum efficiency must be as low as possible. In this respect, FW 130 is the best. The 56 TVP, 9658, and 9558 are much behind. Thus, a small effective photocathode area tube clearly has the edge. Furthermore, FW 130 is the only tube tested by Foord *et al.* (1969) whose cooled dark counts follow Poisson statistics.

Coherence-area limitations often involve the use of apertures of less than 0.05 cm. Thus, the FW 130 tube has a unique advantage since effective cathode diameters of 50 μm can be achieved. The room-temperature dark count rates for such a tube are about 1 count/sec. On the other hand, the FW 130 tube has the lowest quantum-counting efficiency and collection efficiency of all the tubes tested. The search for better PM tubes goes on even though most such studies are not concerned with correlated afterpulses (Lakes and Poultney, 1971; Robinson *et al.*, 1971; Birenbaum and Scarl, 1973; Poultney, 1972; Reisse *et al.* 1973). It should be noted that the evaluation of PM tubes is more complex than it appears (Young and Schild, 1971). In conclusion, the ITT FW 130 or the ITT 4085 tube is clearly a suitable choice for a He–Ne laser at an incident wavelength of 632.8 nm. At other wavelengths, the cathode spectral sensitivity should have no more red response than is needed in the experiment. At low light levels, it is advisable to buy a tube selected for low dark-count rate.

7.4.3. Photomultiplier-Tube Housing Design

Zatzick (1971) has written a very good discussion of the requirements for an effective PM-tube housing to be used with a high gain wide-band

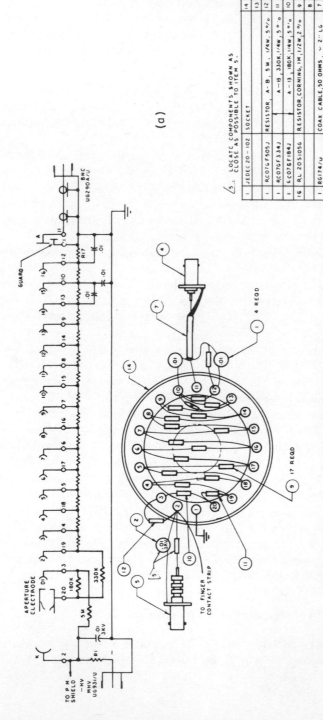

(a)

	14										
1		JEDEC 20 - 102	SOCKET								13
1		RC07GF505J	RESISTOR	A - B , 5 M , 1/4W, 5 %							12
1		RC07GF334J		A - B , 330K, 1/4W, 5 %							11
1		KC07GF184J		A - 13 , 180K, 1/4W, 5 %							10
16		RL 20S105G	RESISTOR, CORNING, 1M , 1/2W, 2 %								9
1		RG174/U	COAX CABLE, 50 OHMS , ~ 2" LG								8
1		U693I/U	CONNECTOR, MHV								7
1		UG290A/U	CONNECTOR, BNC								6
											5
											4
1		30GA-S10	CAPACITOR, SPRAGUE , .01 , 3 KV								3
3		5GA-S10	CAPACITOR, SPRAGUE , .01 , 1 KV								2
REQD		PART NO	DESCRIPTION								1
			LIST OF MATERIALS								ITEM

LOCATE COMPONENTS SHOWN AS CLOSE AS POSSIBLE TO ITEM 5.

Fig. 7.4.3. Suggested schematic and wiring diagram for ITT FW 130 photomulti-plier when used with the SSR 1100 series photon counting system (M. R. Zatzick, SSR Instrument Co., Application Note 71021). Resistors are 1 MΩ, $\frac{1}{2}$ W, 2 %, tin oxide; capacitors are in microfarads, 1 kV; lead lengths to be as short as possible. (a) Typical grounded anode configuration. (b) Typical grounded cathode configuration. Can be used only in the photon-counting mode and eliminates the susceptibility of the PMT focusing as a consequence of potential differences between the photocathode and the grounded assembly at the PMT faceplate (M. R. Zatzick, private communication).

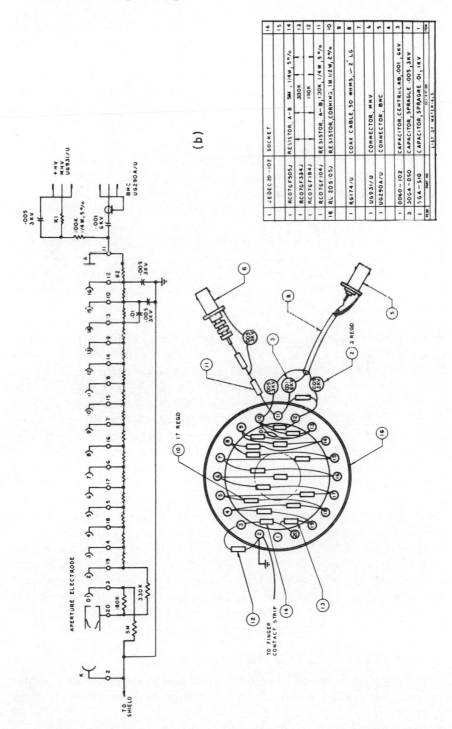

(b)

16	15	14	13	12	11	10	9	8	7	6	5	4	3	2	1	ITEM
JEDEC 20-102 SOCKET	RESISTOR, A—B 5M, 1/4W, 5%	330K	110K	RESISTOR, A—B, 130K, 1/4W, 5%	RESISTOR, CORNING, 1M 1/2W, 2%	COAX CABLE, 50 OHMS, ~2' LG		CONNECTOR, MHV	CONNECTOR, BNC		CAPACITOR, CENTRALAB .001, 6KV	CAPACITOR, SPRAGUE .005, 3KV	CAPACITOR, SPRAGUE .01, 1KV		DESCRIPTION
JEDEC 20-102	RC07GF505J	RC07GF334J	RC07GF1B4J	RC07GF104J	RL 20 S 105J	RG174/U		UG931/U	UG290A/U		D060-102	30GA-D50	5GA-S10		PART NO
1				1	18	1		1	1		1	3	1		REQD	

LIST OF MATERIALS

photon-counting system. PM-tube housings and circuits designed for analog measurements are usually not suitable for use in photon counting. On the other hand, housings and dynode voltage divider circuits designed for photon counting can be used for current measurements, the only precaution being that much lower anode currents are permitted for linear performance. The essential features for good PM-tube housing are summarized as follows.

7.4.3.A. Voltage divider circuit

A typical schematic and wiring diagram of an ITT FW 130 PM-tube voltage divider circuit is shown in Fig. 7.4.3. The input high-voltage line is filtered with a 1-MΩ resistor and a 0.001–0.1 μF capacitor giving an attenuation of 10^{-4}–10^{-6} at 1 MHz. The zener diode (IN 992B) is used to establish a constant potential between the cathode and the first dynode. Older type zeners are high-temperature blackbody emitters and should therefore be coated with opaque material. The bypass capacitor is highly recommended since zeners operating in the avalanche mode are noise sources. The use of 1-MΩ resistors in each dynode stage assures a divider current of about $10^3/10 \times 10^6 = 100$ μA for tubes with ten (or more) stages. Thus, a typical maximum anode current with stable linear performance and without tube fatigue should be less than 5 μA. The tube can maintain linear response with increasing maximum anode current by reducing the dynode resistance per chain. However, dissipation of heat in the base region will then increase and may result in higher dark-count rates. Corning glass, tin oxide resistors are often used because of their good temperature stability and low noise. Disc ceramic or equivalent high frequency capacitors of approximately 0.01 μF with an excess voltage rating of 1 kV are used to bypass the last three dynodes to ground in order to minimize radiofrequency interference pickup via the dynode-to-anode capacitance and to sustain a constant potential at the latter dynodes during high counting rates. The capacitors are grounded at the shield of the anode coax lead. The lead length for all components should be kept as short as possible. Double shielded RG55A, 50-Ω coaxial cable matched at both ends to reduce reflection is used to connect the anode with the (pre)amplifier. The base design should give the optimum pulse shape without a long-time-constant back edge to the pulse. Variation in the position of the same components has been known to change the pulse-counting properties, even the pulse-height distribution. Thus, good base construction is very important.

7.4.3.B. Electromagnetic shielding

Each penetration of the housing for signal and power decreases its isolation from electrical interference. A fairly heavy wall electrostatic shield with an inner magnetic shield can provide good radio frequency shielding. However, sharp edges in the electrostatic shield should be avoided and good insulation between the mμ metal shield and the outer ground shell is essential as corona may become a problem.

7.4.3.C. Choice of housing material

Aluminum for the outer shell and Plexiglass or Teflon for the insulators are recommended. The polymers should be tested for electroluminescence properties, and use of lint-producing materials should always be avoided. The housing subassembly should be properly grounded without electrical contacts through paint or anodized material since oxides are poor conductors.

7.4.3.D. Cleanliness and other considerations

Leakage is generally created by a film of moisture, often caused by finger marks, on the tube base or socket. The leakage current of any good tube can be made negligibly small by keeping the tube and socket assembly *dry* and *clean*. The socket assembly can be potted to avoid contamination by moisture and other material. It is advantageous to avoid using lenses and windows in order to reduce scattering, reflection, and transmission losses.

The above considerations clearly demonstrate that the construction of a good tube housing is a tricky undertaking. Fortunately, good commercial housings, such as those made by SSR and Products for Research, are available. Home construction of coolable tube housings which require additional penetrations from electrical isolation is even more difficult. Therefore, my advice is simply to buy from a reputable manufacturer.

7.4.4. Amplifiers, Discriminators, and Scalers

The configuration of a detection system for measurements of integrated intensity is shown in Fig. 7.4.4. Generally, a single-channel analyzer indicates lower count-rate capability than a discriminator. The amplifier should have a rise time comparable with that of the tube, a gain sufficient to make the single-channel analyzer or discriminator operational, and low correlations or distortions in its output. If the amplifier gain is insufficient, two amplifiers can be cascaded. In cascading amplifiers, the amplifier noise could become a problem. Foord et al. (1969) pointed out that the PM tube, which provides the best high gain, wide-band amplification, should be operated at high supply voltage in order to minimize external amplification. Photomultiplier-tube gains in the range 10^6–10^8 with amplifier gains of

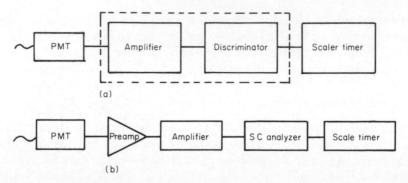

(a)

(b)

Fig. 7.4.4. Block diagram for photon counting of integrated intensity. (a) Fast system (~100 MHz). Example: SSR Instruments or LeCroy Research Systems. (b) Slow System. Example: Ortec 109 PC preamplifier, Ortec 451 amplifier, Ortec 406A SC analyzer, and Ortec 715 counter and timer.

10–100 yield appropriate pulse heights for most single-channel-analyzer or discriminator use. A good amplifier schematic, as designed by Jackson (1965), is shown in Fig. 7.4.5. Amplifiers with 1–2 nsec rise times are available commercially from "nuclear" oriented electronics firms. Foord *et al.* (1969) considered the Jackson design as one of the best tested. This particular amplifier with known and proven physical layout (see Jackson, 1965) could be an interesting project for the novice.

The discriminator should be set at maximum sensitivity so that the overall gain of the combined photomultiplier–amplifier system is kept at a minimum. Young (1969) mentioned that any nonlinear weighting function results in limited dynamic range. In photon counting, the nonlinearity after

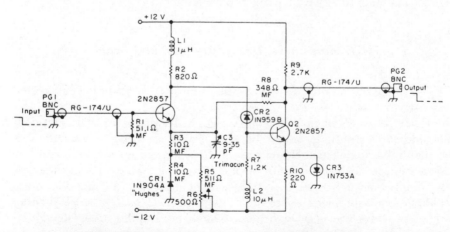

Fig. 7.4.5. Schematic of an amplifier (Jackson, 1965).

corrections for background arises from pulse overlap. Present-day technology permits 100-MHz system without excessive expense, and such a
system is quite adequate for most purposes.

Jonas and Alon (1971) observed that, in the photon-counting mode at a
constant discriminating bias, the signal-to-noise ratio (S/N) improved
with increasing operating voltage in the box-and-grid structure tube such
as the ITT FW 130, but changed little in the venetian-blind structure tube
such as the EMI 6256S. On the other hand, S/N remained relatively constant over a supply-voltage range of 1800–2000 V with the dc method of
detection for the FW 130 PM tube.

In depolarization studies, it is important to realize that the photocathode
sensitivity which usually varies across the photocathode surface could
depend upon the polarization of the light. The surface polarization effects
are wavelength, temperature, and voltage dependent. Furthermore, the
polarization also depends on the angle at which the light strikes the photocathode surface.

7.5. Current Detection

7.5.1. Current Detection versus Photon Counting

The photon-counting technique is the most efficient detection method
(Young, 1969; Jones et al., 1971) even though others, such as Robben
(1971) and Alfano and Ockman (1968), have indicated otherwise. The
work by Jones et al. (1971) was stimulated by the results of Rolfe and Moore
(1970) who draw experimental conclusions with respect to the merits of
various techniques not acceptable by Jones et al. When the tubes are operated under noise-in-signal limited conditions with negligible dark-count
rates, Jones et al. (1971) showed that the photon-counting technique was
superior to the current measurements by a factor of 2.6 in the duration
time required to achieve the same variances. They operated the ITT FW
130 with a cathode-to-dynode 1 voltage of 300 V (Barr and Eberhardt,
1965) and a dynode 1-to-anode voltage of 1800 V in order to achieve an
optimum pulse-height distribution. Regardless of existing arguments and
discussions on the advantages and disadvantages of various techniques, it is
advisable to set up the detection system for pulse counting and photon
correlation rather than current measurements, signal correlation, and spectrum (or wave) analysis. However, in view of the fact that digital photon
correlators are not common, a brief discussion on current measurements,
which remain popular in laser anemometry, is included in this chapter.

7.5.2. Time-Dependent Current Measurements

The linearity of integrated intensity at high light levels by means of current detection needs to be calibrated experimentally. A general compromise is to reduce the dynode resistances by a factor of about 5–10. Good commercial electrometers are readily available. With digital read out, a linearity of 0.2 % over limited ranges is easily attainable. Land (1971) presented a discussion of the region of linear operation of photomultipliers. It should be noted that in general linearity at high current levels ($>10\ \mu A$) is difficult to achieve.

In signal correlation, a preamplifier, preferably connected immediately after the anode output, is recommended. Many commercial signal correlators accept an analog photocurrent signal and then convert its amplitude into digital information. All subsequent processes are performed digitally. Such correlators cannot be used for direct digital photon correlation without modification. Furthermore, its clipping mode inplies "double clipping" whose formalism is quite complex. Nevertheless, signal correlators are quite suitable for very slow decay time studies, especially those related to critical opalescence and diffusion coefficients of large macromolecules in solution measured at small scattering angles. The effect of the detector time response function (RC time constant) on the photocurrent autocorrelation function has been investigated (King and Lee, 1972). A small anode load resistance ensures a fast decay of the instrument response but it also reduces the output voltage of the amplifier for the correlator.

In wave (or spectrum) analysis, the postdetection signal needs to be averaged by using an integration time constant, a signal averager, or both. Long integration times necessitate a reduction in the sweep rates. The relationship between the integration time constant T and the sweep rate can be derived as follows.

We take the signal spectrum to have the form

$$P = A/[\nu^2 + (\Gamma/2\pi)^2] + B \qquad (7.5.1)$$

where P is the power output of the wave analyzer, ν represents the frequency in hertz, A and B are constants, and Γ (in radians per second) is the half-width at half-maximum of the Lorentzian curve centered at $\omega = 2\pi\nu = 0$. As we sweep the analyzer, the rate of change of P is

$$\frac{dP}{dt} = -\frac{2A\nu}{(\nu^2 + (\Gamma/2\pi)^2)^2}\frac{d\nu}{dt} \qquad (7.5.2)$$

where $d\nu/dt$ is the sweep rate. For a Lorentzian curve, the maximum change of P with respect to ν can be obtained by setting

$$\frac{d^2P}{d\nu^2} = -\frac{2A}{[\nu^2 + (\Gamma/2\pi)^2]^2} + \frac{8A\nu^2}{[\nu^2 + (\Gamma/2\pi)^2]^3} = 0 \qquad (7.5.3)$$

which gives $\nu_P^2 = \frac{1}{3}(\Gamma/2\pi)^2$ or $\nu_P = \Gamma/[2\pi(3)^{1/2}]$. Thus, for a normalized Lorentzian curve, the maximum rate of change of P occurs at ν_P and is related to the sweep rate as follows:

$$\frac{1}{P_0}\left(\frac{dP}{dt}\right)_{\max} = -\frac{3\sqrt{3}}{8}\frac{A(2\pi/\Gamma)}{[A + B(\Gamma/2\pi)^2]}\frac{d\nu}{dt} \qquad (7.5.4)$$

where

$$P_0 = \frac{(A + B(\Gamma/2\pi)^2)}{(\Gamma/2\pi)^2}$$

If we set $CA \simeq B(\Gamma/2\pi)^2$ then Eq. (7.5.4) has a simpler form

$$\frac{1}{P_0}\left(\frac{dP}{dt}\right)_{\max} = -\frac{3\sqrt{3}}{8}\frac{2\pi}{\Gamma}\left(\frac{1}{C+1}\right)\frac{d\nu}{dt} \qquad (7.5.5)$$

In actual data collection, we set the change in P over a time constant T (in sec) to be less than $e \%$ in order to assure a distortion of $\leq 1 \%$ because of the RC integration. The above condition requires

$$T\frac{d\nu}{dt} = \frac{e}{100}\frac{8}{3\sqrt{3}}\frac{\Gamma}{2\pi}(C + 1) = 0.04185(C + 1)\frac{\Gamma}{2\pi} \qquad (7.5.6)$$

which relates the integration time constant with the sweep rate. In general, we want the sweep range $>2\Gamma$, $\Delta\nu_B < \Gamma/10\pi$, and $d\nu/dt < [\pi(\Delta\nu_B)^2/10]$ in hertz per second, where $\Delta\nu_B$ is the bandwidth (in hertz) of the wave analyzer. For example, if we have a General Radio model 1900 wave analyzer and want to measure a Lorentzian curve with $\Gamma/2\pi = 100$ Hz, then we set the sweep range from low frequencies up to 200–300 Hz, and use the 10-Hz bandwidth. Without considering the integration time constant for smoothing out the spectrum, the sweep rate has to be slower than $\pi \times 10^2/10 = 31$ Hz/sec. If $C = 1$, Eq. (7.5.6) tells us that an integration time constant of 0.26 sec can be used. Such an integration time is much too short. So we have to first set a time constant T, say $T = 5$ sec, and then determine $d\nu/dt$ by means of Eq. (7.5.6) which in this case corresponds to 1.67 Hz/sec. It is therefore a time-consuming task to measure narrow linewidths by using a wave (or spectrum) analyzer. For broader linewidth, higher sweep rates coupled with appropriate time constants permit the use of a signal averager. In either case, the measurement of signal correlation is much more efficient.

7.5.3. *Wave Analyzer, Signal Correlator, and*
Digital Instrumentation

The rate of data collection with a signal correlator is higher than the rate of data collection with a wave analyzer by a factor which is of the order of the number of bandwidths swept (sweep range per bandwidth). Unfortunately, many commercial signal correlators are limited to relatively long delay times and as we have indicated in Chapter VI, can only accept analog photocurrent. The same limitations are applicable to "real-time" spectrum analyzers which simultaneously sample frequency intervals.

At low count rates, the probability of measuring a count during the sample time interval $T(\ll \tau_{coh})$ is small. Then, the probability of detecting two photons separated by a sample time T could be approximated by the joint count rate at time intervals centered at $t = 0$ and $t = T$ (Glauber, 1968; Blake and Barakat, 1973). Scarl (1968) used the distribution of separation times between individual photons to measure the width of a mercury vapor line. For very fast time correlations, it should be interesting to note that Scarl used a double discriminator system in order to eliminate the time slewing by allowing only pulses well above the threshold of the timing discriminator to be analyzed. The measurement of pulse separations for photoelectrons uses the same time-to-amplitude converter (TAC) and pulse-height analyzer (MCA) approach of nanosecond fluorescence decay studies (Lewis *et al.*, 1973) involving the determination of rotational diffusion coefficients of macromolecules (Tao, 1969) and reaction rates (DeLuca *et al.*, 1971). Unfortunately, such an approach permits only measurements of time arrivals for pairs of individual photons because of the limitation in the time-to-amplitude converter. Nevertheless, correlation times outside the range of present-day digital photon correlators (10–50 nsec per channel) can be measured using the TAC–MCA approach. It is also expected that for intermediately fast decay time studies (50–100 nsec) the double discriminator-coincidence circuit (Scarl, 1968) can be avoided since the rise times of the PM tube and of amplifiers are in the nanosecond range. Thus, measurements of separation times between individual photons provide us with an alternative route to the linewidth problem, and remains the only known technique for very fast correlation time studies with resolutions down to about 100 psec. In the nanosecond region, a "multiple" time-to-amplitude converter in the form of time-to-digital converters (TDC) can be used to measure time correlations for 4 to 64 photons. The techniques are relatively new, and the above approach has not yet been tested. Perhaps, part of the reason is that a 32-channel TDC (made in France) cost about $30,000 in 1973. Chopra and Mandel (1972) have developed a correlator based on digital storage of the arrival times of up to six photo-electric pulses following a start pulse. They have also adapted the same technique to the development of a third-order intensity correlator (Chopra and Mandel, 1973). In fast decay time studies the finite pulsewidth and instrumental dead time have to be taken into account.

Kelly and Blake (1971) and Kelly (1972) measured the width of a Lorentz spectral line using a digital photoelectron correlation device as well as a pulse-separation detector (TAC–MCA) and showed that the pulse-separation measurements can yield information similar to the auto-correlation function measurements over a wide range of count rates if the results are correctly interpreted. For macromolecules in solution and phase-transition studies, the best approach is to use digital photon counting for the integrated intensity and digital photon correlation (clipped or un-clipped) for decay time studies as we have described in detail in Chapter VI. Even in interferometry, an automatic scanning Fabry Perot inter-ferometer using photon counting and multichannel digital data storage has been developed (Jackson and Pike, 1968; Jackson et al., 1968). Digital instrumentation coupled with on-line computer data acquisition is clearly a recommended direction. At Stony Brook, we have observed that, for routine measurements, it now requires about 3 weeks to obtain similar data information that used to take about 1 yr to accomplish. Such a step is essential for laser-light-scattering studies of complex biological systems where we are likely to encounter extensive data collection and analysis.

Finally, a digital PDP-9 computer has been used successfully as a photon correlation spectrometer (Hallett et al., 1972) with a dead time down to 800 nsec and a resolution of 200 nsec. Slower versions using analog cur-rents and analog-to-digital converters have been reported by Schurr and Schmitz (1973) and by Shaya et al. (1974). Thus, the technique can be expected to become accessible to anyone who has a direct on-line computer.

It should be noted that as the power spectrum or the time-dependent correlation function becomes more complex, direct signal processing by means of a digital computer will undoubtedly be a more flexible approach than hard-wired correlators or real-time spectrum analyzers. At present, one drawback of the digital computer is a pile-up of signals when the delay times become short (say 500 nsec), since computer cycle time remains relatively slow with respect to fast photopulse arrival times. Thus an fm tape recorder (Section 10.5.4) for analog signals (or a buffer storage for photon arrival times) is required, and the power spectrum (or the time correlation function) is not truly on-line. However, the flexibility of the computer cannot be overlooked. For example, with signals properly stored, the computer can analyze the *same* data using different bandwidths or delay times, which hard-wired systems cannot do.

7.6. Fabry–Perot Interferometer

The Fabry–Perot (F–P) interferometer can be purchased ready made. Many commercial firms make F–P interferometers that are quite adequate for laser light scattering. In interferometry, like in optical heterodyne spectroscopy, rigidity of the entire optical setup, isolation from mechanical vibrations, and high-quality optics are helpful considerations which we must undertake in order to ensure the success of the experiment. The F–P interferometer should be made of materials with a low thermal coefficient of expansion, such as Invar. In this respect, even stainless steel is better than aluminum. Sometimes, the F–P interferometer is thermally compensated, or situated in a constant temperature environment. The Fabry–Perot etalon spacer *must* be made of materials with a low thermal coefficient of expansion. Wavelength variations of a scanning Fabry–Perot interferometer can be achieved by changing (a) the index of refraction between the interferometer plates and (b) the separation distance between the interferometer plates. In fact, many systems have been used or proposed for the scanning of etalons (see *J. Phys. Radium* **19**, 185–436 (1958); and Jacquinot, 1960), including variation of the plate-separation distance by thermal expansion of the spacer (Burger and van Cittert, 1935), electromagnetic attraction (Bruce and Hill, 1961), magnetostriction (Bennett and Kindlmann, 1962), piezoelectricity, bellow action under pressure, and precision screws. The other approach which varies the ambient gas pressure and thus the refractive index between the etalon plates instead of the etalon geometry has been by far the simplest and most widely used method.

The principle of scanning the wavelength by changing the index of refraction between the interferometer plates was first used by Jacquinot and Dufour (1948), and later by Connes (1956, 1958), and Hindle and Reay (1967). The details may be found in a paper by Chabbal and Jacquinot (1961). Earlier, Biondi (1956) designed a high-speed direct recording Fabry–Perot interferometer. In the pressure-scanning technique, the spacers for the Fabry–Perot etalon could be very crucial. Phelps, III (1965) described procedures for making spacers, even though it is advisable to purchase such spacers, which are usually made of quartz or Invar, from reliable commercial sources.

Piezoelectric scanning of Fabry–Perot interferometers has been becoming increasingly more popular. Piezoelectric elements made of barium titanate (Cooper and Greig, 1963; Peacock *et al.*, 1964) and of lead zirconate (Fray *et al.*, 1969) have been used successfully. Fork *et al.* (1964) have constructed a scanning spherical mirror interferometer for spectral analysis of laser radiation. Their interferometer used a moving-coil driving system of the Tolansky–Bradley (1960) type, which permitted motions of mirror distances to over 70 μm. Stacking of piezoelectric elements also permits sufficient scanning range, even though care should be exercised in testing the linear translation of one of the mirrors in the axial direction without mirror tilt. In addition, piezoelectric scanning, unlike pressure scanning, which needs an etalon spacer for each fixed cavity length, utilizes the same scanning elements over large ranges of cavity length.

Jackson and Pike (1968) used a stack of six 50-mm-diam lead zirconate titanate disks (Mullard MB 1019 PXE5) with a 2-cm aperture as their scanning elements. The piezoelectric rings, separated by pyrophylite or glass annular spacers, are glued together with Araldite 103 and are wired in parallel as shown in Fig. 7.6.1. The Fabry–Perot mirror is mounted on three small feet glued to the free end of the stack. The system can be scanned at low sweep rates (<50 Hz) in order to avoid mechanical resonances. The spacings of Brillouin doublets scattered from liquids are references for calibration. The dc bias controls the fine adjustments in plate separation distance while the MCA can be internally programmed so that it scans through a preset number of channels and returns to channel (1) in a time interval just shorter than the "ramp plus fly back" time of the oscilloscope. Repeated process is achieved by subsequent triggering of the system.

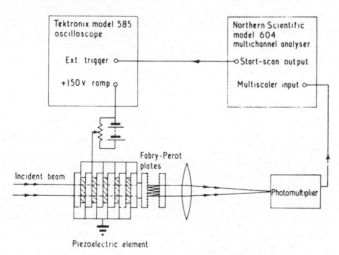

Fig. 7.6.1. Block diagram of a multichannel scanning system (Jackson and Pike, 1968).

Further improvements including servo control of drifts of the laser frequency and of the Fabry–Perot cavity length have been achieved (Fray
et al., 1969). Figure 7.6.2 shows the schematic block diagram of their servo-
controlled digital Fabry–Perot interferometer. A dc level is applied from a
servo loop to stabilize the spectrum. This servo loop is controlled by obtaining a reference spectrum of the laser line on the alternate cycles of the
sawtooth which drives the piezoelectric system. The laser beam, after
passing through the sample, is returned back through the Fabry–Perot
interferometer via a mechanical chopper every second cycle.

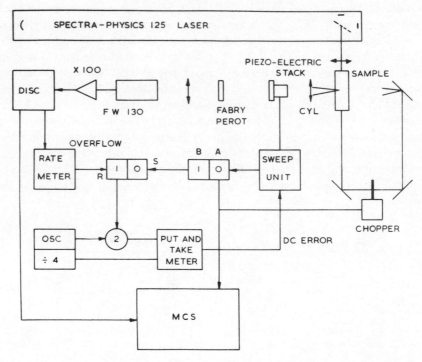

Fig. 7.6.2. Block schematic of a scanning servo-controlled digital Fabry–Perot
interferometer (Fray *et al.*, 1969).

The servo loop has been very cleverly designed. *A* and *B* could be logic
units (flip–flops) which turn on either the MCS scan or the laser beam. When
the laser beam is on, the oscillator signal and the oscillator signal/4 are
started by the flip–flop trigger as shown in Fig. 7.6.3. Then the oscillator
signal is stopped by the rate meter overflow, which is set at maximum of the
laser spectrum. We visualize the function of the put-and-take meter as

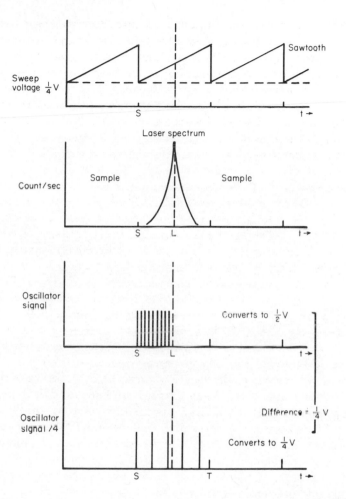

Fig. 7.6.3. A schematic indication of the servo loop which removes drifts of the laser frequency and of the Fabry–Perot cavity length.

follows. The oscillator signal counts accumulated over the time interval $(L–S)$ are compared with the (oscillator signal/4) counts accumulated over the time interval $(T–S)$. The difference signal could be latched, converted to a voltage by a digital-to-analog converter (DAC), amplified, and fed back to the piezoelectric stack on top of the constant-amplitude sawtooth with the correct polarity (negative feed back) to complete the servo loop. The dc output of the put-and-take meter corresponds to $V/4$ of the oscillator signal when the laser peak is located at $\frac{1}{2}(T–S)$. This output is integrated over a number of cycles for better S/N and will move in one direction or the other depending upon whether the laser line appears later or earlier than halfway across the reference sweep.

Such a setup removes drifts of the laser frequency and the Fabry–Perot cavity length at rates slower than the integration time of the servo loop. It should be noted that variation of the incident laser intensity during each sweep will be viewed by the servo loop as drifts of the laser frequency and the Fabry–Perot cavity length because of the overflow setting at the rate meter. In fact a significant decrease in laser intensity should make the servo loop inoperative by not triggering the overflow at all. Thus, the laser must be stabilized for constant intensity.

An improvement of the above scheme has been accomplished by Pike and his co-workers at Malvern, England. Basically they increase the scan rate during the reference sweep by a factor of 5–10. Thus, an 80–90% efficiency can be achieved, and the Rayleigh line also acts as a trigger for the signal sweep. The variable scan rate permits magnification of the spectrum over regions of interest. In addition, Sandercock (1970) has designed a servo system in which the cavity length as well as the tilt of the Fabry–Perot mirrors can be adjusted automatically. The servo for the tilt uses a four-stroke approach where the criterion in the maximum Rayleigh peak intensity controls the parallelisms of the Fabry–Perot mirrors. Hicks et al. (1974) have developed a servo-controlled Fabry–Perot interferometer using capacitance micrometers to sense departures from parallelism and variations in the mean cavity length to an accuracy better than the surface quality of the plates ($\sim\lambda/150$ at 500 nm). McLaren and Stegeman (1973) have reported a digital stabilizer specifically designed to eliminate the effects of long-term frequency shift. Thus, we finally have a satisfactory Fabry–Perot servo system which is readily available commercially and several servo mechanisms based on established techniques.

The application of piezoelectric transducers to spectral scanning using Fabry–Perot interferometers has also been reported in the reviews of Vaughan (1967) and Greig and Cooper (1968). Astronomers have made valuable contributions in improving the parallelism adjustment as well as the long-term stability of Fabry–Perot spectrometers. In the servo loop designed by Fray et al. (1969), the two etalon plates are mounted independently and parallelism adjustment is achieved by alignment of the stationary etalon plate. While finely controlled mirror mount with high accuracy in alignment and good stability exists (Simić-Glavăski and Jackson, 1970), automatic control of both the parallelism and the spacing of Fabry–Perot interferometers have been devised (Ramsay 1962, 1966; Ramsay and Mugridge 1962a,b; Hicks et al., 1974). The reader should consult the references for practical details of the various components in constructing such electronically controlled Fabry–Perot spectrometers.

Smeethe and James (1971) have successfully adopted the active servo system of Ramsay with an optical-electrical loop where the optical path of the servo loop requires a truncated pyramid in the rear edge of one of the two etalon plates. Bates *et al.* (1971) have described a stable, high finesse scanning Fabry–Perot interferometer with different piezoelectric ceramics for plate parallelism adjustment and spectral scanning. Control of mirror position to within 5×10^{-5} wavelength have been achieved by the use of an auxiliary Fabry–Perot interferometer (Tuma *et al.*, 1973). Hernandez and Mills (1973) have been able to stabilize their finished instrument with respect to the reference wavelength and parallelism to approximately $\lambda/1000$ at 546 nm for a 6-hr period. Nevertheless, the development of digitally scanned piezoelectric systems is still in its infancy. Problems exist concerning the linearity of the sweep, the constancy of finesse with sweep, and long-term stability, all of which are essential for high resolution studies of weak lines. Cooper *et al.* (1972) have constructed a digital pressure-scanned Fabry–Perot interferometer where repetitive scans are reproduced within 1/640 of the spectral free range. Their spectrometer is simpler in electronics and design and has virtues which should not be overlooked when compared with the more sophisticated piezoelectric-scanned systems.

Double- or multiple-pass F–P interferometers with very great contrasts, instead of operating F–P interferometers in tandem (Cannell and Benedek, 1970), have been developed to detect weak lines in a spectrum in the presence of nearby intense lines. Sandercock (1971) used retroreflective cubes to pass the light back and forth at different portions of the plates of a flat F–P interferometer. However, the technique requires extremely precise alignment of the interferometer. An alternative approach is to place the interferometer in an optical isolator (Hariharan and Sen, 1961; Cannell *et al.*, 1973). Cannell *et al.* have constructed a double-pass spherical F–P interferometer that has an instrumental profile with a full width of 4.8 MHz. The multiple-pass technique should be very useful in Brillouin scattering of critical fluids and quasielastic light scattering of macromolecules in solution.

7.7. Data Analysis

The importance of data analysis has often been overlooked. Unfortunately, experimental conditions vary so that generalizations in data treatment are dangerous. Nevertheless, we can say that determinations of a single linewidth Γ from the power spectrum or a single decay constant from the correlation function are fairly straightforward, and routine least-squares-fitting techniques are applicable. In practice, we need to pay particular attention to the baseline determination. For example, in power-spectral analysis, the shot-noise contribution (baseline) can be measured either at large frequencies ($\omega > 8\Gamma$) or by using a white-light source which registers the same dc current as the scattered laser light. In signal correlation, the dc contribution (baseline) can be determined by measuring $g^{(2)}(\tau)$ at sufficiently large values of τ where the signal portion of the correlation function has become negligibly small. The advantage of knowing the baseline lies with reducing the parameters in the least-squares-fitting procedure of either the power spectrum or the correlation function by one. The baseline is measured directly in digital photon correlation.

Major difficulties in data analysis arise from multiexponential (or multi-Lorentzian) signals. Extreme care must be exercised in fitting experimental data with a sum of exponentials (or Lorentzians) consisting of arbitrary decay times and amplitudes. Although computer-fitting programs exist, e.g., Ford (1972) suggested the damped least-squares-fitting program of Laiken and Printz (1970), there is no guarantee that the resulting parameters are unique and have real physical meaning. On the other hand, it is advantageous to be able to detect deviations from a single decay time. Pusey *et al.* (1972) fitted a single exponential to every possible set of four consecutive points and plotted the resulting decay times as a function of the delay times at the center of each set. The single exponential gives a line of zero slope while a slope reveals deviations from the single exponential correlation function. The most powerful technique is by the method of cumulants (Koppel, 1972) which will be discussed in Section 8.6.2.

Finally, the effect of dust in influencing the experimental results cannot be overemphasized. It is essential to use all necessary precautions in order to eliminate dust. Its presence corresponds to the introduction of large polydisperse particles into the system. If the decay time of interest is comparable to that of the dust, no measurements can be performed unless $\langle I_D \rangle \ll \langle I_S \rangle$ where $\langle I_D \rangle$ and $\langle I_S \rangle$ are the average intensities of light scattered by the dust and the sample, respectively. For smaller particles, the dust can act as a local oscillator

$$G^{(2)}(\tau) = \langle I_D{}^2 \rangle + 2\langle I_D \rangle \langle I_S \rangle (1 + \beta e^{-\Gamma\tau}) + \langle I_S \rangle^2 (1 + \beta e^{-2\Gamma\tau}) \quad (7.7.1)$$

where we have implicitly neglected the decay time of the dust particles. Equation (7.7.1), which is the inverse Fourier transform of Eq. (4.3.25), clearly indicates that when $\langle I_D \rangle \gg \langle I_S \rangle$, the measurement gives essentially Γ as the linewidth. However, this approach is not usually practical since dust particles tend partially to block the incident beam or give such a strong scattering as to overload the instrument. On the other hand, if $\langle I_S \rangle \gg \langle I_D \rangle$ the linewidth corresponds to 2Γ. Here, a small amount of dust will distort the third self-beating term of Eq. (7.7.1). An accuracy of 1 % in D requires that $\langle I_D \rangle$ be about $\frac{1}{2}$ % of $\langle I_S \rangle$ in view of the coefficient 2 in the second cross-beating term. All large particles, such as dust, scatter light very strongly in the forward direction. Thus, the effect of dust becomes very serious especially at small scattering angles.

McQueen and Hermans (1972a) fitted the power spectra of sodium lauryl sulfate in 0.1-M NaCl and decyltriammonium bromide in water using a trial function of the form

$$S(K, \omega) \approx 2\langle I_S \rangle \langle I_D \rangle \frac{DK^2}{\omega^2 + D^2 K^4}$$

$$+ \langle I_S \rangle^2 \frac{2DK^2}{\omega^2 + 4D^2 K^4} + \text{constant background} \quad (7.7.2)$$

whereby the diffusion coefficient of the dust particles was assumed to be negligibly small. They were able to obtain reasonable answers for D using Eq. (7.7.2) for micelles as well as poly-l-lysine (McQueen and Hermans, 1972b). It is generally advisable not to use such an approach unless dust cannot be eliminated. In the presence of a *small* amount of dust or for *very weak* scattering systems where stray light is likely to introduce partial heterodyning, then Eq. (7.7.2) becomes a possible method to extract the desired diffusion coefficient even though the uncertainties in such multiparameter fits are usually extremely large.

The use of interferometry for linewidth measurements in quasielastic laser scattering sometimes requires a knowledge of the instrumental response function. Since deconvolution is a difficult procedure, the easiest approach is to try to use an instrument with its width much narrower than the linewidth of interest. If the instrumental width becomes a measurable fraction of the true spectral width, the next step is to compare the measured spectrum with a convolution of the model spectrum using the measured instrumental response function which could include uncertainties in the momentum transfer from slit or pin-hole sizes (Yeh, 1969), various possible misalignments (Table 5.2.1), and the intrinsic instrumental bandwidth (Table 5.2.2) of the interferometer. Finally, with the aid of fast Fourier transform programs, we can use a more general approach. There, the true spectrum is the inverse Fourier transform of $\hat{A}$ which is the Fourier transform of the measured spectrum divided by that of the instrumental response function. Rautian (1958) has outlined a general procedure for treating a real spectral apparatus using different forms of the instrumental response function. Such corrections are often important even in linewidth measurements from Brillouin scattering of fluids (Aref'ev *et al.*, 1972). However, the ratio $I_c/2I_B$ [Eq. (3.4.64)] can be obtained directly from the recorded spectrum regardless of the shape or width of the instrumental profile (Cannell, 1970).

References

Adam, M., Hamelin, A., and Berge, P. (1969). *Opt. Acta* **16**, 337.
Akins, D. L., Schwartz, S. E., and Moore, C. B. (1968). *Rev. Sci. Instrum.* **39**, 715.
Alfano, R. R., and Ockman, N. (1968). *J. Opt. Soc. Amer.* **58**, 90.
Aref'ev, I. M., Gladkii, V. A., Stankov, V. A. (1972). *Brief Phys. Commun. (USSR)* **5**, 57.
Barr, F. H., and Eberhardt, E. H. (1965). "Research in the Development of an Improved Multiplier Phototube," ITT Final Rep. Contr. No. NASW-1038.
Bates, B., Conway, J. K., Courts, G. R., McKeith, C. D., and McKeith, N. E. (1971). *J. Phys. E* **4**, 899.
Benedek, G., and Greytak, T. (1965). *Proc. IEEE* **53**, 1623.
Bennett, Jr., W. R., and Kindlmann, P. J. (1962). *Rev. Sci. Instrum.* **33**, 601.
Berge, P. (1967). *Bull. Soc. Fr. Mineral. Cristallogr.* **90**, 508.
Biondi, M. A. (1956). *Rev. Sci. Instrum.* **27**, 36.
Birenbaum, L., and Scarl, D. B. (1973). *Appl. Opt.* **12**, 519.
Blake, J., and Barakat, R. (1973). *J. Phys. A* **6**, 1196.
Born, M., and Wolf, E. (1965). "Principles of Optics," 3rd (revised) ed., p. 312. Pergamon, London.
Bruce, C. F., and Hill, R. M. (1961). *Aust. J. Phys.* **14**, 64.
Burger, H. C., and van Cittert, P. H. (1935). *Physica* (Utrecht) **2**, 87.
Cannell, D. S. (1970). Ph.D. thesis. MIT, Cambridge, Massachusetts.
Cannell, D. S., and Benedek, G. B. (1970). *Phys. Rev. Lett.* **25**, 1157.
Cannell, D. S., Lunacek, J. H., and Dubin, S. B. (1973). *Rev. Sci. Instrum.* **44**, 1651.
Chabbal, R., and Jacquinot, P. (1961). *Rev. Opt.* **40**, 157.
Chodil, G., Hearn, D., Jopson, R. C., Mark, H., Swift, C. D., and Anderson, K. A. (1965). *Rev. Sci. Instr.* **36**, 394.
Chopra, S., and Mandel, L. (1972). *Rev. Sci. Instrum.* **43**, 1489.
Chopra, S., and Mandel, L. (1973). *Rev. Sci. Instrum.* **44**, 466.
Chu, B. (1968). *J. Chem. Educ.* **45**, 224.
Cole, M., and Ryer, D. (1972). Electro Optical Systems Design, 16-19.
Connes, P. (1956). *Rev. Opt.* **35**, 37.
Connes, P. (1958). *J. Phys. Radium* **19**, 262.
Cooper, J., and Greig, J. R. (1963). *J. Sci. Instrum.* **40**, 433.
Cooper, V. G., Gupta, B. K., and May, A. D. (1972). *Appl. Opt.* **11**, 2265.
Cummins, H. Z., Knable, N., and Yeh, Y. (1964). *Phys. Rev. Lett.* **12**, 150.
Cummins, H. Z., Carlson, F. D., Herbert, T. J., and Woods, G. (1969). *Biophys. J.* **9**, 518.
DeLuca, M., Brand, L., Cebula, T. A., Seliger, H. H., and Makula, A. F. (1971). *J. Biol. Chem.* **246**, 6702.
Dressler, K., and Spitzer, L., (1967). *Rev. Sci. Instrum.* **38**, 436.
Dubin, S. B., Clark, N. A., and Benedek, G. B. (1971). *J. Chem. Phys.* **54**, 5158.
Eberhardt, E. H. (1967). *IEEE Trans. Nucl. Sci.* **NS-14** (2), 7.
Fleury, P. A., and Chiao, R. Y. (1966). *J. Acoust. Soc. Amer.* **39**, 751.
Foord, R., Jones, R., Oliver, C. J., and Pike, E. R. (1969). *Appl. Opt.* **8**, 1975.

Foord, R., Jones, R., Oliver, C. J., and Pike, E. R. (1971). *Appl. Opt.* **10**, 1683.

Ford, Jr., N. C. (1972). *Chemica Scr.* **2**, 193.

Ford, Jr., N. C., and Benedek, G. B. (1965). *Phys. Rev. Lett.* **15**, 649.

Fork, R. L., Herriott, D. R., and Kogelnik, H. (1964). *Appl. Opt.* **3**, 1471.

Fray, S., Johnson, F. A., Jones, R., Kay, S., Oliver, C. J., Pike, E. R., Russell, J., Sennett, C., O'Shaughnessy, J., and Smith, C. (1969). *In* "Light Scattering Spectra of Solids" (G. B. Wright, ed.), pp. 139–150. Springer-Verlag, Berlin and New York.

Gadsden, M. (1965). *Appl. Opt.* **2**, 1446.

Glauber, R. J. (1968). "Fundamental Problems in Statistical Mechanics II," (E. G. D. Cohen, ed.), pp. 140–87. North-Holland, Amsterdam.

Greig, J. R., and Cooper, J. (1968). *Appl. Opt.* **7**, 2166.

Hallett, F. R., Gray, A. L., Rybakowski, A., Hunt, J. L., and Stevens, J. R. (1972). *Can. J. Phys.* **50**, 2368.

Hariharan, P., and Sen, D. (1961). *J. Amer. Opt. Soc.* **51**, 398.

Harker, Y. D., Masso, J. D., and Edwards, D. F. (1969). *Appl. Opt.* **8**, 2563.

Hernandez, G., and Mills, O. A. (1973). *Appl. Opt.* **12**, 126.

Hicks, T. R., Reay, N. K., and Scaddan, R. J. (1974). *J. Phys. E* **7**, 27.

Hindle, P. H., and Reay, N. K. (1967). *J. Sci. Instrum.* **44**, 360.

Jackson, H. G. (1965). *Nucl. Instrum. Methods* **33**, 161.

Jackson, D. A., and Paul, D. M. (1969). *J. Phys. E* **2**, 1077.

Jackson, D. A., and Pike, E. R. (1968). *J. Phys. E* **1**, 394.

Jackson, D. A., Jones, R., and Pike, E. R. (1968). *Phys. Lett. A* **28**, 272.

Jacquinot, P. (1960). *Rep. Progr. Phys.* **23**, 267.

Jacquinot, P., and Dufour, C. (1948). *J. Rech. Cent. Nat. Rech. Sci.* **2**, 91.

Jerde, R. L., Peterson, L. E., and Stein, W. (1967). *Rev. Sci. Instrum.* **38**, 1387.

Jonas, M., and Alon, Y. (1971). *Appl. Opt.* **10**, 2436.

Jones, R., Oliver, C. J., and Pike, E. R. (1971). *Appl. Opt.* **10**, 1673.

Kelly, H. C. (1972). *J. Phys. A* **5**, 104.

Kelly, H. C., and Blake, J. G. (1971). *J. Phys. A* **4**, L103.

King, T. A., and Lee, W. I. (1972). *J. Phys. E.* **5**, 1091.

Kittel, C. (1968). "Introduction to Solid State Physics," 3rd Ed., p. 247. Wiley, New York.

Klein, M. V. (1970). "Optics," Chapter 11.3. Wiley, New York.

Kogelnik, H., and Li, T. (1966). *Appl. Opt.* **5**, 1550.

Koppel, D. E. (1972). *J. Chem. Phys.* **57**, 4814.

Klein, M. (1970). "Optics," p. 319. Wiley, New York.

Krall, H. R. (1967). *IEEE Trans. Nucl. Sci.* **NS-14**, 455.

Lai, C. C., and Chen, S. H. (1972). *Phys. Rev. Lett.* **29**, 401.

Laiken, S. L., and Printz, M. P. (1970). *Biochemistry* **9**, 1547.

Lakes, R. S., and Poultney, S. K. (1971). *Appl. Opt.* **10**, 797.

Land, P. L. (1971). *Rev. Sci. Instrum.* **42**, 420. *See also* Lush, H. J. (1965). *J. Sci. Instrum.* **42**, 597; Sloman, A. W. (1972). *Rev. Sci. Instrum.* **43**, 362; Land, P. L. (1972). *Rev. Sci. Instrum.* **43**, 363.

Lastovka, J. B. (1967). Ph.D. thesis. MIT Press, Cambridge, Massachusetts.

Lastovka, J. B., and Benedek, G. B. (1966a). *In* "Physics of Quantum Electronics," Conf. Proc. San Juan, Puerto Rico, 1965 (P. L. Kelley, B. Lax, P. E. Tannenwald, eds.), pp. 231–40. McGraw-Hill, New York.

Lastovka, J. B., and Benedek, G. B. (1966b). *Phys. Rev. Lett.* **17**, 1039.

Lewis, C., Ware, W. R., Doemey, L. J., and Nemzek, T. L. (1973). *Rev. Sci. Instrum.* **44**, 107.

Maes, J. P., and Moore, M. (1973). *J. Phys. E* **6**, 15.

Marshall, L. (1971). *Laser Focus* **7**, 26.

McLaren, R. A., and Stegeman, G. I. A. (1973). *Appl. Opt.* **12**, 1396.

McQueen, D. H., and Hermans, J. J. (1972a). *J. Colloid Interface Sci.* **39**, 389.

McQueen, D. H., and Hermans, J. J. (1972b). *Proc. Kon. Ned. Akad. Wetensch., Ser. B* **75**, 48.

Morton, G. A. (1968). *Appl. Opt.* **7**, 1.

Oliver, C. J., and Pike, E. R. (1968). *J. Phys. D* **2**, 1459.

Pao, Y. H., and Griffiths, J. E. (1967). *J. Chem. Phys.* **46**, 1671.

Pao, Y. H., Zitter, R. N., and Griffiths, J. E. (1966). *J. Opt. Soc. Amer.* **56**, 1133.

Peacock, N. J., Cooper, J., and Greig, J. R. (1964). *Proc. Phys. Soc. London*, **83**, 803.

Phelps, F. M., III (1965). *J. Opt. Soc. Amer.* **55**, 293.

Poultney, S. K. (1972). *In* "Advances in Electronics and Electron Physics" (L. Marton, ed.), Vol. 31. Academic Press, New York and London.

Pusey, P. N., Schaefer, D. W., Koppel, D. E., Camerini-Otero, R. D., and Franklin, R. M. (1972). *J. Phys. (Paris)* **33**, C1-163.

Ramsay, J. V. (1962). *Appl. Opt.* **1**, 411.

Ramsay, J. V. (1966). *Appl. Opt.* **5**, 1297.

Ramsay, J. V., and Mugridge, E. G. V. (1962a). *J. Sci. Instrum.* **39**, 636.

Ramsay, J. V., and Mugridge, E. G. V. (1962b). *Appl. Opt.* **1**, 538.

Rautian, S. G. (1958). *Uspekhi Fis. Nauk.* **66**, 475; *Sov. Phys. Uspekhi* **1**, 245.

Reisse, R., Creecy, R., and Poultney, S. K. (1973). *Rev. Sci. Instrum.* **44**, 1666.

Robben, F. (1971). *Appl. Opt.* **10**, 776.

Robinson, W. Williams, J., and Lewis, T. (1971). *Appl. Opt.* **10**, 2560.

Rodman, J. P., and Smith, H. J. (1963). *Appl. Opt.* **2**, 181.

Rolfe, J., and Moore, S. E. (1970). *Appl. Opt.* **9**, 63.

Sandercock, J. R. (1970). *Opt. Commun.* **2**, 73.

Sandercock, J. R. (1971). *In* "Light Scattering in Solids" (M. Balkanski, ed.). Flammarion Sciences, Paris.

Scarl, D. B. (1968). *Phys. Rev.* **175**, 1661.

Schurr, J. M., and Schmitz, K. S. (1973). *Biopolymers* **12**, 1021.

Shaya, S. A., Han, C. C.-C., and Yu, H. (1974). *Rev. Sci. Instrum.* **45**, 280.

Simic-Glavaski, B., and Jackson, D. A. (1970). *J. Phys. E* **3**, 660.

Smeethe, M. J., and James, J. F. (1971). *J. Phys. E* **4**, 429.

Tao, T. (1969). *Biopolymers* **8**, 669.

Tolansky, S., and Bradley, D. J. (1960). *In* "Symposium on Interferometry," N.P.L. Symposium No. 11, pp. 375–86. H. M. Stationary Office, London.

Tuma, W., and Van der Hoeven, C. J. (1973). *J. Phys. E* **6**, 169.

Uzgiris, E. E. (1972). *Rev. Sci. Instrum.* **43**, 1383.

Vaughan, A. H. (1967). *Annu. Rev. Astron. Astrophys.* **5**, 139.

Wada, A., Suda, N., Tsuda, T., and Soda, K. (1969). *J. Chem. Phys.* **50**, 31.

Wada, A., Soda, K., Tanaka, T., and Suda, N. (1970). *Rev. Sci. Instrum.* **41**, 845.

Wada, A., Tsuda, T., and Suda, N. (1972). *Jap. J. Appl. Phys.* **11**, 266.

Yeh, Y. (1969). *Appl. Opt.* **8**, 1254.

Young, A. T., (1966). *Rev. Sci. Instrum.* **37**, 1472.

Young, A. T. (1969). *Appl. Opt.* **8**, 2431.

Young, A. T. (1971). *Appl. Opt.* **10**, 1681.

Young, A. T., and Schild, R. E. (1971). *Appl. Opt.* **10**, 1668.

Zatzick, M. R. (1971). Application Note F1021. SSR Instruments Co., Santa Monica, California.

Chapter VIII

|| MACROMOLECULES

Principal applications in laser light scattering include dynamics of macro-molecules in solution, phase transitions, reaction kinetics, and velocity of fluid flow, which we shall examine here and in subsequent chapters. In phase-transition studies, dramatic changes in thermodynamic and transport properties of a system produce drastic changes in linewidths. The collapse of linewidths because of the critical slowing down of the local fluctuations has been extensively studied. Laser anemometry, which is being developed rapidly, is an accomplished fact. The potential of laser light scattering lies with the dynamics of macromolecules and chemical reaction kinetics. There the applications are in their infancy, partly because the scientists who developed this technique are not biologists or polymer chemists and most biologists do not yet fully understand this form of spectroscopy, and partly because digital photon correlators have only been made available recently. Now, there are already two very good digital photon correlation spectrometers on the market; one made by Precision Devices and Systems (U.K.) Ltd., Marvern, England; the other by A. T. N. Electronique, Orsay, France. Both have 24 channels (expandable) with delay times down to 50 and 10 nsec, respectively. However, they did cost U.S. $15,000–25,000 in 1974. On the other hand, more such instrumentation and hope-fully less expensive ones, will undoubtedly be made available as the field matures, e.g., Signal Analysis Industries Corporation, Hauppauge, New York, has modified its signal correlator to accept digital photon correla-tion with delay times down to the microsecond region.

For careful work in laser light scattering, the sample must be free of dust because dust particles can act as local oscillators as well as have their own line-broadening contributions. Furthermore, linewidths from different effects superimpose on one another, all centered at zero frequency owing to the difference technique used. Although the ambiguity in resolving the line-widths can sometimes be removed by varying other physical parameters such as temperature, pH, scattering angle, concentration, applied electric field, etc., we should also remember to combine the information obtained by this technique with other traditional approaches in order to answer more complex questions. The possibility of detecting slow molecular reorientation in polymers (Jackson *et al.*, 1973) and plastic crystals (Boyer *et al.*, 1971; Jackson *et al.*, 1971) has also been proposed. In this chapter, we shall limit our discussion to macromolecules in solution.

8.1. Basic Particle Scattering Theory

Application of laser light scattering, which deals mainly with the low-frequency line broadening of the central Rayleigh component of the scattered light, to the study of dynamical properties of macromolecules has been extensively reviewed (Chu, 1968, 1970; Yeh and Keeler, 1969; Benedek, 1969; French *et al.*, 1969; Pecora, 1970a, b, 1971, 1972; Cummins and Swinney, 1970; Pike, 1970; Fujime, 1972; Ford, Jr., 1972; Ford Jr., *et al.*, 1973). Aside from the short reviews, the rapid development of quasielastic laser scattering for applications to macromolecular systems can best be perceived by comparing the earlier discussions of this topic (Benedek, 1969; Cummins and Swinney, 1970; and Chu, 1970) with the later ones (Pecora, 1972; Ford, Jr., 1972; and Ford, Jr. *et al.*, 1973). The reader should pay particular attention to the excellent reviews by Pecora (1972) who has emphasized the theory of light-scattering spectroscopy from a molecular (rather than hydrodynamic) viewpoint, and by Ford (1972) who has summarized biochemical applications of laser Rayleigh scattering.

The hydrodynamic approach is suitable for pure fluids (Mountain, 1966a, 1966b, 1968, 1970) and binary fluids (Miller, 1967; Miller and Lee, 1968; Mountain and Deutch, 1969; Fishman and Mountain, 1970). However, these theories are generally not applicable to macromolecular solutions. In Chapters III and IV we approached the problem from a simple hydrodynamic viewpoint in order to provide a reasonable explanation for the existence of line broadening in the central Rayleigh component and of the Brillouin doublets in a simple fluid. For dilute macromolecular solutions, the molecular viewpoint is simpler and takes into account the depolarized as well as the polarized spectrum even though the depolarized spectrum of pure fluids has been treated using "generalized" hydrodynamics (Keyes and Kivelson, 1971; Ben Reuven and Gershon, 1971; Andersen and Pecora,

1971; Ailawadi *et al.*, 1971; Volterra, 1969; Chung and Yip, 1971). Komarov and Fisher (1963), Pecora (1964), and Pecora and Steel (1965) extended the Van Hove (1954) two-particle space–time correlation function to light scattering. The basic theory has been summarized as follows (Pecora, 1972). The power spectral density for an incident plane electromagnetic wave of polarization $\hat{n}_I$, wave vector k_I, and angular frequency ω_I, has the form

$$S(K, \omega) = \text{const} \int \exp[i(\omega_s - \omega_I)\tau]$$

$$\times \langle [\hat{n}_I \cdot \alpha(K, \tau) \cdot \hat{n}_s][\hat{n}_I \cdot \alpha(-K, 0) \cdot \hat{n}_s] \rangle \, d\tau \quad (8.1.1)$$

where the angular brackets denote an equilibrium ensemble average, and $\hat{n}_s$, k_s, and ω_s are the corresponding quantities for the scattered wave. $\alpha(K, t)$ is the spatial Fourier component of the local fluid polarization tensor $\alpha(r, t)$:

$$\alpha(K, t) \equiv \int \alpha(r, t) \exp(-iK \cdot r) \, dr \quad (8.1.2)$$

with $K = k_s - k_I$ and $K = (4\pi/\lambda) \sin(\tfrac{1}{2}\theta)$. Equation (8.1.1) is applicable to pure fluids, fluid mixtures, and macromolecular solutions. Pecora (1972) has confined his discussions mainly to *dilute* polymer solutions where the solvent is assumed to be invisible. Then, the scattering comes from identical polymer segments each with a given segment-fixed polarizability tensor. Infinite dilution also implies that there are no space–time correlations between segments of *different* molecules. For a single polymer molecule of polarizability density $\alpha(r, t)$, we have

$$\alpha(r, t) = \sum_{i=1}^{n_s} \alpha_i(\Omega(t)) \, \delta[r - r_i(t)] \quad (8.1.3a)$$

and

$$\alpha(K, t) = \sum_{i=1}^{n_s} \alpha_i(\Omega(t)) \, \exp[+iK \cdot r_i(t)] \quad (8.1.3b)$$

where n_s is the number of segments per molecule. $r_i(t)$ and $\Omega(t)$ are, respectively, the position and orientation of segment i in a laboratory-fixed coordinate system at time t. By neglecting fluctuations in segment-fixed polarizabilities due to solvent–segment intersegmental interactions, we take α_i to be independent of the whole set of r_j. Substitution of Eq.

(8.1.3) into Eq. (8.1.2) yields

$$S(K, \omega) \propto \sum_{i,j}^{n_s} \int \exp[+i(\omega_s - \omega_I)\tau] \langle [\hat{\mathbf{n}}_I \cdot \boldsymbol{\alpha}_i(\Omega(\tau)) \cdot \hat{\mathbf{n}}_s]$$

$$\times [\hat{\mathbf{n}}_I \cdot \boldsymbol{\alpha}_j(\Omega(0)) \cdot \hat{\mathbf{n}}_s] \exp\{i\mathbf{K} \cdot [\mathbf{r}_i(\tau) - \mathbf{r}_j(0)]\}\rangle \, d\tau \quad (8.1.4)$$

where i and j are segments on the same molecule. Equation (8.1.4) has been applied to specific macromolecular problems ranging from optically iso-tropic molecules, large optically isotropic molecules—such as flexible coils (Pecora, 1965, 1968a), rigid rods (Pecora, 1968b), and once-broken rods—optically anisotropic molecules (Pecora, 1968c, Tagami, 1971) to poly-disperse rods and Gaussian coils (Tagami and Pecora, 1969; Pecora and Tagami, 1969). Silbey and Deutch (1972) briefly considered quasielastic light scattering from large macromolecules. In particular, experimental results of quasielastic light scattering from solutions of DNA (Schmidt, 1973; Schmitz and Schurr, 1973) and of polyacrylamide (Jamieson and Presley, 1973) do not conform with simple coupling of internal molecular relaxation terms and the center-of-mass translational diffusion term. In these systems, two modes of translational diffusion have been proposed, and Schmitz (1974) has developed a general (although not yet useful) form for the photocurrent autocorrelation function. Thus the discussions presented in this chapter merely try to point out a way to obtain dynamic information from spectra. The detailed interpretation for specific systems, especially large polydisperse marcomolecular solutions, should always be treated with care.

8.2. Translational Diffusion Coefficient

8.2.1. Optically Isotropic Molecules

Fc optically isotropic molecules, the molecular polarizability α is a scalar. Equation (8.1.4) is reduced to

$$S_{\text{isotropic}}(K, \omega) = \frac{1}{2\pi} \int_{-\infty}^{\infty} e^{+i\omega\tau} R_I(K, \tau) \, d\tau \quad (8.2.1)$$

where $\omega = \omega_s - \omega_I$ and

$$R_I(K, \tau) = (\hat{\mathbf{n}}_I \cdot \hat{\mathbf{n}}_s)^2 A \rho \alpha^2 \frac{1}{n_s^2} \sum_{i,j}^{n_s} \langle \exp\{i\mathbf{K} \cdot [\mathbf{r}_i(\tau) - \mathbf{r}_j(0)]\}\rangle \quad (8.2.2)$$

where A and ρ are a constant and density of the macromolecules in solution, respectively. Equation (8.2.1) accounts for most of the scattering from solutions of macromolecules which are usually only weakly anisotropic. If we take $\mathbf{r}_i = \mathbf{R} + \mathbf{b}_i$ where $\mathbf{R}$ is the vector locating the center of mass and $\mathbf{b}_i$ is the vector from the center of mass to segment i, then

$$R_{\perp}(K, \tau) \propto \frac{1}{n_s^2} \langle \exp\{i\mathbf{K}\cdot[\mathbf{R}(\tau) - \mathbf{R}(0)]\}$$

$$\times \sum_{i,j}^{n_s} \exp\{i\mathbf{K}\cdot[\mathbf{b}_i(\tau) - \mathbf{b}_j(0)]\}\rangle \quad (8.2.3)$$

When the molecule is small, $\mathbf{b}_i(t) - \mathbf{b}_j(0)$ must be small. Similarly, at small angles, $K\ [\equiv (4\pi/\lambda) \sin(\tfrac{1}{2}\theta)]$ is small. Then,

$$\sum_{i,j}^{n_s} \exp\{i\mathbf{K}\cdot[\mathbf{b}_i(t) - b_j(0)]\} \approx n_s^2 \quad (8.2.4)$$

provided that $|\ \mathbf{K}\cdot[\mathbf{b}_i(t) - \mathbf{b}_j(0)]\ | \ll 1$. By substituting Eq. (8.2.4) into Eq. (8.2.3), we have

$$R_{\mathrm{I}}(K, \tau) \propto \langle \exp\{i\mathbf{K}\cdot[\mathbf{R}(\tau) - \mathbf{R}(0)]\}\rangle \quad (8.2.5)$$

which is determined only by the translational motion due to the center of mass of the molecule. Pecora (1964) obtained the signal spectrum for a heterodyne experiment:

$$S_{\mathrm{isotropic}}(K, \omega) = (\hat{\mathbf{n}}_{\mathrm{I}}\cdot\hat{\mathbf{n}}_s)^2 (A\rho/\pi)\alpha^2 DK^2/[\omega^2 + (DK^2)^2] \quad (8.2.6)$$

where ρ is the number density of the macromolecules in solution, A is a constant, and D is the translational macromolecular (self-diffusion) coefficient. Equation (8.2.6) represents a Lorentzian curve whose half-width at half-maximum is

$$\Gamma = \Delta\omega_{1/2} = 1/\tau = DK^2 \quad (8.2.7)$$

Both the shot noise and the dc terms have been neglected. For more concentrated solutions, Debye (1965) recognized that in the absence of temperature and pressure gradients, concentration fluctuations δC decay away in accordance with Fick's second law of diffusion:

$$\partial\ \delta C(\mathbf{r}, t)/\partial t = D\nabla^2 \delta C(\mathbf{r}, t) \quad (8.2.8)$$

where D is the mass diffusion coefficient (or the macromolecular relative-diffusion coefficient for polymer solutions). According to Eq. (8.2.8), a concentration fluctuation of wave vector $\mathbf{K}$ dies away with time t as

$$\delta C(\mathbf{K}, t) = \delta C(\mathbf{K}, 0)e^{-\Gamma t} \quad (8.2.9)$$

with $\Gamma = DK^2$. In fact, the spectrum of the light scattered quasielastically by a binary system is composed of several Lorentzian curves since the local fluctuations in the dielectric constant κ_e of a macromolecular solution depend upon the local fluctuations in solute concentration C, solution density ρ, and temperature T. We shall now change the notation for the dielectric constant from κ_e to the more familiar symbol ϵ and express

$$\delta\epsilon(\mathbf{r}, t) = (\partial\epsilon/\partial C)_{\rho,T}\,\delta C(\mathbf{r}, t) + (\partial\epsilon/\partial\rho)_{C,T}\,\delta\rho(\mathbf{r}, t)$$

$$+ (\partial\epsilon/\partial T)_{C,\rho}\,\delta T(\mathbf{r}, t) \quad (8.2.10)$$

In macromolecular solutions, concentration fluctuations usually dominate Eq. (8.2.10). Thus,

$$\delta\epsilon(\mathbf{r}, t) \approx (\partial\epsilon/\partial C)_{\rho,T}\,\delta C(\mathbf{r}, t) \quad (8.2.11)$$

whose spatial Fourier transform is

$$\delta\epsilon(\mathbf{K}, t) = (\partial\epsilon/\partial C)_{\rho,T}\,\delta C(\mathbf{K}, t) \quad (8.2.12)$$

The corresponding signal power spectral density has the form

$$S_{\text{isotropic}} \equiv S_\text{I} \propto (\partial\epsilon/\partial C)^2_{\rho,T}\langle(\delta C)^2\rangle DK^2/[\omega^2 + (DK^2)^2] \quad (8.2.13)$$

The difference between Eqs. (8.2.6) and (8.2.13) can be eliminated by reinterpreting $\rho\alpha^2$ as being proportional to $(\partial\epsilon/\partial C)^2\langle(\delta C)^2\rangle$. In relating the fluctuations in the local dielectric constant to fluctuations in the local thermodynamic quantities, the choice of C, ρ, and T is not unique. We may also choose, say, pressure p, solute concentration C, and temperature T. Then

$$\delta\epsilon(\mathbf{r}, t) = (\partial\epsilon/\partial p)_{C,T}\,\delta p(\mathbf{r}, t) + (\partial\epsilon/\partial T)_{C,p}\,\delta T(\mathbf{r}, t)$$

$$+ (\partial\epsilon/\partial C)_{p,T}\,\delta C(\mathbf{r}, t) \quad (8.2.14)$$

Mountain and Deutch (1969) have shown that in the limit of zero thermal diffusion ratio (Landau and Lifshitz, 1959), heat conduction and diffusion are uncoupled. Then the central Rayleigh line consists of the superposition of two Lorentzians with widths that are directly proportional to the thermal diffusivity χ due to entropy fluctuations at constant pressure and the diffusion coefficient D due to concentration fluctuations:

$$S_\text{I}(K, \omega) \propto \left(\frac{\partial\epsilon}{\partial C}\right)^2 \langle(\delta C)^2\rangle_{T,p} \frac{DK^2}{(DK^2)^2 + \omega^2}$$

$$+ \left(\frac{\partial\epsilon}{\partial T}\right)^2_{C,p} \left(\frac{k_\text{B}T^2}{C_p}\right) \frac{\chi K^2}{(\chi K^2)^2 + \omega^2} \quad (8.2.15)$$

DuBois and Berge (1971) have first resolved the two components of the central peak and obtained an experimental determination of D and χ in a binary solution. Further improvements have been reported by Jamieson and Walton (1973). Oliver *et al.* (1972) have used photon-correlation spectroscopy to measure the thermal diffusivity of carbon tetrachloride.

If the heterodyne spectrum is a sum of Lorentzians, the power spectral density in the absence of shot noise and dc terms becomes

$$S(K, \omega) = \frac{1}{\pi} \sum_i R_i \frac{\Gamma_i}{\omega^2 + \Gamma_i^2} \qquad (8.2.16)$$

and the corresponding time correlation function is

$$R(K, \tau) = \sum_i R_i \exp(-\Gamma_i \tau) \qquad (8.2.17)$$

where $1/\Gamma_i \ [\equiv (\tau_i)]$ is the decay time of i, and R_i, which denotes the scattering power of i, depends upon the number of i and its particle scattering factor. On the other hand, the self-beating technique gives

$$R(K, \tau) = \sum_{i,j} R_i R_j \exp[-(\Gamma_i + \Gamma_j)\tau] \qquad (8.2.18)$$

and

$$S(K, \omega) = \frac{1}{\pi} \sum_{i,j} R_i R_j \frac{\Gamma_i + \Gamma_j}{\omega^2 + (\Gamma_i + \Gamma_j)^2} \qquad (8.2.19)$$

which can become very complex if the spectrum has several decay times.

Many determinations of translational diffusion coefficients of macromolecules in solution by quasielastic light scattering have been reported. Table 8.2.1 lists D for a few typical biological macromolecular systems. Equation (8.2.13) has been verified by many authors using polystyrene latex spheres (Cummins *et al.*, 1964; Arecchi *et al.*, 1967; Dubin *et al.*, 1967; Chu and Schoenes, 1968). Translational diffusion coefficients for coliphages and coliphage DNA (Dubin *et al.*, 1970), viruses MS-2 (French *et al.*, 1969) and R-17 (Pusey *et al.*, 1972), poly-γ-benzyl-L-glutamate (Ford *et al.*, 1969), polystyrene in 2-butanone (Ford, *et al.*, 1970), poly[d(AT)] (Yeh, 1970), RNase (Rimai *et al.*, 1970), bovine milk casein micelles (Lin *et al.*, 1971), myosin (Carlson and Herbert, 1972), *E. coli* ribosomes (Hocker *et al.*, 1973), colloidal silica suspensions-Ludox (Sellen, 1970), and colloidal gold (Chu and Schones, 1968) have been determined. There is no doubt that more such studies will follow.

Foord *et al.* (1970) used only 15 μliters of solution to measure the translational diffusion coefficient of haemocyanin. Their cell was a piece of capillary tubing of 1 mm internal radius and 5 mm length. Using digital photon correlation and a Spectra Physics model 125 He–Ne laser (est. output

Table 8.2.1

Translational Diffusion Coefficients of Typical Biomacromolecules by Light Scattering

Sample	Concentration (mg/cm³)	T (°C)	pH	Salt content	D_T (10⁻⁷ cm²/sec)	Reference
Bovine serum albumin (BSA)[a]	30	room	6.91	—	10.2 ± 0.2	Dubin et al., 1967
	30	room	6.80	0.5M KCl	6.7 ± 0.1	Dubin et al., 1967
Ovalbumin	50	room	6.80	0.5M KCl	7.1 ± 0.2	Dubin et al., 1967
Lysozyme	60	room	5.60	—	11.5 ± 0.3	Dubin et al., 1967
Tobacco mosaic virus (TMV)	0.1	room	7.20	0.01M sodium phosphate buffer	0.40 ± 0.02	Dubin et al., 1967
DNA (calf thymus)[b]	0.5	room	7.00	0.15M NACl +0.015M trisodium citrate	0.2 ± 0.1	Dubin et al., 1967
TMV	0.1	20	7.5	0.001M sodium phosphate buffer	0.280 ± 0.006	Cummins et al., 1969
TMV	3	20	6.0	0.025M acetate buffer	0.29 ± 0.01	Fujime, 1970b
	0.12	20	6.0	0.025M acetate buffer	0.35	Fujime, 1970b
	0.1	20	6.0	0.025M acetate buffer	(0.37)	Fujime, 1970b
	(0)	20	6.0	0.025M acetate buffer	0.45	Fujime, 1970b

		Temp (°C)	pH			
BSA[a]	0.5–20.0	20	6.0	0.1M NaCl +0.01M phosphate buffer	5.76 ± 0.05	Foord et al., 1970
Lysozyme	3–20	20	6.0	0.1M NaCl +0.01M phosphate buffer	10.6 ± 0.2	Foord et al., 1970
M. trunculus haemocyanin (M.W. = 9.2 × 10^6)	0.08–5 12	20 20	5.7 5.7	0.1M NaCl +0.1M acetate buffer	1.03 ± 0.01 1.08 ± 0.01	Foord et al., 1970 Foord et al., 1970
TMV[c]	0.2 0.4 0.4–1.63	25 25 25	7.5 7.5 7.5	$10^{-3}M$ EDTA[d] buffer $10^{-3}M$ EDTA buffer $10^{-3}M$ sodium phosphate buffer	0.39 ± 0.01 0.365	Schaefer et al., 1971 Schaefer et al., 1971 Wada et al., 1972
E. coli ribosome 50s subunit Monomer Dimer	0.12–0.36	25 25 25		0.01M MgCl$_2$ + 0.01M Tris + KCl	2.1 ± 0.1 1.75 ± 0.1 1.35 ± 0.1	Hocker et al., 1973 Hocker et al., 1973 Hocker et al., 1973

[a] The effect of charge on the light-scattering spectrum has been discussed by Stephen (1971) and Schaefer and Berne (1974).
[b] Nonsingle exponential behavior in the time-correlation function has also been observed by Schmidt (1973) and Schmitz and Schurr (1973).
[c] The interpretation includes the effect on the spectrum of both rotational and anisotropic translational diffusion of rodlike molecules of length L.
[d] Ethylene-diaminetetraacetic acid

power $\sim$60 mW at 632.8 nm), they were able to determine D to ± 1 % in 3 min at a concentration of 0.08 mg/mliter. The statistical accuracy is roughly proportional to the square root of the total time of the experiment and the inverse of the concentration.

Maeda and Fujime (1972) have succeeded in studying quasielastic light scattering under an optical microscope. They were able to observe sample areas as small as $100 \times 100 \ \mu m^2$. The lower limit would be determined by the sensitivity of the electronic detection system including the photomultiplier tube which, in their case, was not the best available. Figure 8.2.1 shows a

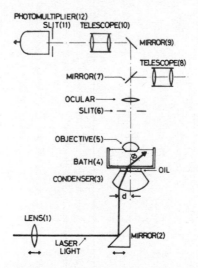

Fig. 8.2.1. Schematic diagram of an optical system for quasielastic light scattering under an optical microscope (Maeda and Fujime, 1972).

schematic diagram of their optical system. The laser beam, which is parallel to the optical axis of the condenser lens (3), is displaced from the center of the condenser so that the angle of the incident light into the sample in the bath (4), θ, is $n_2 \sin \theta = n_1 \sin[\tan^{-1}(f/d)]$ where n_2 and n_1 are the refractive indices of solution and glass, respectively. d is the distance between the incident beam and the optical axis before the condenser lens (3), and f is the focal length of the condenser lens (3). The scattering angle θ can be varied from 0° to about 80°, by changing the distance d. A slit (6) located on the image plane of the water-immersion-type objective lens (5) works as a field selecting diaphragm. The diffusion pattern of the sample is projected by another telescope (10) onto a slit (11) in front of a photomultiplier tube. Slit (11) can be utilized as an aperture stop. Instrumentation in laser light scattering will continue to improve. The important point in inserting the works of Foord *et al.* (1970) and of Maeda and Fujime (1972) here is that we have demonstrated experimentally that only very small samples and even living cells can be studied by means of laser light scattering.

In biological macromolecular solutions, we are usually dealing with weak scattering systems. It is therefore advantageous to have a knowledge of the Rayleigh ratio [Eq. (3.3.0)] of the system. We shall now proceed to calculate the Rayleigh ratio due to concentration fluctuations. In other words, we shall try to estimate the order of magnitude of the coefficients and the proportionality constant in Eq. (8.2.13).

Following the considerations similar to the derivation of entropy and pressure fluctuations [Eq. (3.3.59)], we can obtain the contribution in the integrated scattered intensity due to concentration fluctuations by evaluating $\langle |\, \delta C(\mathbf{K}, t)\, |^2 \rangle$ in the computation of the mean-square electric field $\langle |\, E(\mathbf{K}, t)\, |^2 \rangle$ using Eqs. (3.3.8) and (8.2.12) and the relation that the dielectric constant is equal to the square of the refractive index of the medium n (Dubin, 1970):

$$\frac{I_s}{I_I} = \left(\frac{k}{n}\right)^4 \frac{\sin^2\vartheta}{(4\pi R)^2} \left(2n\,\frac{\partial n}{\partial C}\right)^2 \frac{CMv}{N_A} \qquad (8.2.20)$$

where I_s and I_I are the scattered and the incident intensities, respectively. $k = 2\pi/\lambda$ with λ being the wavelength of light in the medium. ϑ is the angle between the direction of polarization of the incident plane-polarized light and the direction of the scattered beam. $C\ (\equiv NM/N_A v)$ is the average solute concentration expressed in grams per cubic centimeter in the scattering volume v. M, N, and N_A are the molecular weight of the solute, the number of solute molecules in the scattering volume, and Avogadro's number, respectively. R is the large distance from an arbitrary center in the scattering volume to the detector. Equation (8.2.20) is the basic formula used in the determination of molecular weight of macromolecular solute molecules. By substituting the definition of C into Eq. (8.2.20), we find

$$I_s \propto NM^2/v \qquad (8.2.21)$$

which implies that the excess scattered intensity (due to concentration fluctuations) is proportional to the concentration and the square of the solute molecular weight. The Rayleigh ratio [Eq. (3.3.65)] has the form

$$\mathcal{R}^* = \frac{I_s R^2}{I_I 2v \sin^2\vartheta} = \left(\frac{k}{n}\right)^4 \frac{[\sqrt{2}n\,(\partial n/\partial C)]^2}{(4\pi)^2} \frac{CM}{N_A} \qquad (8.2.22)$$

or

$$\mathcal{R}^* = HCM \qquad (8.2.23)$$

where $H \{ \equiv (k/n)^4 [\sqrt{2}n(\partial n/\partial C)]^2 [N_A (4\pi)^2]^{-1} \}$ has the units of $(\text{cm/gm})^2$. $\Re^*$ has the units of cm^{-1} and can be considered as an attenuation coefficient. For biological macromolecules, the aqueous solution at $\lambda_{air} = 632.8$ nm has $n \simeq 1.33$, and $\partial n/\partial C \simeq 0.19$. Thus, $H \simeq 1.3 \times 10^{-7}$ $(\text{cm/gm})^2$ which is remarkably constant and permits us to estimate the relationship between the scattering power and molecular weight of the sample by means of Eq. (8.2.23). In deriving Eq. (8.2.23) by means of the fluctuation theory, we have neglected the finite size of the macromolecule and interactions between the solutes. The classical light-scattering technique can provide us information on the molecular weight, size, shape, and thermodynamic interactions between solutes and solvent by measuring the absolute scattered intensity as well as the angular distribution as a function of concentration. In this respect, Eq. (8.2.23) represents the limiting behavior for the integrated scattered intensity at infinite dilution and zero scattering angle. Reviews of this technique are readily available (Geiduschek and Holtzer, 1958; Chu, 1967; Timasheff and Townend, 1970).

8.2.2. Molecular Weight Determination

Diffusion coefficients and molecular weight of the macromolecular solute can be related in three ways: (a) by utilizing the Stokes–Einstein relation and its equivalents, (b) by combining with sedimentation velocity data, and (c) by consideration of homologous polymer solutions.

8.2.2.A. Stokes–Einstein relation and its equivalents

According to the Einstein relation, the diffusion coefficient is inversely proportional to the translational frictional coefficient f_t at infinite dilution by the expression:

$$D^0 = k_B T/f_t \qquad (8.2.24)$$

The frictional coefficient can in turn be expressed according to the hydrodynamic shape of the molecule using Stokes law for a sphere of radius a and solvent viscosity η:

$$f_t = 6\pi\eta a \qquad (8.2.25)$$

or for the ellipsoids of revolution (Tanford, 1961) of semiaxes a, b, b:

$$f_t = \frac{6\pi\eta a(1 - b^2/a^2)^{1/2}}{\ln\left[\dfrac{1 + (1 - b^2/a^2)^{1/2}}{b/a}\right]} \qquad \text{(prolate ellipsoid)} \qquad (8.2.26)$$

and of semiaxes a, a, b:

$$f_t = \frac{6\pi\eta b(a^2/b^2 - 1)^{1/2}}{\tan^{-1}(a^2/b^2 - 1)^{1/2}} \qquad \text{(oblate ellipsoid)} \qquad (8.2.27)$$

where a is the semimajor axis of the ellipsoid and b, the semiminor axis. f_t is an angle-averaged translational frictional coefficient. If we take R_0 as the radius of a sphere of volume equal to that of the ellipsoid, i.e., $\frac{4}{3}\pi R_0^3 = \frac{4}{3}\pi ab^2$ (prolate ellipsoid) or $\frac{4}{3}\pi a^2 b$ (oblate ellipsoid), then the volume of the solute molecule, which is assumed to have the geometrical shape of either a sphere or an ellipsoid of revolution, has the form

$$\frac{4}{3}\pi a^3 = \bar{v}M/N_A \qquad \text{(sphere)} \qquad (8.2.28)$$

or

$$\frac{4}{3}\pi R_0^3 = \bar{v}M/N_A \qquad \text{(ellipsoids of revolution)} \qquad (8.2.29)$$

where $\bar{v}$ is the partial specific volume of the solute molecule, and M its molecular weight. Equations (8.2.28) and (8.2.29) are valid only for the unsolvated solute molecules. In the absence of hydration, the molecular weight can be computed from known $\bar{v}$, D, and η for spherical particles. If the molecular weight is known, a comparison of the measured D with those computed using Eqs. (8.2.24), (8.2.25), (8.2.28), and (8.2.29) permits us to distinguish the hydrodynamic shape between a sphere and ellipsoids of revolution provided that the particle is unsolvated. However, the correct choice for a prolate or an oblate ellipsoid requires additional information. Alternatively, if the molecular volume is known from other studies, we can use the above approach to determine the degree of solvation. In fact, it is more likely to have a certain amount of solvent molecules adhere to the diffusing solute macromolecule so that in computing the equivalent hydrodynamic shape, Eqs. (8.2.28) and (8.2.29) give the "dry" dimension while Eqs. (8.2.24) and (8.2.25) give the "hydrated" dimension. For example, Pusey *et al.* (1972) computed the hydrated radius R_h for virus R-17 by means of Eqs. (8.2.24) and (8.2.25):

$$R_h = \frac{293k_B}{6\pi\eta_{20,w}D_{20,w}{}^0} = 139 \pm 1.4 \text{ Å}$$

where the diffusion coefficient $D_{T,S}$, determined at arbitrary temperature $T°K$, in solvent S, was corrected to standard conditions of 20°C and water as solvent by the equation

$$D_{20,w} = D_{T,S} \frac{\eta_{T,S}}{\eta_{20,w}} \frac{293.16}{T} \qquad (8.2.30)$$

and $D_{20,w}{}^0$ is the diffusion coefficient under standard conditions extrapolated to zero virus concentration, and is equal to $(1.54 \pm 0.015) \times 10^{-7}$ cm²/sec for virus R-17. A comparison of the solvated volume $\frac{4}{3}\pi R_h{}^3$ with the dry volume $M\bar{v}/N_A$ yields the degree of solvation. In their case, $\bar{v} = 0.673 \pm 0.007$ cm³/g (Zipper *et al.*, 1971) and $M = (3.81 \pm 0.14) \times 10^6$. The degree of solvation found is 1.11 ± 0.13 cm³ solvent/g virus. A note of caution is needed here as a change in diffusion coefficient could be due to a change in the degree of solvation or a change in the conformation of the solute, or both. Furthermore, the effects of ions (Schaefer and Berne, 1974) and polydispersity (see Section 8.6) will also complicate the interpretation. Approach (a) is limited to rigid molecules of spherical and ellipsoidal shapes. A more general approach is to combine D with the sedimentation coefficient S in order to compute M and then use approach (a) for determining the degree of solvation if the macromolecules are rigid spheres or ellipsoids.

8.2.2.B. Sedimentation–diffusion method

The centrifugal acceleration $(\omega^2 r)$ on a solute molecule of mass $(M/N_A)(1 + \delta_1)$ is $(M/N_A)\omega^2 r(1 + \delta_1)$ where ω is the angular velocity of the rotor and r the distance from the center of rotation. The parameter δ_1 signifies the number of grams of solvent associated with 1 gm of the unsolvated macromolecular solute. The countering buoyant force exerted by the solvent is $v_h\rho_1\omega^2 r$ where ρ_1 is the solvent density and

$$v_h \left[\equiv (M/N_A)(\bar{v} + \delta_1 v_1{}^0) \right]$$

is the total volume of a solvated hydrodynamic particle. Thus, the net force per particle is

$$F = \omega^2 r(M/N_A)(1 - \bar{v}\rho_1) \tag{8.2.31}$$

where $v_1{}^0 = \rho_1{}^{-1}$ by definition and $\bar{v}$ is the partial specific volume of the solute. Equation (8.2.31) is valid for two-component systems at infinite dilution. At finite concentrations, we replace ρ_1 by ρ and get

$$F = \omega^2 r(M/N_A)(1 - \bar{v}\rho) \tag{8.2.32}$$

The sedimentation coefficient S defined as

$$S = u/\omega^2 r = (M/N_A f_t)(1 - \bar{v}\rho) \tag{8.2.33}$$

is a quantity determined by experiment and depends only on molecular parameters where u $(\equiv F/f_t)$ is the flow velocity. By combining Eq. (8.2.24) with (8.2.33) we get

$$M = S^0 RT/D^0(1 - \bar{v}\rho_1) \tag{8.2.34}$$

where R is the gas constant. The superscript zero represents values extrapolated to zero concentration, and ρ_1 is the density of the solvent. Alternatively, at finite concentrations, Eq. (8.2.24) may be replaced by (Tanford, 1961; Ford *et al.*, 1973):

$$D = \frac{C}{N_A f_t}\left(\frac{\partial \mu_2}{\partial C}\right)_{p,T}(1 - \bar{v}C) \qquad (8.2.35)$$

where C, $\bar{v}$, and μ_2 are the concentration, partial specific volume, and chemical potential of the solute, respectively. For an ideal solution, $(\partial \mu_2/\partial C)_{p,T} = RT/C$. The factor $(1 - \bar{v}C)$ corrects for the fact that the solute and the solvent have fluxes in opposite directions.

Equation (8.2.35) is a general expression for the translational diffusion coefficient measured by means of quasielastic laser scattering in the volume fixed frame at finite concentrations, while D^0 in Eq. (8.2.24) can be valid at finite concentrations only in the solvent-fixed frame. Usually, e.g., with polystyrene latex spheres (Lee *et al.*, 1972) $\bar{v}C \ll 10^{-3}$. Thus, the reference frame correction is often insignificant. Recently, Phillies (report prior to publication) predicted that the mutual diffusion coefficient has an intrinsic dependence on the momentum transfer vector $\mathbf{K}$ for spatially sinusoidal concentration gradients. However, the K-dependent correction becomes important only when the interaction potential U is long range and $\partial U/\partial r \neq 0$ for a distance comparable to K^{-1}. For example, the K dependence might be present in isoionic and minimum-salt protein solutions.

The $(\partial \mu/\partial C)_{p,T}$ term can be expressed in terms of the activity coefficient y referred to the concentration in moles per liter:

$$D = (RT/N_A f_t)(1 - \bar{v}C)[1 + C(\partial \ln y/\partial C)_{p,T}] \qquad (8.2.36)$$

or in terms of a virial expansion

$$D = (RT/N_A f_t)(1 - \bar{v}C)(1 + BC + \cdots) \qquad (8.2.37)$$

where B is the second virial coefficient. By combining Eqs. (8.2.36) and (8.2.33) we get

$$\frac{S}{D} = \frac{M(1 - \bar{v}\rho)}{RT[1 + C(\partial \ln y/\partial C)_{T,p}](1 - \bar{v}C)} \qquad (8.2.38)$$

where values of y or the equivalent virial coefficients can be evaluated from the concentration dependence of S/D. Both S and D depend upon the solvent and should therefore be measured in solutions of identical composition and T, p. Pyun and Fixman (1964) have also computed the concentration dependence of f_t.

The determination of molecular weight by combined measurements of diffusion and sedimentation coefficients is particularly valuable for very large molecules. For example, Pusey used Eq. (8.2.34) to obtain

$$M = 293R_{20,w}{}^0/D_{20,w}{}^0(1 - \bar{v}\rho_{20,w}) = (3.81 \pm 0.14) \times 10^6$$

for the R-17 virus molecule where

$$S_{20,w} = S_{T,\text{s}} \frac{1 - \bar{v}\rho_{20,w}}{1 - \bar{v}\rho} \frac{\eta_{T,\text{s}}}{\eta_{20,w}} \tag{8.2.39}$$

and $S_{20,w}{}^0$ is $S_{20,w}$ extrapolated to zero concentration. Table 8.2.2 shows the determination of M by means of Eq. (8.2.34), which covers a wide molecular weight range. Dubin (1970) was even able to deduce a diffusion coefficient for guanidinium chloride: $\bar{D}_{20,w} = 79 \times 10^{-7}$ cm²/sec. Thus, the technique that involves independent measurements of D, S, and $\bar{v}$ should be useful over an extremely wide molecular weight range including intact red blood cells (Bargeron et al., 1972), and is valid for any size or shape molecules. In Table 8.2.2, if we take the weight percent of DNA in coliphages T4, T5, and T7, as determined chemically by Bancroft and Freifelder (1970), the molecular weights of DNA in T4, T5, and T7 could be determined without actually working with the DNA itself.

Table 8.2.2
Molecular Weight Determination by the Diffusion–Sedimentation Method

Sample	M (in daltons)	M_{DNA}	Reference
Lysozyme	$14,500 \pm 300$		Dubin et al., 1971
Virus R-17	$(3.81 \pm 0.14) \times 10^6$		Pusey et al., 1972
Phage λ	$(45.2 \pm 2.0) \times 10^6$		Dubin et al., 1970
Phage T7	$(50.4 \pm 1.8) \times 10^6$	$(25.8 \pm 1.0) \times 10^6$	Dubin et al., 1970
Phage T5	$(109.2 \pm 4.0) \times 10^6$	$(67.3 \pm 3.1) \times 10^6$	Dubin et al., 1970
Phage T4	$(192.5 \pm 6.6) \times 10^6$	$(105.7 \pm 3.8) \times 10^6$	Dubin et al., 1970

8.2.2.C. Homologous polymers

The translational diffusion coefficient should decrease as the molecular size of a homologous polymer increases. Ford et al. (1970) have measured the diffusion coefficients of a homologous series of polystyrene in 2-butanone. The application of linewidth spectroscopy to experimental determination of translational diffusion coefficients of flexible polymer coils in solution has also been reported by others (Frederick *et al.*, 1971; Kramer and Frederick, 1971, 1972). While Kramer and Frederick (1972) paid particular attention on the effects of intramolecular motions in random-coil polymers on the Rayleigh line spectrum of macromolecules in solution, Ford *et al.* found an empirical relationship between the translational diffusion coefficient extrapolated to zero concentration and the molecular weight of the macromolecule

$$D^0 = K_D M^{-b} \tag{8.2.40}$$

where K_D and b are constants whose values depend on the nature of the polymer and solvent and on the temperature, $K_D = (3.1 \pm 0.2) \times 10^{-4}$ cm²/sec and $b = 0.53 \pm 0.02$ for polystyrene in 2-butanone at $T = 298°K$. The exponent b is related to the corresponding exponent a for the intrinsic viscosity $[\eta]$:

$$[\eta] = K_\eta M^a \tag{8.2.41}$$

by the relation $1 + a = 3b$ (Scheraga and Mandelkern, 1953), with a ranging from 0.58 to 0.64, $b = 0.527$ to 0.547, in excellent agreement with the results from linewidth studies. The reader is advised to read Chapter 6 of Tanford (1961) in order to be familiar with the elements of transport processes. Lee (1970) obtained similar relationships for poly-γ-benzyl-L-glutamate (PBLG) in a helical conformation with $D^0 = 1.96 \times 10^{-3} M^{-0.77}$ cm²/sec in 1,2-dichloroethane and in a random-coil conformation with $D^0 = 2.95 \times 10^{-5} M^{-0.585}$ cm²/sec in dichloroacetic acid. Tanford *et al.* (1967) have shown that many protein molecules act as random coils in a denaturing agent such as guanidinium chloride. In a known solvent composition such as $6M$ guanidinium chlorde and $0.1M$ β-mercaptoethanol and at a fixed temperature, Ford (1972) predicted that many proteins should obey the relationship

$$D^0 \approx 7.58 \times 10^{-5} M^{-0.53} \tag{8.2.42}$$

where b [$= 0.53$] represents the exponent value for random coils, and K_D is taken to be about the same for most random-coiled proteins in the above solvent. Thus, one measurement of the diffusion coefficient at very dilute concentrations gives an estimate of the molecular weight of the protein. For example, Dubin (1970) obtained that $D_{20,w} = (7.3 \pm 0.1) \times 10^{-7}$ cm²/sec for a lysozyme denatured in guanidinium chloride. After correction for solvent viscosity, we find $D_{20,6M\ \text{GuHCl}} = 4.56 \times 10^{-7}$ cm²/sec, which compares very well with $D = 4.7 \times 10^{-7}$ cm²/sec computed from Eq. (8.2.42) using $M = 14,500$.

8.2.3. Conformational Changes

In a helix-coil phase transition, quasielastic light scattering can be used to monitor the dramatic changes in the hydrodynamic shape of a molecule from helix to coil or vice versa. Measurements of the translational diffusion coefficients of poly-γ-benzyl-L-glutamate (PBLG) as a function of solvent composition [ranging from pure 1,2-dichloroethane (DCE) to pure dichloroacetic acid (DCA) (Ford et al., 1969)] and of temperature (Lee, 1970) as well as the isothermal helix-to-coil transition of poly-L-lysine HBr (Jamieson et al., 1972) have been reported. The sharp change in the corrected diffusion coefficient D_{cor} ($\equiv D\eta_s/\eta_{DCE}$ with η_s being the viscosity of the mixed solvent, and η_{DCE} that of DCE) at about 76 % dichloroacetic acid and at 25°C is consistent with the corresponding data for the optical rotation (at 589 nm) of PBLG as a function of solvent composition (Doty and Yang, 1957). The translational diffusion coefficient for a 0.5 wt/volume % of PBLG in a 1:4 mixture of DCE and DCA changes from about 1.47 × 10^{-7} cm²/sec at about 25–29°C to about 1.2 × 10^{-7} cm²/sec at about 40°C. However, the helix–coil transition represents large conformational changes. More subtle shape changes associated with protein chemistry require more precise determination of D as a monitor for these changes. As Ford (1972) has pointed out the binding of the allosteric activator potassium succinate to aspartate transcarbamylase decreases the sedimentation coefficients by about 4 % (Gerhart and Schachman, 1968) and the binding of oxygen to hemoglobin increases S by about 4 % (Goers and Schumaker, 1970). Such changes can be detected using quasielastic light scattering. Thus, enzyme conformational changes can be studied using measurements of translational diffusion coefficient as a probe. Other parameters, such as the stiffness of a semiflexible coil in terms of a relaxation time of the internal mode of motion of the macromolecule may also be utilized with success (see Section 8.5). The important point is that several quantities which are related to the dynamic properties of the macromolecule are measurable by means of quasielastic light scattering, and we can use these dynamical quantities to study other changes in a biological process, such as elastin coacervation (Jamieson et al., 1972). Furthermore, quasielastic light scattering requires no external perturbation such as electric, centrifugal, shear forces, etc.; it requires only a spontaneous fluctuation. However, this is not to imply that the use of external forces will not be helpful, as we shall see in Section 8.7 on electrophoretic light scattering.

Koppel (1973) was able to overcome limitations of lack of specificity in laser light scattering by combining it with the technique of band or zonal sedimentation in a sucrose gradient for his ribosome solutions.

8.3. Rotational Diffusion Coefficient

8.3.1. Ellipsoids of Revolution

A very small portion of the scattered light with the same polarization as the incident light arises from anisotropy of the macromolecule which has a nonscalar optical polarizability. Pecora (1964) and Caroli and Parodi (1969) have presented the complete form of the depolarized light-scattering spectrum. In the simplest case, if we take the macromolecule as being rigid and having a geometrical shape corresponding to the ellipsoids of revolution, symmetry requires that two of the three rotational diffusion coefficients be equal and that corresponding polarizabilities be equal. Then, the spectrum of the depolarized scattered light has the form

$$S_R(\omega) \propto (\omega^2 + \Gamma_R^2)^{-1} \qquad (8.3.1)$$

where $\Gamma_R = l(l+1)D_R$ with D_R being the rotational diffusion coefficient for motion of the ellipsoids of revolution about either of its two equal axes $(l = 2)$. The rotational diffusion coefficient is related to the rotational frictional coefficient f_R by the expression

$$D_R = k_B T / f_R \qquad (8.3.2)$$

where k_B and T are the Boltzmann constant and the absolute temperature, respectively. f_R is given by

$$f_R = \tfrac{8}{9} f_t a^2 \left(\frac{1 - (b/a)^4}{2 - b^2/a^2 - (f_t/f_t^0)(b/a)^{2/3}} \right) \qquad (8.3.3)$$

for a prolate ellipsoid of revolution. With $f_t^0 = 6\pi\eta R_0 = 6\pi\eta(ab^2)^{1/3}$ and f_t from Eq. (8.2.26), we get

$$f_R = \frac{16\pi a^3 \eta}{3} \left(\frac{1 - (b/a)^4}{(2 - b^2/a^2)G(b/a) - 1} \right) \qquad (8.3.4)$$

where

$$G\left(\frac{b}{a}\right) = \ln\left(\frac{1 + (1 - b^2/a^2)^{1/2}}{b/a} \right) \Big/ \left(1 - \frac{b^2}{a^2} \right)^{1/2} \qquad (a > b).$$

For an oblate ellipsoid of revolution with semiaxes a, a, b,

$$f_R = \tfrac{8}{9} f_t b^2 \left(\frac{1 - (a/b)^4}{2 - (a/b)^2 - (f_t/f_t^0)(a/b)^{2/3}} \right) \qquad (8.3.5)$$

where $f_t^0 = 6\pi\eta(a^2b)^{1/3}$. Together with Eq. (8.2.27) for f_t, we obtain

$$f_R = \frac{16\pi b^3 \eta}{3}\left(\frac{1 - (a/b)^4}{(2 - a^2/b^2)G(a/b) - 1}\right) \qquad (8.3.6)$$

where

$$G\left(\frac{a}{b}\right) = \frac{\tan^{-1}[(a^2/b^2) - 1]^{1/2}}{[(a^2/b^2) - 1]^{1/2}} \qquad (a > b)$$

The theory on the rotational diffusion coefficients of cylindrical particles and the corresponding translational frictional factor has been derived by Broersma (1960). If we assume the macromolecule of interest to have a rigid geometrical shape, such as spheres or ellipsoids of revolution, and measure D and D_R and hence f_t and f_R, we may then solve f_t and f_R simultaneously to obtain the hydrodynamic *dimensions* and *shape* of the particle. Additional knowledge of $\bar{v}$ and S permits us to determine the unsolvated particle volume, and thus the degree of solvation. Under the assumption that the lysozyme molecules behave like independent uncharged microscopic bodies, Dubin *et al.* (1971) have shown that their data are consistent with an unsolvated prolate ellipsoid with a major axis a of 48 ± 1 Å, minor axis b of 26 ± 0.8 Å, and covered with a shell of solvent 3.5 Å thick.

8.3.2. Rigid Rods

For large molecules, the condition $|\mathbf{K}\cdot[\mathbf{b}_i(t) - \mathbf{b}_j(0)]| \ll 1$ no longer holds. The intramolecular factor of Eq. (8.2.3) must be taken into account. The simplest case for which the light-scattering spectrum has been calculated is that of the rigid rodlike macromolecule (Pecora, 1964,1968b). The time-dependent signal correlation function has the form

$$R(K, \tau) = R_0(KL) \exp(-DK^2\tau) + R_1(KL)$$

$$\times \exp[-(DK^2 + 6D_R)\tau] + \cdots \qquad (8.3.7)$$

where

$$R_0(KL) = \left(\frac{2}{KL}\int_0^{KL/2}\frac{\sin z}{z}\,dz\right)^2 \qquad (8.3.8)$$

and

$$R_1(KL) = 5\left[(KL)^{-1}\left(-3j_1(\tfrac{1}{2}KL) + \int_0^{KL/2}\frac{\sin z}{z}\,dz\right)\right]^2 \qquad (8.3.9)$$

j_1 is the spherical Bessel function of order 1 and L is the length of the rigid rod. Figure 8.3.1 shows R, R_0, R_1, and R_h as a function of KL (Pecora,

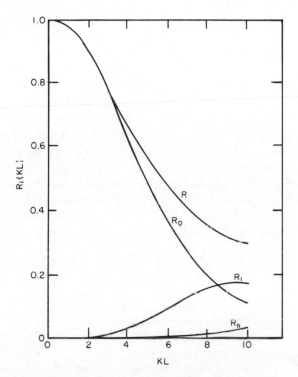

Fig. 8.3.1. Relative integrated intensities of light scattered from optically isotropic rigid rods. R is the total relative integrated scattered intensity; R_0 is the intensity of the pure translational part; R_1 is the first nonzero term whose spectral width contains the rotational diffusion coefficient; R_h is the sum of intensities of all other terms; and $R(KL) = R_0(KL) + R_1(KL) + R_h(KL)$ (Pecora, 1972). [Reproduced with permission, copyright by Annual Reviews, Inc., 1972. All rights reserved.]

1972). For $KL < 3$, R_1 is less than 1 % of the total scattered intensity, so R_0 dominates, and only the translational diffusion coefficient is measurable. For $KL > 5$, R_1 is sufficiently strong so that the total spectral width is related to both D and D_R. Thus, for long rigid rods ($L > 1000$ Å), D can be measured at small $KL < 2$–3, and then D_R can be obtained at large KL from the mixed spectrum. The rotational diffusion coefficients of tobacco mosaic virus (TMV) have been measured by Cummins *et al.* (1969) with $D_{R,20} = 320 \pm 18$ sec^{-1} at 0.1 mgm/mliter, by Fujime (1969; 1970b,c) with $D_{R,20} = 360 \pm 20$ sec^{-1} at 3 mgm/mliter and $D_{R,20} = 390 \pm 40$ sec^{-1} at 0.5 mgm/mliter, by Wada *et al.* (1969, 1970) with $D_R = 350 \pm 20$ sec^{-1} at 1 mgm/mliter, and by Wada *et al.* (1971) with $D_{R,25,\,w} = 400$ sec^{-1}. It should be noted that the clever depolarized light-mixing technique (see Section 8.3.3) by Wada *et al.* (1969) enabled them to obtain the rotational diffusion coefficient of TMV directly, without decomposition of the spectral line. Unfortunately, possible experimental difficulties have not been discussed in detail in their article. Dust is usually a problem and could become particularly serious at small scattering angles. The reader should read the articles by Cummins *et al.* (1969), Fujime (1970b,c), Wada *et al.* (1969, 1970), Wada (1974), and Schurr and Schmitz (1973) for further details. In particular, Cummins *et al.* (1969) have presented a simpler derivation for the light-scattering spectrum of rigid rods than the more rigorous approach of Pecora (1964). In the treatment by Pecora, translational diffusion of the center of mass of the molecule in solution and rotational diffusion of the rigid-rod molecule are not coupled. Maeda and Saito (1969) have generalized the theory for rodlike molecules in order to study the coupling effect of translational and rotational motions. According to them, the spectral density $S_{MS}(K, \omega)$ for a rodlike molecule has the form

$$S_{MS}(K, \omega) = S_T(K, \omega) + S_R(K, \omega) + S_{TR}(K, \omega)$$

$$= S(K, \omega) + S_{TR}(K, \omega) \qquad (8.3.10)$$

where S_T and S_R are Lorentzians of half-widths DK^2 and $DK^2 + 6D_R$, respectively. The coupling term $S_{TR}(K, \omega)$ comes from the anisotropy in the mobility of a rodlike molecule and $S(K, \omega) \left[= S_T(K, \omega) + S_R(K, \omega) \right]$ is the same as the one given by Pecora (1968). Maeda and Saito (1969) calculated for a TMV particle that the coupling term contributes to less than 1 % for $\theta = 50°$ but becomes about 8 % for $\theta = 120°$. Fujime detected these corrections for TMV at $\theta = 160°$ (Fujime, 1969) and at $\theta = 180°$ (Fujime, 1970b) even though no numerical values for the anisotropy of the translational diffusion tensor were obtained.

8.3.3. Theory of Anisotropy Scattering

The light scattered by a solution of macromolecules composed of optically anisotropic segments including intramolecular interference terms contains (a) a polarized component which has the same polarization as the incident polarization and comprises contributions due to local concentration fluctuations and optical anisotropy, and (b) the depolarized component which is due solely to molecular anisotropy. The molecular anisotropy could arise from different refractive indices along different axis of the molecule, often referred to as intrinsic anisotropy, or from geometrical properties of the molecule, known as form anisotropy. For example, TMV is intrinsically optically isotropic and the depolarization is due to form anisotropy. We shall follow the scattering geometry used by Pecora (1972) as shown in Fig. 8.3.2. The incident wave is polarized in the z direction and travels along

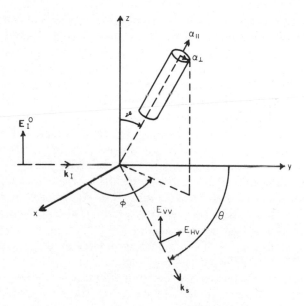

Fig. 8.3.2. Scattering geometry for a small rigid cylindrical molecule. The incident beam travels in the y direction and is polarized in the z direction. The scattered wave is measured in the x–y plane. S_{VV} refers to the polarized light spectrum where the incident and the scattered light have the same polarization. S_{HV} refers to the depolarized light spectrum where the polarization of the incident beam is in the z direction and that of the scattered beam in the x–y plane. $\alpha_{||}$ and $\alpha_{\perp}$ are the molecule-fixed polarizability components along and perpendicular to the cylindrical axis, respectively (Pecora, 1972).

the y axis with E_I^0 along the z direction, and $\mathbf{k}_I$ along the y direction. $\mathbf{k}_s$ is in the xy plane. E_V and E_H are components of the scattered field in the z direction and the x–y plane, respectively. The intensity associated with the E_V component is I_{VV}, and with the E_H component is I_{HV} since the incident wave is polarized in the z direction. For a small rigid molecule of cylindrical symmetry undergoing independent translational and rotational diffusion, Eq. (8.1.4) can be reduced to (Pecora, 1968c, 1970a)

$$S_{VV}(K, \omega) = (A\rho/9\pi)(\alpha_{||} + 2\alpha_{\perp})^2$$

$$\times \{DK^2/[\omega^2 + (DK^2)^2]\} + \tfrac{4}{3}S_{HV} \quad (8.3.11)$$

and

$$S_{HV}(K, \omega) = (A\rho/15\pi)(\alpha_{||} - \alpha_{\perp})^2$$

$$\times (DK^2 + 6D_R)/[\omega^2 + (DK^2 + 6D_R)^2] \quad (8.3.12)$$

where D_R is reserved for the rotational diffusion coefficient of the cylinder long axis. $\alpha_{||}$ and $\alpha_{\perp}$ are the molecule-fixed polarizability components along and perpendicular to the cylindrical axis, respectively. For optically isotropic molecules $\alpha_{||} = \alpha_{\perp}$. Therefore, $S_{HV} = 0$ and we essentially get S_{VV} from which D can be determined. The determination of TMV discussed in Section 8.3.2 is in fact based on Eqs. (8.3.11) and (8.3.12) where measurements of the polarized spectrum at small angles give essentially D while measurements at large angles give D and D_R, because of the changes in the magnitudes of R_0, R_1, and R_h [Eqs. (8.3.8) and (8.3.9)]. Furthermore, measurements of the depolarized spectrum at very low scattering angles permit the determination of D_R (Wada *et al.*, 1969, 1970). Dubin *et al.* (1971) have measured the rotational diffusion coefficient of lysozyme using a spherical Fabry–Perot etalon with the assumption that $DK^2 \ll D_R$. It is interesting to note that D_R ($\equiv \Theta$) for TMV is about 350 sec^{-1} which is very different from $D_{R,20,w}$ of $(16.7 \pm 0.8) \times 10^6$ sec^{-1} for lysozyme. Thus, we need both photon correlation and interferometry for studies dealing with rotational diffusion coefficients of macromolecules in solution. In general, the depolarized component I_{HV} depends upon the optical anisotropy $(\alpha_{||} - \alpha_{\perp})$ which is very small compared with the average polarizability $\frac{1}{3}(\alpha_{||} + 2\alpha_{\perp})$. So far, a very high concentration had to be used in scattering experiments involving the depolarized light-scattering spectrum of macromolecular solutions.

Equations (8.3.11) and (8.3.12) are valid only for cylindrical molecules. Pecora (1968b) has obtained for the more general case where the spectrum is a sum of five Lorentzians:

$$S_{HV}(K, \omega) = \sum_i A_i \frac{(DK^2 + F_i)}{\omega^2 + (DK^2 + F_i)^2} \qquad (8.3.13)$$

where A_i depends on various combinations of elements of the rotational diffusion tensor and the polarizability, and F_i only on the elements of the rotational diffusion tensor. The five Lorentzians are reduced to two when the principal axes for rotation and polarizability coincide, and to one for cylindrically symmetric molecules. Theory on the depolarized light scattering from a helix-coil system has been proposed (Marshall and Pecora, 1971) although no definitive experiments of this nature have been reported. Hess and Müller (1974) have considered the correlation between the translational motion and the orientation of the particles.

8.4. Depolarization Ratio

Measurements of the depolarization ratio for macromolecules have always been difficult and usually show values which are too high. Geiduschek (1954) reported that imperfections in polarizers and analyzers, optical activity, fluorescence, photodetector sensitivity to light polarization, multiple and stray light scattering, and finite acceptance solid angle can all contribute to improper depolarization ratio studies. Even the strains in sample cell windows can make improper contributions to the depolarization ratio. Dubin *et al.* (1971) have shown that measurements of the spectra of the scattered light transmitted by the Glan–Thompson prism when set to pass the polarized and the depolarized components from the sample permit determination of the depolarization ratio (Fig. 8.4.1). The polarized spectrum is *usually* a single Lorentzian which depicts the translational motions of the macromolecule. Contributions from dust or rotational motions, such as those expressed by Eqs. (8.3.7)–(8.3.9) can be subtracted. For the lysozyme, the large particles contribute less than 1 % of the intensity because the polarized spectrum is so accurately a single Lorentzian. The main advantage of measuring the spectra lies with the depolarized spec-

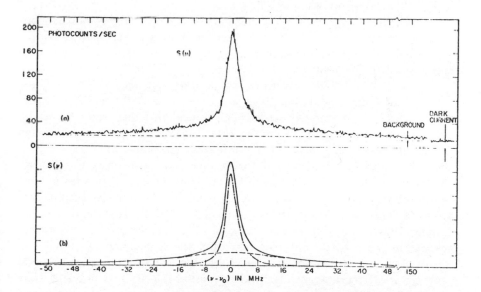

Fig. 8.4.1. (a) Power spectrum of the depolarized light scattered by a 15 % solution of lysozyme in a $0.1M$ sodium acetate–acetic acid buffer at a temperature of 24°C. ●: the best least-squares fit to the spectrum, a convolution of the experimental profile $I(\nu)$ with a Lorentzian of half-width half-height of 18.1 MHz and a δ function of area $\frac{2}{3}$ as large as the Lorentzian. These components rest on a 5-count/sec background. The experimental trace was swept out in 15 min. Wiggly line: observed power spectrum; dotted line: background; ●: best fit to data. (b) Breakdown of the measured spectrum in terms of the component having the instrumental profile and the broad component from the lysozyme. The measured spectrum is the sum of these components. Solid line: best fit to data; dashed-dot line: instrumental profile; dotted line: broad component (Dubin *et al.*, 1971).

trum where there are three significant components: (1) an extremely narrow component produced by large particles such as dust or aggregates; (2) a broader Lorentzian component, produced by the macromolecule (lysozyme); and (3) a very broad component produced possibly by reorientation of the buffer molecules and/or by fluorescence. This extremely broad component represents a background in the measured depolarized spectrum. By distinguishing the contributions, we can then obtain the correct depolarization ratio ρ_v by taking the ratio of the area under the broader Lorentzian component, which arises from the macromolecule, divided by the area of the polarized spectrum. Dubin *et al.* (1971) found $\rho_v = (1.4 \pm 0.1) \times 10^{-3}$ for lysozyme.

8.5. Flexible Coils

In addition to the rigid-body motions, some macromolecules can flex with dimensions comparable to the wavelength of light; the corresponding relaxation times of such long-range configurational fluctuations may appear in the spectrum as additional Lorentzians.

Pecora (1965, 1968a) has used the bead-and-spring model of Zimm (1956) and Zimm and Kilb (1959) to compute the light-scattering spectrum of flexible coils and has extended the consideration to once-broken-rod molecules (Pecora, 1969). Fujime (1970d) has written a formal expression for the light-scattering spectrum of semiflexible molecules, in other words, of molecules of greater rigidity than the random coil, by utilizing the theories of Harris and Hearst (1966), and of Saito *et al.* (1967). Quasielastic light scattering from solutions of semiflexible polymers, F-actin, by Fujime and Ishiwata (Fujime, 1970a, d; 1971; Fujime and Ishiwata, 1971; Ishiwata and Fujime, 1971a, b, c; Fujime and Hatano, 1972) should be very interesting reading to those who want to understand the developments of internal modes of motion of macromolecules in solution. F-actin, one of the muscle proteins, is a very long, two stranded, semiflexible, helical polymer. The spectral density for a semiflexible molecule is a superposition of Lorentzians and can be written as (Fujime, 1970a, d)

$$S(K, \omega) = \sum_{m,n} R_{m,n} \frac{\Gamma_{n,m}}{\omega^2 + \Gamma_{n,m}{}^2} \qquad (8.5.1)$$

where the nth normal mode of the molecule contributes an infinite series of Lorentzians with decay time τ_n:

$$\Gamma_{n,m} = DK^2 + m/\tau_n \qquad (8.5.2)$$

m is an integer, and $R_{m,n}$ measures the contribution from various modes of motion. The corresponding time correlation function in the heterodyne scheme has the form

$$g^{(1)}(\tau) = \sum_m \sum_n R_{m,n} \exp[-(DK^2 + m/\tau_n)\tau] \qquad (8.5.3)$$

The relaxation time of the conformational fluctuation of a Gaussian random coil is (Fujime, 1970d):

$$\tau_n = \langle R^2 \rangle / 3Dn\pi \qquad (8.5.4)$$

where $\langle R^2 \rangle$ is the mean-square end-to-end distance of the chain and D is the translational diffusion coefficient in the free draining case. The relaxation time τ_n of the bending motion of a stiff chain is given by (Fujime and Ishiwata, 1971)

$$\tau_n = \tfrac{4}{3}[L^2/D\pi^4(n + \tfrac{1}{2})^4](\lambda_s L) \qquad (8.5.5)$$

where L is the extended length of the chain and $1/\lambda_s$ is the so-called statistical length. The parameter λ_s is connected to the flexural rigidity ϵ, which is an elastic constant related to the bending of a chain, and $\langle R^2 \rangle$ according to the relations

$$\epsilon = 3k_D T/4\lambda_s \qquad (8.5.6)$$

and

$$\langle R^2 \rangle = [\exp(-2\lambda_s L) - 1 + 2L\lambda_s]/2\lambda_s^2 \qquad (8.5.7)$$

Pecora (1968a) has found that if $\langle R^2 \rangle$ is less than 2000 Å, only the $R_0 = \sum_n R_{0,n}$ term is important, and internal motions of the chain cannot be observed by means of quasielastic light scattering.

In the case of F-actin, the molecule is very long and $L \sim 2.5$ μm so that

$$S(K, \omega) \approx R_2(K)(DK^2 + 1/\tau)/[\omega^2 + (DK^2 + 1/\tau)^2] \qquad (8.5.8)$$

An increase of $1/\tau$ means a decrease in the flexibility of the polymer. In fact, Eq. (8.5.8) implies that only the relaxation time of the first normal mode of bending of the molecule contributes to the spectral density of Eqs. (8.5.1) and (8.5.2) so that

$$S(K, \omega) = \sum_m R_m(K) \frac{DK^2 + m/\tau_1}{\omega^2 + (DK^2 + m/\tau_1)^2} \qquad (8.5.9)$$

where $1/\tau$ is thought to be an average of m/τ_1 of Eq. (8.5.9). The corresponding self-beat spectral density has the form

$$\sum_m \sum_l R_m(K) R_l(K) \frac{2DK^2 + (m + l)/\tau_1}{\omega^2 + (2DK^2 + (m + l)/\tau_1)^2} \qquad (8.5.10)$$

Fujime simply took

$$\Gamma = DK^2 + 1/\tau \qquad (8.5.11)$$

and obtained D and $1/\tau$ from a plot of Γ vs K^2. Since the rotational Brownian motion also has the form

$$\Gamma = DK^2 + 6D_R \qquad (8.5.12)$$

Fujime first computed $1/6D_R$ from Perrin's formula and obtained a value of 500–1000 msec for F-actin as a rod; such a value is far greater than the experimental value of 4.5 msec which he identified as the relaxation time of the lowest-order internal mode of motion (τ). He also found that $D = 0.03 \times 10^{-7}$ cm²/sec for his F-actin at about 4 mg/mliter concentration in 0.4 mM adenosine triphosphate (ATP) at pH 7.5–8.0. Fujime and Ishiwata (1971) then used quasielastic light scattering to investigate the effect of binding on the stiffness of F-actin with various other muscle proteins. They studied the interactions between (1) F-actin and heavy meromyosin or S-1 in the absence of ATP; (2) F-actin and tropomyosin at various salt concentrations; and (3) the interaction between heavy meromyosin and the complex of F-actin and tropomyosin in the absence of ATP. They also showed that the flexibility of an F-actin-tropomyosin-troponin and heavy meromyosin complex (Fujime *et al.*, 1972) in the absence of ATP is regulated by Ca^{2+} (Ishiwata and Fujime, 1971, 1972). Fujime and Hatano (1972) have studied the dynamic properties of plasmodium actin polymers by examining their flexibility under different conditions. Intramolecular Brownian motion should also be detectable for synthetic high polymers. Unfortunately, the effects of polydispersity, and critical scattering have so far prevented any determination of the relevant relaxation times from these experiments (Reed and Frederick, 1971; Kramer and Frederick, 1972).

Bacterial flagella are organelles of locomotion. Flexural rigidity of bacterial flagella has been studied by quasielastic light scattering (Maruyama and Asakura, 1972). The bacterial flagellum was found to be very stiff.

8.6. Polydispersity

8.6.2. General Consideration

All synthetic macromolecules are more or less polydisperse. The effect of polydispersity on the spectrum of light scattered by macromolecules in solution has been examined by Dubin (1970). He considered a mixture of equal numbers of molecules of the same molecular weight but of different diffusion coefficients D_1 and D_2. The signal portion of the heterodyne spectrum is given by

$$S(K, \omega) \propto \frac{D_1 K^2}{\omega^2 + (D_1 K^2)^2} \mid \frac{D_2 K^2}{\omega^2 + (D_2 K^2)^2} \qquad (8.6.1)$$

He then fitted Eq. (8.6.1) using a single Lorentzian. For $D_2/D_1 = 2$, the rms deviation of this single Lorentzian fit is less than 1 % indicating the inability of quasielastic laser scattering to distinguish Eq. (8.6.1) and a single Lorentzian fit. Thus, only for large macromolecules with quite broad molecular weight distributions can we consider light-scattering spectrum as a tool to learn something about polydispersity. For narrower molecular weight distributions, we simply obtain an averaged D. As a rule, very precise measurements are required to examine the effects of polydispersity.

Thompson (1971a) has studied the bimodal distribution with sharp peaks using suspensions of polystyrene latex spheres in water as his test system. He observed that the self-beat method was quite sensitive to small amounts of large particles in the presence of large numbers of small particles. Analysis of intensity correlation spectra of a bimodal distribution of polystyrene latex suspensions has been presented by Bargeron (1973, 1974) and Chen et al. (1974) using a straightforward least-squares method and by Lee and Chu (1974) using an integration least-squares method. Under favorable conditions, the precision of data permits a deduction of scattering amplitude ratios and particle diameters.

Pecora and Tagami (1969) have used the two-parameter unimodal Schulz molecular weight distribution to compute the light-scattering spectra from solutions of rigid rods and flexible coils. Their calculations showed that polydispersity effects could produce small deviations from a single Lorentzian fit and a breakdown of $\Gamma = DK^2$. On the other hand, intramolecular interference effects on the Rayleigh line spectrum of macromolecules in solution also become observable when the scattering species are comparable in size with the incident wavelength. For random-coil polymers, such large sizes can only be achieved at high molecular weights where the polydispersity also increases. Thus, the deviations are likely to become important for large synthetic random coils observed at large values of K where intramolecular interference effects also occur. The polydispersity effects have been investigated by Frederick et al. (1971) and by Kramer and Frederick (1972).

We shall consider a Schulz molecular weight distribution $f(M)$ which has been widely used in fractionation and polymerization of many condensation and vinyl polymers:

$$f(M) = (1/Z!)[(Z + 1)/\bar{M}_w]^{Z+1}M^Z \exp[-(Z + 1)M/\bar{M}_w] \quad (8.6.2)$$

where $f(M)$ is the weight fraction of the molecule in the sample of molecular weight M, $\bar{M}_w$ is the weight average molecular weight, and Z is the degree of polydispersity which is an adjustable parameter governing the breadth of the distribution. The distribution changes from monodisperse to infinitely broad as Z varies from ∞ to 0. We shall follow the discussion outlined by Ford *et al.* (1973).

The normalized correlation function according to Eq. (4.3.28) has the form

$$R_N(\tau) = \frac{\langle \delta\epsilon(t)\ \delta\epsilon(t + \tau)\rangle^2}{\langle \delta\epsilon(t)^2\rangle^2} = \frac{R_i(\tau) - R_i(\infty)}{R_i(0) - R_i(\infty)} = \frac{R_E^2(\tau)}{R_E^2(0)} \quad (8.6.3)$$

For a polydisperse system with a Schulz distribution, we get

$$R_N(\tau) = \frac{1}{\bar{M}_w^2}\left[\int Mf(M)e^{-\Gamma(M)\tau}\,dM\right]^2 \quad (8.6.4)$$

where $\Gamma(M) = DK^2$. If we take $D = K_D M^{-b}$ as expressed in Eq. (8.2.40), Eq. (8.6.4) may be evaluated for a Schulz distribution to yield

$$R_N(Y, Z, b) = \{[(Z + 1)^{Z+1}/Z!]\}\int X^{Z+1}\exp[-(Z + 1)X]$$

$$\times \exp(-Y/X^b)\,dX \quad (8.6.5)$$

where $X = M/\bar{M}_w$ and $Y = \tau K_D K^2/\bar{M}_w^b$. Equation (8.6.4) is the basic theoretical expression for analysis of the time-dependent correlation function in the presence of a polydisperse solute. Equation (8.6.5) restricts the consideration to a Schulz distribution (Frederick *et al.*, 1971; Pecora and Tagami, 1969), and unfortunately it still cannot be evaluated explicitly. Ford *et al.* (1973) have devised an approximate procedure which can yield Z and $\bar{M}_w$.

If the solution contains only two species of macromolecules, then

$$g^{(1)}(\tau) \propto A \exp(-\Gamma_1\tau) + B \exp(-\Gamma_2\tau)$$

$$\propto \exp(-\Gamma_1\tau) + f \exp(-\Gamma_2\tau) \quad (8.6.6)$$

where

$$f\left[\equiv \frac{B}{A} = \frac{C_2 I_2(M_2, K)}{C_1 I_1(M_1, K)}\right]$$

is the relative strength of Γ_2 with respect to Γ_1. C_i is the concentration of species i and $I_i(M_i, K)$ is the intensity of scattering per unit concentration due to species i with molecular weight M_i and at $K = (4\pi/\lambda)\sin(\frac{1}{2}\theta)$. If Γ_1 and Γ_2 are not too different, $g^{(1)}(\tau)$ can be analyzed using a single exponential curve where we have

$$g_0^{(1)}(\tau) \propto \exp(-\Gamma_0\tau) \qquad (8.6.7)$$

Thus, if we know Γ_1 and Γ_2 as well as the scattering powers of each component, namely I_1 and I_2, a single measurement of $g_0^{(1)}(\tau)$ determines the relative concentration of the two species. Such an analysis may be useful in the concentration determination of monomer–dimer equilibria when very precise data are available.

Calculations of Rayleigh spectra from translational motions of flexible coils assuming various forms of distribution functions, such as Schulz, Tung, and exponential functions, yield an average molecular weight essentially equivalent to M_Z for values of M_W/M_n up to 15 and $K^2\langle R_g^2\rangle \leq 0.2$, where $\langle R_g^2\rangle$ is the mean-square radius of gyration (Huang et al., 1973). A more general approach to the same problem is expressed by Eqs. (8.6.15) and (8.6.16). Inelastic light scattering has been used to study the size distribution of bovine milk casein micelles (Lin et al., 1971). Spectrum of light scattered from polydisperse polymer solutions has also been considered by Thompson (1971b) who developed a graphical technique to characterize the average size and standard deviation of particles obeying the log normal distribution. Welch and Bloomfield (1973) extended the graphical treatments by indicating additional ways of analyzing the light-scattering spectrum of polydisperse macromolecular solutions.

8.6.2. Method of Cumulants

The method of cumulants, as devised by Koppel (1972), appears to be a very powerful technique for analysis of macromolecular polydispersity in quasielastic light scattering. The coefficients give successively the average, width, skewness, and higher moments of the molecular weight distribution function. Careful determinations of the time correlation function give significance to at least the first three moments. We shall follow the derivation by Koppel.

For a monodisperse macromolecular solution,

$$| g^{(1)}(\tau) | = e^{-\Gamma\tau} \qquad (8.6.8a)$$

where $\Gamma = DK^2$ and we have neglected the $\exp(-i\omega_I\tau)$ term and set $A = 1$.

For a polydisperse solution, Eq. (8.6.8a) must be generalized to a sum or distribution of exponentials:

$$| g^{(1)}(\tau) | = \int_0^\infty G(\Gamma) e^{-\Gamma\tau} \, d\Gamma \qquad (8.6.8b)$$

where $G(\Gamma)$ is the normalized distribution function of the decay rates. $G(\Gamma) \, d\Gamma$ is the fraction of the total (normalized and integrated) intensity scattered by molecules which obey $\Gamma = DK^2$, within the increment $d\Gamma$, and

$$\int_0^\infty G(\Gamma) \, d\Gamma = 1$$

The evaluation of $G(\Gamma)$ can be approached in at least three ways. First, $G(\Gamma)$ can be calculated in principle by inverting the Laplace integral equation (8.6.8b) with Fourier transforms. Extremely precise data over extended ranges are required and such inversions have never worked out well so far. Second, we can assume a specific form for $G(\Gamma)$. This has been the approach of the previous Section 8.6.1 (Tagami and Pecora, 1969; Frederick *et al.*, 1971; Ford et *al.*, 1973). The third approach does not assume a particular distribution function and is based on the formalism of the statistical cumulant generating function.

The moment generating function (Kendall and Stuart, 1958; Cantrell, 1970; Schaefer *et al.*, 1971) is defined as

$$\mathfrak{M}(-\tau; \Gamma) \equiv \overline{\exp(-\Gamma\tau)} = | g^{(1)}(\tau) | \qquad (8.6.9)$$

where the bar signifies an average over Γ, weighted by the distribution function $G(\Gamma)$ as defined in Eq. (8.6.8b). The moments of the distribution $\mu_m(\Gamma)$ can be expressed as

$$\mu_m(\Gamma) \equiv \overline{\Gamma^m} = [d^m/d(-\tau)^m] \mathfrak{M}(-\tau; \Gamma) \, |_{-\tau=0} \qquad (8.6.10)$$

and the cumulant generating function $\mathfrak{K}(-\tau; \Gamma)$ as

$$\mathfrak{K}(-\tau, \Gamma) \equiv \ln \mathfrak{M}(-\tau; \Gamma) = \ln | g^{(1)}(\tau) | \qquad (8.6.11)$$

The mth cumulant of Γ, $K_m(\Gamma)$, is the coefficient of $(-\tau)^m/m!$ in the MacLaurin expansion of $\mathfrak{K}(-\tau; \Gamma)$, i.e.,

$$K_m(\Gamma) \equiv [d^m/d(-\tau)^m] \mathfrak{K}(-\tau; \Gamma) \, |_{-\tau=0} \qquad (8.6.12)$$

and

$$\mathfrak{K}(-\tau; \Gamma) = \sum_{m=1}^\infty K_m(\Gamma) [(-\tau)^m/m!] \qquad (8.6.13)$$

Equation (8.6.11) tells us that $\mathfrak{K}(-\tau; \Gamma)$ is linear in τ for a single exponential correlation function.

The cumulants can be written explicitly in terms of the moments (Cantrell, 1970) with

$$K_1 = \bar{\Gamma} = \int_0^\infty \Gamma G(\Gamma)\, d\Gamma, \qquad K_2 = M_2$$

$$K_3 = M_3, \qquad\qquad\qquad K_4 = M_4 - 3(M_2)^2, \ldots \quad (8.6.14)$$

where $M_m \equiv \overline{(\Gamma - \bar{\Gamma})^m}$. If the intensity of light scattered by macromolecular species i is proportional to the molecular weight m_i [note: we change the notation for molecular weight from M to m because here M_i is used to define $\overline{(\Gamma - \bar{\Gamma})^i}$], times the *weight* concentration C_i:

$$G(\Gamma) = \sum_i C_i m_i\, \delta(\Gamma - \Gamma_i) \Big/ \sum_i C_i m_i \qquad (8.6.15)$$

then

$$\bar{D} = \bar{\Gamma}/K^2 = D_Z \equiv \sum_i C_i m_i D_i \Big/ \sum_i C_i m_i \qquad (8.6.16)$$

where D_Z is the so-called Z-average diffusion coefficient. When D_Z is combined with the weight-average sedimentation coefficient S in the Svedberg equation (8.2.34) for a polydisperse system, we can obtain the weight-average molecular weight provided the partial specific volume is the same for all species. The second cumulant K_2, when normalized by $(K_1)^2$, is related to the width of the distribution, while K_3 and K_4 measures the skewness or asymmetry, and the kurtosis of the distribution. For a Gaussian distribution, $K_{m>2} \equiv 0$.

The corresponding heterodyne spectrum has the form

$$S(\omega) = \frac{A}{2\pi} \int_{-\infty}^{\infty} |g^{(1)}(\tau)|^2 e^{+i\omega\tau}\, d\tau$$

$$= \frac{A}{\pi(\omega^2 + \bar{\Gamma}^2)} \left[1 + \frac{\bar{\Gamma}^2 - 3\omega^2}{(\bar{\Gamma}^2 + \omega^2)^2} M_2 - \frac{\bar{\Gamma}^4 - 6\bar{\Gamma}^2\omega^2 + \omega^4}{\bar{\Gamma}(\bar{\Gamma}^2 + \omega^2)^3} M_3 + \cdots \right]$$

$$(8.6.17)$$

where A is the integrated spectral intensity. Koppel has devised a detailed procedure for calculating the cumulants starting with the correlation data of a digital homodyne experiment. The reader is advised to find out the details from his original work.

A slightly simpler but less rigorous approach has been proposed by Pusey *et al.* (1972) who expanded $\exp(-\Gamma\tau)$ in Eq. (8.6.8b) around

$\exp(-\bar{\Gamma}\tau):$

$$\exp(-\Gamma\tau) = \exp(-\bar{\Gamma}\tau) \exp[-(\Gamma - \bar{\Gamma})\tau]$$

$$= \exp(-\bar{\Gamma}\tau)$$

$$\times \left(1 - (\Gamma - \bar{\Gamma})\tau + \frac{(\Gamma - \bar{\Gamma})^2\tau^2}{2!} - \frac{(\Gamma - \bar{\Gamma})^3}{3!}\tau^3 + \cdots\right)$$

$$(8.6.18)$$

where $\bar{\Gamma}$ is the mean decay rate defined by

$$\bar{\Gamma} = \int_0^\infty \Gamma G(\Gamma) \, d\Gamma \qquad (8.6.19)$$

Substitution of Eq. (8.6.18) into Eq. (8.6.8b) gives

$$|g^{(1)}(\tau)| = \exp(-\bar{\Gamma}\tau)\{1 + \mu_2\tau^2/2! - \mu_3\tau^3/3! + \cdots\} \quad (8.6.20)$$

where the μ's are moments about the mean of $G(\Gamma)$. Thus,

$$\mu_1 \equiv \int (\Gamma - \bar{\Gamma})G(\Gamma) \, d\Gamma = 0 \qquad (8.6.21)$$

$$\mu_2 \equiv \int (\Gamma - \bar{\Gamma})^2 G(\Gamma) \, d\Gamma \qquad (8.6.22)$$

etc. With $\ln(1 + X) = X - \frac{1}{2}X^2 + \cdots$, we then get from Eq. (8.6.20)

$$\ln[\beta \, |g^{(1)}(\tau)|] = \ln \beta - \bar{\Gamma}\tau + \frac{1}{2!}\left(\frac{\mu_2}{\bar{\Gamma}^2}\right)(\bar{\Gamma}\tau)^2$$

$$- \frac{1}{3!}\left(\frac{\mu_3}{\bar{\Gamma}^3}\right)(\bar{\Gamma}\tau)^3 + \cdots \quad (8.6.23)$$

The μ's are identically zero for a single exponential. To evaluate $\bar{\Gamma}$ and the μ's, Pusey *et al.* used a procedure of numerical differentiation of $\ln|g^{(1)}(\tau)|$ with respect to τ. They take all possible sets of four (an arbitrary choice) consecutive data points and obtain m-3 values of Γ_i where

$$\Gamma_i = -\frac{d}{d\tau}\ln|g^{(1)}(\tau)|\bigg|_{\tau=\tau_i} \qquad (8.6.24)$$

with τ_i and m being the delay time at the midpoint of the four-point segment and the total number of delay points. The derivatives of Eq. (8.6.23) are

$$\frac{d}{d\tau}\ln|g^{(1)}(\tau)| = -\bar{\Gamma} + \mu_2\tau - \frac{1}{2!}\mu_3\tau^2 + \frac{1}{3!}(\mu_4 - 3\mu_2^2)\tau^3 - \cdots \quad (8.6.25)$$

and

$$\frac{d^2}{d\tau^2} \ln| \ g^{(1)}(\tau)| \ = \ \mu_2 \ - \ \mu_3\tau + \frac{1}{2!} \ (\mu_4 \ - \ 3\mu_2{}^2)\tau^2 \ - \ \cdots \tag{8.6.26}$$

Thus, we can obtain the mean, spread, and skewness of $G(\Gamma)$ as follows:

(1)   The initial slope of a plot of $\ln| \ g^{(1)}(\tau) \ |$ vs τ or alternatively the intercept at $\tau = 0$ of a plot of $(d/d\tau) \ln| \ g^{(1)}(\tau) \ |$ vs τ is the negative mean decay rate $\bar{\Gamma}$ of the distribution $G(\Gamma)$,

$$(2) \quad \lim_{\tau \to 0} \frac{d^2}{d\tau^2} \ln| \ g^{(1)}(\tau) \ | \ = \ \mu_2 \tag{8.6.27}$$

and

$$(3) \quad \lim_{\tau \to 0} \frac{d^3}{d\tau^3} \ln| \ g^{(1)}(\tau) \ | \ = \ -\mu_3 \tag{8.6.28}$$

In practice, statistical errors often prevent evaluation of derivatives higher

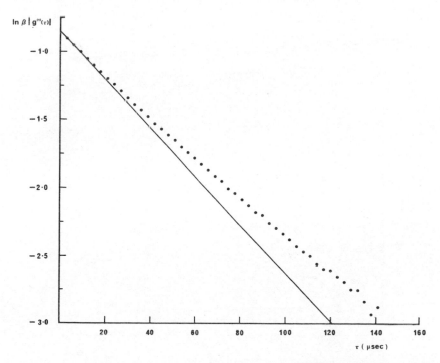

Fig. 8.6.1.   A plot of $\ln \beta | \ g^{(1)}(\tau) \ |$ vs τ for a mixture of polystyrene ($\bar{M}_w = 4.1 \times 10^5$ and 5.1×10^4; weight ratio 40:60) in cyclohexane at $\theta = 90°$, (Pusey, 1973; Brown and Pusey, 1974).

than μ_2 even though we know that they are related to the higher moments of $G(\Gamma)$.

Pusey *et al.* (1972b) used a "quality parameter" defined by $Q \equiv (\mu_2)_{\text{est}}/\bar{\Gamma}_{\text{est}}{}^2$ to test the single exponentiality of the time correlation function. $(\mu_2)_{\text{est}}$ and $\bar{\Gamma}_{\text{est}}$ are obtained by fitting $(d/d\tau) \ln| g^{(1)}(\tau) |$ to a straight line. Q is zero for the single exponential. We also note

$$\mu_2/\bar{\Gamma}^2 = [(\overline{D^2})_Z - \bar{D}_Z{}^2]/\bar{D}_Z{}^2 \qquad (8.6.29)$$

which is the Z-average normalized variance of the D distribution. Figure 8.6.1 shows a semilogarithmic plot of a typical correlation function for a 40:60 by weight mixture of $\bar{M}_w = (4.1 \pm 0.2) \times 10^5$ and $(5.1 \pm 0.25) \times 10^4$ of polystyrene at about 0.1 wt % in cyclohexane with $\theta = 90°$ and $\bar{\Gamma}\tau_{\max} \simeq 2$. $\tau_{\max}$ is the longest delay time used. Figure 8.6.2 is the first numerical derivative of Fig. 8.6.1 (Pusey, 1973; Brown and Pusey, 1974). The effects of polydispersity have been demonstrated even though intensity fluctuation spectroscopy is relatively insensitive in resolving a superposition of multiple decay times, and there is little hope of determining the detail form of $G(\Gamma)$.

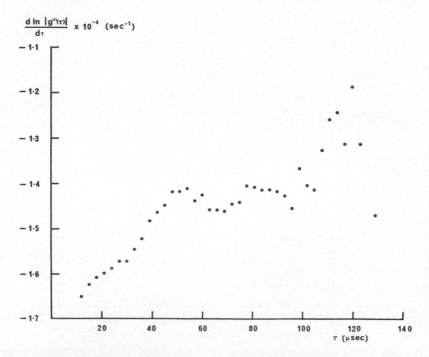

Fig. 8.6.2. First numerical derivative of data of Fig. 8.6.1 (Pusey, 1973; Brown and Pusey, 1974).

8.7. Electrophoresis and Light Scattering

Ware and Flygare (1971) have successfully combined electrophoresis with quasielastic light scattering. Their idea can best be demonstrated by considering the two original light-beating experiments of Cummins *et al.* (1964) and of Yeh and Cummins (1964). Cummins *et al.* (1964) verified that the spectrum of light scattered from a solution of polystyrene latex spheres has a width proportional to the diffusion coefficient of the polystyrene spheres ($\Gamma = DK^2$). Subsequently, Yeh and Cummins (1964) measured the Doppler-shifted spectrum from a flowing solution of polystyrene latex spheres and observed that the flow velocity of the latex spheres is related to the magnitude of the Doppler-shifted frequency. Therefore, measurements of Doppler-shifted spectra from a flowing solution of macromolecules give us information on the diffusion coefficient as well as the flow velocity of the macromolecule. A natural extension of the idea would be to try to set the macromolecules in motion by some external forces. The use of an external electric field on charged species is especially appealing since if the charged species move with different velocities, the spectrum of each charged species are Doppler shifted according to its terminal flow velocity, and the width of each spectrum characterizes the corresponding species by means of its translational diffusion coefficient. Thus, such a technique may be useful for the quantitative analysis of mixtures of charged macromolecules in solution. Ware and Flygare (1971) first employed a combination of electrophoresis with quasielastic light scattering to measure the Doppler shift of the Rayleigh scattered light from a solution of charged bovine serum albumin molecules in an electric field. We shall summarize the theory according to Ware and Flygare (1971, 1972). It is important to note that the electric field is used to move the charged macromolecules. In principle, any means which will move (or even reorient) the different molecular species will be helpful in analyzing and identifying a mixture of such species in solution. Other disturbances, such as the application of a magnetic field, an inhomogeneous electric field, or a centrifugal field, may eventually be utilized in combination with quasielastic light scattering for the quantitative analysis of mixtures of macromolecules in solution. The use of a centrifugal field is especially attractive since the ultracentrifuge technique is well developed and the separation can be performed for charged as well as uncharged species. Chapter X, especially Section 10.5, provides further discussions of this technique. It should be noted that electrophotetic light scattering complements electric field light scattering (Jennings, 1972) in a special way since the same instrumentation, with the exception of an interchange of a signal correlator and a storage oscilloscope, could yield different molecular information.

Consider the autocorrelation function for N independent isotropic spherical scatterers of equal size. Equation (8.2.5) can be written as

$$R_I(K, \tau) = N E_s^{02} \langle \exp\{i\mathbf{K}\cdot[\mathbf{R}(\tau) - \mathbf{R}(0)]\}\rangle \qquad (8.7.1)$$

where E_s^0 is the amplitude factor of the scattered electric field. According to the ergodic hypothesis, the time average can be replaced by an ensemble average so that

$$\langle \exp\{i\mathbf{K}\cdot[\mathbf{R}(\tau) - \mathbf{R}(0)]\}\rangle$$

$$= \int w(R_0, t \mid R_0 + r, t + \tau) \exp(-i\mathbf{K}\cdot\mathbf{R}_0)$$

$$\times \exp(i\mathbf{K}\cdot(\mathbf{R}_0 + \mathbf{r})\} \, dr \qquad (8.7.2)$$

where $w(R_0, t \mid R_0 + r, t + \tau)$ is the conditional probability that a scattering center in a unit volume element located at R_0 at time t will be at $R_0 + r$ at time $t + \tau$. w is independent of R_0 and t for a homogeneous, isotropic, and stationary system. Then,

$$R_I(K, \tau) = N E_s^{02} \int G_s(r, \tau) \exp(i\mathbf{K}\cdot\mathbf{r}) \, d\mathbf{r} \qquad (8.7.3)$$

where $G_s(r, \tau)$ is the ensemble averaged conditional probability that a particle in a unit volume element located at $r = 0$ at $t = 0$, will be at r and at time τ.

In the absence of an electric field, the time evolution of G_s is given by the macroscopic diffusion equation:

$$\partial G_s/\partial t = D\nabla^2 G_s \qquad (8.7.4)$$

with

$$G_s(r, \tau) = (4\pi D\tau)^{-3/2} \exp(-r^2/4D\tau) \qquad (8.7.5)$$

Substituting Eq. (8.7.5) into Eq. (8.7.3) gives

$$R_I(K, \tau) = N E_s^{02} \exp(-DK^2\tau) \qquad (8.7.6)$$

In the presence of an electric field, the macromolecule will reach a constant drift velocity v_d which is equal to the electrophoretic mobility u of the macromolecule times the electric field strength E.

$$v_d = Eu \qquad (8.7.7)$$

If we take v_d as the velocity along the x axis, the time evolution of G_s under the conditions of both random thermal motion and the constant drift velocity v_d along the x axis is

$$\partial G_s/\partial t = D\nabla^2 G_s + Eu(\partial G_s/\partial x) \qquad (8.7.8)$$

where

$$G_s(r, \tau) = (4\pi D\tau)^{-3/2} \exp\{-[(x + v_d\tau)^2 + y^2 + z^2]/4D\tau\} \quad (8.7.9)$$

with

$$r^2 = x^2 + y^2 + z^2$$

Substituting Eq. (8.7.9) into Eq. (8.7.3) gives the correlation function for a solution of homogeneous, isotropic, independent macromolecules with an electric field applied along the x axis:

$$R_I(K, \tau) = NE_s^{02} \exp(-iK_x v_d\tau) \exp(-DK^2\tau) \quad (8.7.10)$$

If $x \perp \mathbf{k}_I$, $K_x = K \cos(\tfrac{1}{2}\theta)$, as shown in Fig. 8.7.1. Then

$$R_I(K, \tau) = NE_s^{02} \exp[-iK v_d \cos(\tfrac{1}{2}\theta)\tau] \exp(-DK^2\tau) \quad (8.7.10a)$$

whose Fourier transform gives

$$S(K, \omega) = NE_s^{02}DK^2/\{[\omega - K v_d \cos(\tfrac{1}{2}\theta)]^2 + (DK^2)^2\} \quad (8.7.11)$$

Equation (8.7.11) represents a Lorentzian curve of half-width $\Delta\omega_{1/2} = DK^2$ which has been Doppler shifted by

$$\Delta\omega_{shift} = K v_d \cos(\tfrac{1}{2}\theta) = KEu \cos(\tfrac{1}{2}\theta) \quad (8.7.12)$$

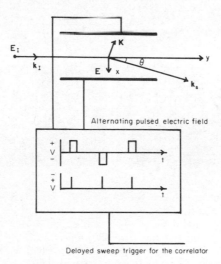

Fig. 8.7.1. Scattering geometry among the directions of the incident electric field $\mathbf{k}_I$, of polarization $\mathbf{E}_I$, and of the applied electric field $\mathbf{E}$ and the scattering plane x-y; $\mathbf{E}$ and $\mathbf{k}_I$ are in the x and y directions, respectively. $\mathbf{K}$ and $\mathbf{k}_s$ are in the x-y plane.

If we define the resolving power $[\mathcal{R}^\dagger]$ as

$$[\mathcal{R}^\dagger] = \frac{\Delta\omega_{shift}}{\Delta\omega_{1/2}} = \frac{KEu\cos(\frac{1}{2}\theta)}{DK^2} = \frac{Eu\cos(\frac{1}{2}\theta)}{DK} \qquad (8.7.13)$$

the resolution increases without bound as $\theta \to 0$, and it increases with increasing electric field and electrophoretic mobility. Thus, the technique is limited by the experimental restrictions of observing small angle light scattering and the use of field strength to such an extent so that excessive heating is avoided. Furthermore high electrophoretic mobility comes from macromolecules which can support high charges.

According to Eq. (8.7.10), the heterodyne autocorrelation function is a damped cosine wave whose frequency is equal to the Doppler shift $[\Delta\omega_{shift} = KEu\cos(\frac{1}{2}\theta)]$ and whose decay time constant is $(DK^2)^{-1}$, which is the same as that in the absence of an external electric field. Figure 8.7.2 shows a typical series of autocorrelation functions for a fixed scattering angle $\theta = 4.5°$. The zero field autocorrelation function is an exponential decay, and the autocorrelation functions in the presence of an electric field are exponentially damped cosine waves whose frequencies are proportional to

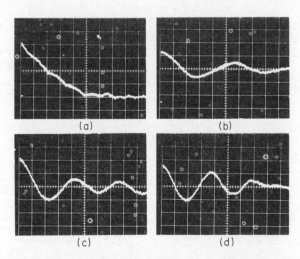

Fig. 8.7.2. The autocorrelation function at (a) zero field and fields of (b) 115, (c) 135, and (d) 154 V/cm respectively in a 5% solution of bovine serum albumin in $0.004M$ NaCl titrated to pH 9.2 with n-butylamine. $\lambda_0 = 5145$ Å, $T = 10°C$, and $\theta = 0.079$ rad $= 4.5°$. The correlation functions shown here are computed by the Fabry–Tek correlator-computer and contain 256 points. The time base is 0.3 msec/point or 5.12 msec/cm in the curves. Each curve is a sum of 256 scans which took 13 sec of measurement time. The field-off time when no data was being collected added another 2–3 min to the total time for each curve. The average mobility from these data, corrected to 20°C, is $u = 10 \times 10^{-5}$ cm²/sec V (Ware and Flygare, 1971).

the magnitude of the electric field. If we define

$$\Delta\tau = 2\pi/uEK\cos(\tfrac{1}{2}\theta) \qquad (8.7.14)$$

then

$$\frac{1}{E\Delta\tau} = \frac{uK\cos(\tfrac{1}{2}\theta)}{2\pi} = u\,\frac{2\pi n}{2\pi\lambda_{air}}\,2\sin(\tfrac{1}{2}\theta)\,\cos(\tfrac{1}{2}\theta)$$

$$= u\,\frac{n}{\lambda_{air}}\sin\theta \qquad (8.7.15)$$

A plot of $1/E\Delta\tau$ vs $\sin\theta$ yields a straight line with a slope of nu/λ_{air} and an intercept of zero. Ware and Flygare have been able to work at scattering angles as low as 3° and achieved $[\mathcal{R}^{\dagger}] \simeq 20$ for bovine serum albumin. In their experiment, the electric potential to the Ag–AgCl electrodes in the scattering cell which resembles a Tiselius electrophoresis cell is controlled by an electronic switching circuit. The electric field is pulsed to allow any heat generated by the current to be dissipated. The correlator is set to delay a short time before sampling to ensure that the system has achieved a steady state. The ratio of on-time to off-time is variable. Ware and Flygare used a 1:10 ratio. Alternating pulses of opposite polarity are used to prevent the accummulation of concentration gradients. The technique requires no maintenance of concentration gradients, permits the use of higher fields than typically used in electrophoresis, and has potentials for much higher resolution. A typical measurement can be done in a few minutes while electrophoresis takes hours. Furthermore, no macroscopic

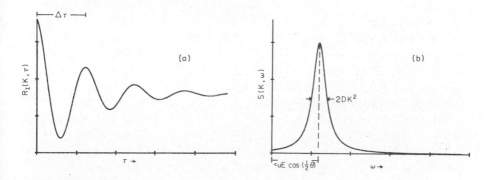

Fig. 8.7.3. Simulated time-dependent correlation function and heterodyne spectrum of light scattered from a solution of charged macromolecules in the presence of an electric field. (a) $R_I(K,\tau) \propto N\exp(-DK^2\tau)\exp(-iKuE\cos\tfrac{1}{2}\theta)$; $\Delta\tau = 2\pi/uEK\cos\tfrac{1}{2}\theta$; (b) $S(K,\omega) \propto N(DK^2/\{[\omega - KuE\cos(\tfrac{1}{2}\theta)]^2 + (DK^2)^2\})$. Shot noise and dc terms neglected.

separation is required with this analytical technique. It should be noted that the use of Eq. (8.7.10) is not so convenient as Eq. (8.7.11) as shown schematically in Fig. 8.7.3. For multicomponent systems in the absence of chemical relaxations, $R_I(K, \tau)$ is complex while $S(K, \omega)$ in a heterodyne spectrum has separate peaks for each species with corresponding linewidth equal to each translational diffusion coefficient. (See *Note*, p. 249.)

8.8. Scattering from Polymer Gels

Scattering from polymer gels is a relatively new application. Prins *et al.* (1972) first observed a broad "resonance" in the frequency spectrum by two dilute polymer gels: 1 % aqueous solution of agarose (an alternating copolymer of 3,6-anhydro-α-L-galactopyranose and β-D-galactopyranose) at 70°C as well as that of the gel obtained by cooling the solution to a temperature below the gel point at 42°C, and a 5 % poly(vinyl alcohol) gel in a mixture of water and ethylene glycol obtained by quenching the solution from 80 to 5°C, and subsequently measuring at room temperature. In the later case, the "resonance" disappears upon aging of the gel. The heterodyne frequency spectrum was represented by means of a modified Eq. (8.7.11):

$$S(K, \omega) \propto N\{DK^2/[(\omega - \Omega)^2 + (DK^2)^2]\} \qquad (8.8.1)$$

where Ω represented an audio "resonance" frequency of the gel. The "resonance" occurred at a few kilohertz and was traced erroneously to underdamped, oscillatory behavior of viscoelastic, microscopic inhomogeneities in the gel structure. In fact, this underdamped, oscillatory behavior derives from a mass or heat flow.

The reader should note that Doppler shifts due to the translational motion of solute molecules can often be present and be interpreted as some other effects. Bargeron *et al.* (1972) measured the light-beating spectrum of a suspension of ATP containing erthrocyte ghosts (red blood cells which have had their hemoglobin removed) in a nutrient solution. They observed a displaced spectral component at about 170 Hz in addition to the expected line centered at 0 Hz and first suggested the shifted component as being due to the Na$^+$–K$^+$ "pump", an ion-active transport mechanism across the cell membrane. However, subsequent studies revealed that the initial interpretation was premature and the shifted component could be derived from convection (Bargeron *et al.*, 1973). In fact, the effects of mass motion due to heating by the incident laser beam, especially on absorbing particles, are often not negligible. Ben-Yosef *et al.* (1972) observed a shifted component centered at ∼2 kHz in the power spectrum of laser light scattered from silver chloride colloids in water at 90° scattering angle. Thus, there is no experimental evidence for the existence of "resonance" scattering, which requires careful elimination of such experimental artifacts. In this respect, the interpretation of Prins et al. (1972) becomes an open question. Tanaka et al. (1973) have demonstrated that the spectrum of light scattered from thermal fluctuations of the gel fiber network provides a detailed quantitative characterization of the viscoelastic properties of gels. It measures the collective motion of the network structure and differs from dynamic measurements of the propagation of shear waves (through gels) which give information about the motions of individual polymers that form the fiber network (Ninomiya and Ferry, 1967). The reader should consult the original article (Tanaka et al., 1973) for details.

8.9. Motile Microorganisms and Chemotactic Response

8.9.1. Motile Microorganisms

The spectra of self-propelled living organisms no longer lead to the exponential correlation function characteristic of Brownian motion. Berge et al. (1967) first reported an experimental study on the motion of sperm cells. Nossal (1971) and Nossal et al. (1971) have treated the general theoretical problem on the spatially isotropic bacterial movement (with the later publication being simpler in its derivations) and have performed experiments on E. Coli motility. Combescot (1970) has computed the light-scattering spectrum of active sperm-cell dispersions.

Light scattering from motile bacteria has also been reviewed by Nossal and Chen (1972a). Bacteria are large particles with sizes comparable to the wavelength of light. At large angles, the scattering spectrum may contain contributions due to rotational diffusion as well as translational diffusion (see Section 8.3). However, at small scattering angles, Eq. (8.3.11) is reduced mainly to only Eq. (8.2.6). In this case, the total scattering spectrum can be described by Eq. (8.2.1). The corresponding time-dependent correlation function $R_I(K, \tau)$ is given by

$$R_I(K, \tau) = |E_s^0|^2 \left\langle \sum_{i=1}^{N} \sum_{j=1}^{N} \exp[-i\mathbf{K} \cdot \mathbf{R}_i(0)] \exp[i\mathbf{K} \cdot \mathbf{R}_j(\tau)] \right\rangle \quad (8.9.1)$$

where $\mathbf{R}_i(0)$ and $\mathbf{R}_j(t)$ are, respectively, the positions of the ith particle at time $t = 0$, and of the jth particle at time τ, and we have again taken $I = E^*E$. Equation (8.9.1) is valid provided that $KL/4 \leq 1$ where L is the maximum dimension of the particle, and the scattering amplitude E_s^0 is assumed to be the same for all particles. If the particles are independent, we have rederived Eq. (8.7.1)

$$R_I(K, \tau) = N \mid E_s^0 \mid^2 \langle \exp\{i\mathbf{K} \cdot [\mathbf{R}_i(\tau) - \mathbf{R}_i(0)]\} \rangle$$

$$= N \mid E_s^0 \mid^2 \left\langle \exp\left[i\mathbf{K} \cdot \int_0^\tau \mathbf{v}_i(t) \, dt \right] \right\rangle \qquad (8.9.2)$$

where $\mathbf{v}_i(t)$ is the velocity of the ith (arbitrary) particle at time t. Let us first take all particles to have the same speed. If the velocity is spatially isotropic, all odd terms of Eq. (8.9.2) in a Taylor series expansion vanish so that

$$\left\langle \exp\left[i\mathbf{K} \cdot \int_0^\tau \mathbf{v}(t) \, dt \right] \right\rangle = 1 - \frac{1}{2!} \int_0^\tau dy \int_0^\tau dz \langle [\mathbf{K} \cdot \mathbf{v}(y)][\mathbf{K} \cdot \mathbf{v}(z)] \rangle$$

$$+ \frac{1}{4!} \int_0^\tau dx \int_0^\tau dw \int_0^\tau dy \int_0^\tau dz$$

$$\times \langle [\mathbf{K} \cdot \mathbf{v}(x)][\mathbf{K} \cdot \mathbf{v}(w)]$$

$$\times [\mathbf{K} \cdot \mathbf{v}(y)][\mathbf{K} \cdot \mathbf{v}(z)] \rangle + \cdots \qquad (8.9.3)$$

If the movement of the particle is distributed as a Gaussian random variable with *zero* mean as for the case of Brownian particles due to thermal motions, Eq. (8.9.3) is reduced to (Kubo, 1963)

$$\left\langle \exp\left[i\mathbf{K} \cdot \int_0^\tau \mathbf{v}(t) \, dt \right] \right\rangle = \exp[-\tfrac{1}{2} W(\tau)] \qquad (8.9.4)$$

and

$$W(\tau) = \int_0^\tau \int_0^\tau \langle [(\mathbf{K} \cdot \mathbf{v}(y)][\mathbf{K} \cdot \mathbf{v}(z)] \rangle \, dy \, dz$$

$$= \frac{K^2}{3} \int_0^\tau \int_0^\tau \langle \mathbf{v}(0) \cdot \mathbf{v}(z - y) \rangle \, dy \, dz$$

$$= \tfrac{2}{3} K^2 \int_0^\tau (t - \xi) \langle \mathbf{v}(0) \cdot \mathbf{v}(\xi) \rangle \, d\xi$$

$$= \tfrac{2}{3} K^2 \int_0^\tau (t - \xi) \langle [\mathbf{v}(0)]^2 \rangle e^{-f t/m} \, d\xi$$

$$= \frac{2K^2 m^2}{3f^2} \left(e^{-f\tau/m} - 1 + \frac{f\tau}{m} \right) \langle [v(0)]^2 \rangle \qquad (8.9.5)$$

where f and m are the friction coefficient and the mass of the particle. If

$ft/m \gg 1$, Eq. (8.9.5) is further simplified to

$$W(\tau) = (2K^2 m\tau/3f)\langle[v(0)]^2\rangle \qquad (8.9.6)$$

Now with $D = (m/3f)[v(0)]^2$ (Zwanzig, 1965), we finally get

$$R_1(K, \tau) = N \mid E_s^0 \mid^2 \exp(-DK^2\tau) \qquad (8.9.7)$$

which is equivalent to Eq. (8.7.6). The above derivation was illustrated by Nossal (1971) who pointed out that $f\tau/m \gg 1$ is appropriate for light-scattering experiments since experimental resolution times are of the order of 10^{-5} sec or greater whereas molecular relaxation times m/f are of the order of 10^{-7}–10^{-8} sec.

For swimming microorganisms, Nossal and Chen (1972a) used motile strains of $E.$ $Coli$ K_{12} bacteria (Adler and Dahl, 1967) as their test example because these bacteria move at constant speeds in straight lines for time of the order of seconds before changing directions. Such times are long compared with typical decay times of bacterial scattering spectra. Thus, we may assume that the velocities of the individual bacteria remain unchanged over measurement times relevant to the scattering experiments. In other words, $v(t) \simeq v(0)$. Then (Kubo, 1963),

$$\int_0^\tau \int_0^\tau \langle[\mathbf{K}\cdot\mathbf{v}(y)][\mathbf{K}\cdot\mathbf{v}(z)]\rangle\, dy\, dz \approx \tfrac{1}{3}K^2\tau^2\langle[v(0)]^2\rangle \qquad (8.9.8)$$

Since the particles move in random directions in the absence of external forces,

$$\langle[v(0)]^2\rangle = 3\langle[v_x(0)]^2\rangle = 3\int_{-\infty}^{\infty} v_x^2 W(v_x)\, dv_x \qquad (8.9.9)$$

where $W(v_x)$ is the directed velocity distribution function of the swimming particles all swimming with the same speed v_s, and moving in random directions. By definition,

$$W(v_x) = \int_{-\infty}^{\infty} P(v)\, dv_y\, dv_z \qquad (8.9.10)$$

where $P(v)$ is the joint probability distribution for the total velocity v. If all the particles have the same speed v_s,

$$P(v) = \frac{1}{4\pi v_s^2}\delta(\mid v \mid - v_s) \qquad (8.9.11)$$

which is normalized since

$$\int P(v)\ dv = \frac{1}{4\pi v_{\mathrm{s}}^2} \int_0^{2\pi} d\phi \int_0^{\pi} \sin\theta\ d\theta \int_0^{\infty} \delta(|\ v\ | - v_{\mathrm{s}})v^2\ dv = 1 \quad (8.9.12)$$

By substituting Eq. (8.9.11) into Eq. (8.9.10), we get

$$W(v_x) = \begin{cases} 1/2v_{\mathrm{s}} & \text{for } |\ v_x\ | \le v_{\mathrm{s}} \\ \\ 0 & \text{for } |\ v_x\ | > v_{\mathrm{s}} \end{cases} \quad (8.9.13)$$

and with Eq. (8.9.9), we find

$$\langle [v(0)]^2 \rangle = v_{\mathrm{s}}^2 \quad (8.9.14)$$

Equation (8.9.3) can be computed using Eqs. (8.9.14) and (8.9.8) so that

$$\left\langle \exp\left[i\mathbf{K}\cdot \int_0^{\tau} \mathbf{v}(t)\ dt \right] \right\rangle \approx 1 - \frac{K^2\tau^2}{2!}\ (\tfrac{1}{3}v_{\mathrm{s}}^2) + \frac{K^4\tau^4}{4!}\left(\frac{v_{\mathrm{s}}^4}{5} \right) - \cdots$$

$$= \sum_{j=0}^{\infty} \frac{(-1)^j(K\tau v_{\mathrm{s}})^{2j}}{(2j+1)!} = \frac{\sin K v_{\mathrm{s}}\tau}{K v_{\mathrm{s}}\tau} \quad (8.9.15)$$

Substituting Eq. (8.9.15) into Eq. (8.9.2), we get the time correlation function of the signal for isotropic particles all swimming with the same speed and in totally random motions:

$$R_{\mathrm{SW}}(K, \tau) = N\ |\ E_{\mathrm{s}}^0\ |^2\ (\sin K v_{\mathrm{s}}\tau / K v_{\mathrm{s}}\tau) \quad (8.9.16)$$

and the corresponding frequency spectrum:

$$S_{\mathrm{SW}}(K, \omega) = N\ |\ E_{\mathrm{s}}^0\ |^2 \left(\frac{H(|\ \omega\ | - |\ K\ |\ v_{\mathrm{s}})}{2\ |\ K\ |\ v_{\mathrm{s}}} \right) \quad (8.9.17)$$

where

$$H(X) = \begin{cases} 1 & \text{if } X < 0 \\ \\ 0 & \text{if } X > 0 \end{cases}$$

The subscript sw denotes swimming particles.

More generally, bacteria have a velocity distribution which is isotropic in the absence of external forces. Then, Eq. (8.9.2) can be written as

$$R_{\mathrm{SW}}(K, \tau) = N\ |\ E_{\mathrm{s}}^0\ |^2\ \langle \exp[i\mathbf{K}\cdot\mathbf{v}_{\mathrm{s}}\tau] \rangle \quad (8.9.18)$$

where the ensemble average is performed over the velocity distribution.

$$\langle \exp[i\mathbf{K}\cdot\mathbf{v}_s\tau]\rangle \equiv \int_0^{2\pi} d\phi \int_0^{\pi} d\theta \int_0^{\infty} \exp(i\mathbf{K}\cdot\mathbf{v}_s\tau) \sin\theta [v_s^2 P(v_s)]\, dv_s$$

$$= \int_0^{\infty} \frac{\sin Kv_s\tau}{Kv_s\tau} \lceil 4\pi v_s^2 P(v_s)\rceil\, dv_s$$

$$= \int_0^{\infty} \frac{\sin Kv_s\tau}{Kv_s\tau} W(v_s)\, dv_s \qquad (8.9.19)$$

where $W(v_s)$ $[= 4\pi v_s^2 P(v_s)]$ is the swimming-speed distribution. The swimming-speed distribution $W(v_s)$ can be obtained by the Fourier sine transform of Eq. (8.9.19):

$$W(v_s) - N \mid E_s^0 \mid^2 \frac{2v_s}{\pi} \int_0^{\infty} \sin Kv_s\tau [K\tau R_{SW}(K,\tau)]\, d(K\tau) \qquad (8.9.20)$$

Nossal and Chen (1972a) have also considered a mixture of motile and non-motile scatterers, i.e., the assembly of microorganisms is composed of two types, the live ones which are swimming and the still ones which are either dead or of low metabolic activity. Let α be the fraction of motile particles. Then,

$$R(K,\tau) = \alpha R_{SW}(K,\tau) + (1-\alpha)N \mid E_s^0 \mid^2 \exp(-DK^2\tau) \qquad (8.9.21)$$

At low population densities, number fluctuation spectroscopy (Section 6.5) becomes an additional tool which gives us information on the mean-free swimming distance and/or the swimming-speed distribution.

8.9.2. Chemotactic Response†

The physiological mechanism by which bacteria sense the chemo-attractants and then move towards them is little known. Quasielastic light scattering can be used to detect spatially anisotropic (directed) motion and thus provide a means to study chemotactic response. The developments by Nossal and Chen are summarized as follows.

The scattering geometry is shown in Fig. 8.9.1. In a heterodyne spectrometer, when the local oscillator field is much greater than the scattered field, all the information about bacterial motion is represented in the cor-

† Nossal and Chen, 1972b, 1973.

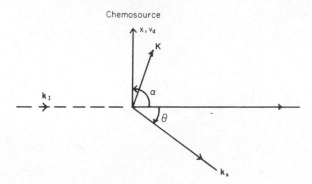

Fig. 8.9.1. Experimental geometry for chemotactic motion within the scattering plane.

relation function according to Eq. (4.3.28):

$$R(K, \tau) \propto \langle E_s^*(0) E_s(\tau) \rangle + \langle E_s(0) E_s^*(\tau) \rangle \qquad (8.9.22)$$

If the bacteria move independently, $R(K, \tau)$ may be evaluated the same way as Eq. (8.9.2) with

$$R(K, \tau) \propto \left\langle \exp\left[i\mathbf{K} \cdot \int_0^\tau \mathbf{v}_i(t)\, dt \right] \right\rangle + \left\langle \exp\left[-i\mathbf{K} \cdot \int_0^\tau \mathbf{v}_i(t)\, dt \right] \right\rangle$$

Nossal and Chen introduced a directed velocity v_d defined as

$$\mathbf{v}_d = \mathbf{v}_i - \mathbf{v}_s$$

and let the chemosource be located in the x direction as shown in Fig. 8.9.1. The components of $\mathbf{v}_d$ and $\mathbf{v}_s$ can be represented by

$$\mathbf{v}_d = (v_d, 0, 0), \qquad \langle \mathbf{v}_s \rangle = (0, 0, 0)$$

$$\langle v_{sx}^2 \rangle = \langle v_{sy}^2 \rangle = \langle v_{sz}^2 \rangle = \tfrac{1}{3}[\langle |v_i|^2 \rangle - v_d^2)] \qquad (8.9.23)$$

They then assumed the directed and the isotropic motions to be stochastically independent and obtained

$$R(K, \tau) = \left\langle \cos \int_0^\tau \mathbf{K} \cdot \mathbf{v}_d(t)\, dt \right\rangle \left\langle \cos \int_0^\tau \mathbf{K} \cdot \mathbf{v}_s(t)\, dt \right\rangle$$

$$= R_{ch}(K, \tau) R_{SW}(K, \tau) \qquad (8.9.24)$$

We again recall that bacterial velocities persist for times long compared with typical decay times of bacterial scattering spectra so that

$$R_{ch}(K, \tau) = \langle \cos[\mathbf{K} \cdot \mathbf{v}_d] \tau \rangle \qquad (8.9.25)$$

According to Fig. 8.9.1,

$$\mathbf{K} \cdot \mathbf{v}_d = K v_d \cos(\theta/2) \qquad (8.9.26)$$

when $\alpha = \frac{1}{2}\pi$, and

$$\mathbf{K} \cdot \mathbf{v}_d = (2\pi n v_d / \lambda_{air}) \sin \theta \qquad (8.9.27)$$

Substitution of Eq. (8.9.27) into Eq. (8.9.25) yields

$$R_{ch}(K, \tau) = \int_0^\infty \cos\left(\frac{2\pi n v_d}{\lambda_{air}} (\sin \theta) \tau\right) W_{ch}(v_d) \, dv_d \qquad (8.9.28)$$

where $W_{ch}(v_d)$ is the velocity distribution due to chemotactic response. $W_{ch}(v_d)$ can be evaluated from a Fourier cosine inversion of Eq. (8.9.28):

$$W_{ch}(v_d) = \frac{2}{\pi} \int_0^\infty \cos(Z v_d) R_{ch}(Z) \, dZ \qquad (8.9.29)$$

where $Z = 2\pi n (\sin \theta) \tau / \lambda_{air}$. Berg (1974) has studied how bacteria move about. He observed that the probability of abrupt changes in direction by a swimming bacterium is biased by chemoreception (Berg and Brown, 1972).

Note added in proof: In more practical terms, the laser Doppler effect has been used to study the electrophoretic mobility and diffusion coefficient of bovine serum albumin (Ware and Flygare, 1971), fibrinogen (Ware and Flygare, 1972), erythrocytes (Uzgiris, 1972), and model colloids (Uzgiris and Costashuk, 1973). The major experimental difficulties for examining such electrokinetic phenomena often result from the application of an electric field to a conducting solution. These deleterious effects include Joule heating, gas bubbling, electrode polarization, and surface reactions. Uzgiris (1974) has given fairly careful considerations to those effects, which cannot be ignored. Although further improvements are conceivable and should be forthcoming, his article (Uzgiris, 1974) does provide a very good experimental starting point on electrodes design for those interested in electrophoretic light scattering. We shall summarize his findings as follows:

Uzgiris (1974) tried to minimize convective instabilities due to Joule heating by using electrodes with a very narrow gap (200 μm to 1 mm). For a closely spaced pair of parallel plate electrodes, the temperature rise ΔT due to Joule heating at the center of the gap can be approximated by

$$\Delta T \propto d^2 E^2 / R_e \Lambda \qquad (8.7.16)$$

where d, E, R_e and Λ are, respectively, the distance between the electrodes, the electric field strength, the electrical resistivity, and the thermal conductivity. Thus, for a given system of interest, the gap (d) between the electrodes should be as small as possible. Furthermore, for a horizontal layer of water heated from below, Uzgiris referred to Schmidt and Saunders (1938), who reported no turbulent motion provided that the Rayleigh number R^* is less than 1700:

$$R^* = (\alpha g c' / \Lambda \eta_w) \Delta T d^3 \qquad (8.7.17)$$

where α, g, c', and η_w are the thermal coefficient of expansion, the gravitational acceleration, the specific heat per unit volume, and the kinematic viscosity of water at the mean temperature between the plates, respectively.

An alternating square wave (instead of pulsed alternating square wave) electric field could be used to prevent gas bubbling and electrode polarization. Bennett and Uzgiris (1973) considered the harmonic structures in the Doppler spectra due to the applied alternating square wave electric field. Furthermore, the electro-osmotic effects for narrow gap electrodes are negligible because of the small electric fields at solid–liquid interfaces.

Platinized Pt electrodes gave the best results, and the RC time constants of such electrodes were discussed. Uzgiris and Kaplan(1974) further described a simple method for coating platinized Pt electrodes with bovine serum albumin to prevent surface reactions.

References

Adler, J., and Dahl, M. M. (1967). *J. Gen. Microbiol.* 46, 161.

Ailawadi, N. K., Berne, B. J., and Forster, D. (1971). *Phys. Rev. A* 3, 1472.

Andersen, H. C., and Pecora, R. (1971). *J. Chem. Phys.* 54, 2584.

Arecchi, F. T., Giglio, M., and Tartari, U. (1967). *Phys. Rev.* 163, 186.

Bancroft, F. C., and Freifelder, D. (1970). *J. Mol. Biol.* 54, 537.

Bargeron, C. B. (1973). *Appl. Phys. Lett.* 23, 379.

Bargeron, C. B. (1974). *J. Chem. Phys.* 60, 2516.

Bargeron, C. B., McCally, R. L., Tatham, P. E. R., Cannon, S. M., and Hart, R. W. (1972). *Phys. Rev. Lett.* 28, 1105.

Bargeron, C. B., McCally, R. L., Cannon, S. M., and Hart, R. W. (1973). *Phys. Rev. Lett.* 30, 205.

Benedek, G. B. (1969). *In* "Polarization, Matiere and Rayonnement." Presses Universitaires de France, Paris.

Bennett, A. J., and Uzgiris, E. E. (1973). *Phys. Rev. A* 8, 2662.

Ben Reuven, A., and Gershon, N. D. (1971). *J. Chem. Phys.* 54, 1049.

Ben-Yosef, N., Zweigenbaum, S., and Weitz, A. (1972). *Appl. Phys. Lett.* 21, 436.

Berg, H. C. (1974). *Bull. Amer. Phys. Soc.* 19, 243.

Berg, H. C., and Brown, D. A. (1972). *Nature* 239, 500.

Bergé, P., Volochine, B., Billard, R., Hamelin, A. (1967). *C. R. H. Acad. Sci. Ser. D.* 265, 889.

Boyer, L., Vacher, R., Cecchi, L., Adam, M., and Bergé, P. (1971). *Phys. Rev. Lett.* 26, 1435.

Broersma, S. (1960). *J. Chem. Phys.* 32, 1626, 1632. [*See also* van Holde, K. E. (1971) "Physical Biochemistry," Table 4.1. Prentice-Hall, Englewood Cliffs, New Jersey.]

Brown, J. C., and Pusey, P. N. (1974). *J. Phys. D* 7, L31.

Cantrell, C. D. (1970). *Phys. Rev. A* 1, 672.

Carlson, F. D., and Herbert, T. J. (1972). *J. Phys. (Paris)* 33, C1-157.

Caroli, C., and Parodi, O. (1969). *J. Phys. B* 2, 1229.

Chen, F. C., Tscharnuter, W., Schmidt, D., and Chu, B. (1974). *J. Chem. Phys.* 60, 1675.

Chu, B. (1967). "Molecular Forces," based on the Baker Lectures of Peter J. W. Debye. Wiley, New York.

Chu, B. (1968). *J. Chem. Educ.* 45, 224.

Chu, B. (1970). *Annu. Rev. Phys. Chem.* 21, 145.

Chu, B. and Schoenes, F. J. (1968). *J. Colloid Interface Sci.* 27, 424.

Chung, C. H., and Yip, S. (1971). *Phys. Rev. A* 4, 928.

Combescot, R. (1970). *J. Phys. (Paris)* 31, 767.

Cummins, H. Z., and Swinney, H. L. (1970). *Progr. Opt.* 8, 133.

Cummins, H. Z., Carlson, F. D., Herbert, T. J. and Woods, G. (1969). *Biophys. J.* **9**, 518.
Cummins, H. Z., Knable, N., and Yeh, Y. (1964). *Phys. Rev. Lett.* **12**, 150.
Debye, P. (1965). *Phys. Rev. Lett.* **14**, 783.
Dubin, S. B. (1970). Ph.D. thesis. M.I.T., Cambridge, Massachusetts.
Dubin, S. B., Benedek, G. B., Bancroft, F. C., Freifelder, D. (1970). *J. Mol. Biol.* **54**, 547.
Dubin, S. B., Clark, N. A., and Benedek, G. B. (1971). *J. Chem. Phys.* **54**, 5158.
DuBois, M., and Borge, P. (1971). *Phys. Rev. Lett.* **26**, 121.
Doty, P., and Yang, J. T. (1957). *J. Amer. Chem. Soc.* **79**, 671.
Dubin, S. B., Lunacek, J. H., and Benedek, G. B. (1967). *Proc. Nat. Acad. Sci. U. S.* **57**, 1164.
Fishman, L., and Mountain, R. D. (1970). *J. Phys. Chem.* **74**, 2178.
Foord, R., Jakeman, E. Oliver, C. J., Pike, E. R., Blagrove, R. J., Wood, E., and Peacocke, A. R. (1970). *Nature* **227**, 242.
Ford Jr., N. C. (1972). *Chemica Scr.* **2**, 193.
Ford, Jr., N. C., Gabler, R., and Karasz, F. E. (1973). *In* "Polymer Molecular Weight Methods" (M. Ezrin, ed.). Amer. Chem. Soc.
Ford, N. C., Lee, W., and Karasz, F. E. (1969). *J. Chem. Phys* **50**, 3098.
Ford, N. C., Karasz, F. E., and Owen, J. E. M. (1970). *Discuss. Faraday Soc.* **49**, 228.
Frederick, J. E., Reed, T. F., and Kramer, O. (1971). *Macromolecules* **4**, 242.
French, M. J., Angus, J. C., and Walton, A. G. (1969). *Science* **163**, 345.
Fujime, S. (1969). *J. Phys. Soc. Japan* **27**, 1370.
Fujime, S. (1970a). *J. Phys. Soc. Japan* **28**, 267.
Fujime, S. (1970b). *J. Phys. Soc. Japan* **29**, 416.
Fujime, S. (1970c). *J. Phys. Soc. Japan* **29**, 527.
Fujime, S. (1970d). *J. Phys. Soc. Japan* **29**, 751.
Fujime, S. (1971). *J. Phys. Soc. Japan* **31**, 1805.
Fujime, S. (1972). *Advan. Biophys.* **3**, 1.
Fujime, S., and Hatano, S. (1972). *J. Mechanochem. Cell Motility* **1**, 81.
Fujime, S., and Ishiwata, S. (1971). *J. Mol. Biol.* **62**, 251.
Fujime, S., Ishiwata, S., and Maeda, T. (1972). *Biochim. Biophys. Acta,* **283**, 351.
Geiduschek, E. P. (1954). *J. Polym. Sci.* **13**, 408.
Geiduschek, E. P., and Holtzer, A. (1958). *Advan. Biol. Med. Phys.* **6**, 431.
Gerhart, J. C., and Schachman, H. K. (1968). *Biochemistry* **7**, 538.
Goers, J. W., and Schumaker, V. N. (1970). *J. Mol. Biol.* **54**, 125.
Harris, R. A., and Hearst, J. E. (1966). *J. Chem. Phys.* **44**, 2595.
Hess, S., and Müller, R. (1974). *Opt. Commun.* **10**, 172.
Hocker, L., Krupp, J., Benedek, G. B., and Vournakis, J. (1973). *Biopolymers* **12**, 1677.
Huang, W. N., Vrancken, E., Frederick, J. E. (1973). *Macromolecules* **6**, 58.
Ishiwata, S., and Fujime, S. (1971a). *J. Phys. Soc. Japan* **30**, 302.
Ishiwata, S., and Fujime, S. (1971b). *J. Phys. Soc. Japan* **30**, 303.
Ishiwata, S., and Fujime, S. (1971c). *J. Phys. Soc. Japan* **31**, 1601.
Ishiwata, S., and Fujime, S. (1972). *J. Mol. Biol.* **68**, 511.
Jackson, D. A., Bird, M. J., Pentecost, H. T. A., and Powles, J. G. (1971). *Phys. Lett. A* **35**, 1.
Jackson, D. A., Pike, E. R., Powles, J. G., and Vaughan, J. M. (1973). *J. Phys. C* **6**, L55.
Jamieson, A. M., Mack, L., and Walton, A. G. (1972). *Biopolymers* **11**, 2267.
Jamieson, A. M., and Presley, C. T. (1973). *Macromolecules* **6**, 358.
Jamieson, A. M., and Walton, A. G. (1973). *J. Chem. Phys.* **58**, 1054.
Jamieson, A. M., Downs, C. E., and Walton, A. G. (1972). *Biochim. Biophys. Acta* **271**, 34.
Jennings, B. R. (1972). *In* "Light Scattering from Polymer Solutions" (M. Huglin, ed.) Chap. 13. Academic Press, New York.

Kendall, M. G., and Stuart, A. (1958). "The Advanced Theory of Statistics," Vol. 1. Griffin, London.

Keyes, T., and Kivelson, D. (1971). *J. Chem. Phys.* **54**, 1786.

Komarov, L. I., and Fisher, I. Z. (1963). *Sov. Phys. JETP* **16**, 1358.

Koppel, D. E. (1972). *J. Chem. Phys.* **57**, 4814.

Koppel, D. E. (1973). Ph.D. thesis. Columbia Univ., New York.

Kramer, O., and Frederick, J. E. (1971). *Macromolecules* **4**, 613.

Kramer, O., and Frederick, J. E. (1972). *Macromolecules* **5**, 69.

Kubo, R. (1963). *J. Math. Phys.* **4**, 174.

Landau, L., and Lifshitz, E. (1959). "Fluid Mechanics," Chap. 6. Addison-Wesley, Reading, Massachusetts.

Lee, W. (1970). Ph.D. thesis. Univ. of Massachusetts, Amherst, Massachusetts.

Lee, S. P., and Chu, B. (1974). *Appl. Phys. Lett.* **24**, 261.

Lee, S. P., Tscharnuter, W., and Chu, B. (1972). *J. Polym. Sci.* **10**, 2453.

Lin, S. H. C., Dewan, R. K., Bloomfield, V. A., and Morr, C. V. (1971). *Biochemistry* **10**, 4788.

Maeda, T., and Fujime, S. (1972). *Rev. Sci. Instrum.* **43**, 567.

Maeda, H., and Saito, N. (1969). *J. Phys. Soc. Japan* **27**, 984.

Marshall, A. G., and Pecora, R. (1971). *J. Chem. Phys.* **55**, 1245.

Maruyama, M., and Asakura, S. (1972). *J. Mol. Biol.* **68**, 347.

Miller, G. A. (1967). *J. Phys. Chem.* **71**, 2305.

Miller, G. A., and Lee, C. S. (1968). *J. Phys. Chem.* **72**, 4644.

Mountain, R. D. (1966a). *Rev. Mod. Phys.* **38**, 205.

Mountain, R. D. (1966b). *J. Res. Nat. Bur. Stand. Sect. A* **70**, 207.

Mountain, R. D. (1968). *J. Res. Nat. Bur. Stand. Sect. A* **72**, 95.

Mountain, R. D. (1970). *CRC Critical Rev. Solid State Sci.* **1**, 5.

Mountain, R. D., and Deutch, J. M. (1969). *J. Chem. Phys.* **50**, 1103.

Ninomiya, K., and Ferry, J. D. (1967). *J. Polymer Sci.* **A-2**, **5**, 195.

Nossal, R. (1971). *Biophys. J.* **11**, 341.

Nossal, R., and Chen, S. H. (1972a). *J. Phys. (Paris)* **33**, C1-171.

Nossal, R., and Chen, S. H. (1972b). *Opt. Commun.* **5**, 117.

Nossal, R., and Chen, S. H. (1973). Nature New Biology **244**, 253.

Nossal, R., Chen, S. H., and Lai, C. C. (1971). *Opt. Commun.* **4**, 35.

Oliver, C. J., Pike, E. R., and Vaughan, J. M. (1972). *Proc. Rochester Conf.*

Pecora, R. (1964). *J. Chem. Phys.* **40**, 1604.

Pecora, R. (1965). *J. Chem. Phys.* **43**, 1562.

Pecora, R. (1968a). *J. Chem. Phys.* **49**, 1032.

Pecora, R. (1968b). *J. Chem. Phys.* **48**, 4126.

Pecora, R. (1968c). *J. Chem. Phys.* **49**, 1036.

Pecora, R. (1969). *Macromolecules* **2**, 31.

Pecora, R. (1970a). *In* "Photochemistry of Macromolecules" (R. F. Reinisch, ed.). Plenum, New York.

Pecora, R. (1970b). *Discuss. Faraday Soc.* **49**, 222.

Pecora, R. (1971). *Nature Phys. Sci.* **231**, 73.

Pecora, R. (1972). *Annu. Rev. Biophys. Bioeng.* **1**, 257.

Pecora, R., and Steele, W. A. (1965). *J. Chem. Phys.* **42**, 1863.

Pecora, R., and Tagami, Y. (1969). *J. Chem. Phys.* **51**, 3298.

Phillies, G. D. J. (report prior to publication). Effects of Intermacromolecular Interactions on Diffusion I. Two-Component Solutions.

Pike, E. R. (1970). *Rev. Phys. Technol.* **1**, 180.

Prins, W., Rimai, L., and Chompff, A. J. (1972). *Macromolecules* **5**, 104.

Pusey, P. N. (1973). *In* "Industrial Polymers: Characterization by Molecular Weight" (J. H. S. Green and R. Dietz, eds.). Transcripta Books, London.

Pusey, P. N., Schaefer, D. W., Koppel, D. E., Camerini-Otero, R. D., Franklin, R. M. (1972a). *J. Phys. (Paris)* **33**, C1-163.

Pusey, P. N., Koppel, D. E., Schaefer, D. W., and Camerini-Otero, R. D. (1972b). IBM Res. Rep. No. RC3924.

Pyun, C. W., and Fixman, M. (1964). *J. Chem. Phys.* **41**, 937.

Reed, T. F., and Frederick, J. E. (1971). *Macromolecules* **4**, 72.

Rimai, L., Hickmott, J. T., Cole, T., and Carew, E. B. (1970). *Biophys. J.* **10**, 20.

Saito, N. Takahashi, K., and Yunoki, Y. (1967). *J. Phys. Soc. Japan* **22**, 219.

Schaefer, D. W., and Berne, B. J. (1974). *Phys. Rev. Lett.* **32**, 1110.

Schaefer, D. W., Benedek, G. B., Schofield, P., and Bradford, E. (1971). *J. Chem. Phys.* **55**, 3884.

Scheraga, H. A., and Mandelkern, L. (1953). *J. Amer. Chem. Soc.* **75**, 179.

Schmidt, R. L. (1973). *Biopolymers* **12**, 1427.

Schmidt, R. L., and Saunders, O. A. (1938). *Proc. Roy. Soc.* **A165**, 216.

Schmitz, K. S. (1974). *Macromolecules* **7**, 146.

Schmitz, K. S., and Schurr, J. M. (1973). *Biopolymers* **12**, 1021.

Schurr, J. M., and Schmitz, K. S. (1973). *Biopolymers* **12**, 1543.

Sellen, D. B. (1970). *Polymer* **11**, 374.

Silbey, R., and Deutch, J. M. (1972). *J. Chem. Phys.* **57**, 5010.

Stephen, M. J. (1971). *J. Chem. Phys.* **55**, 3878.

Tagami, Y. (1971). *J. Chem. Phys.* **54**, 4990.

Tagami, Y., and Pecora, R. (1969). *J. Chem. Phys.* **51**, 3293.

Tanaka, T., Hocker, L. O., and Benedek, G. B. (1973). *J. Chem. Phys.* **59**, 5151.

Tanford, C. (1961). "Physical Chemistry of Macromolecules," p. 327. Wiley, New York.

Tanford, C., Kawahara, K., and Lapanje, S. (1967). *J. Amer. Chem. Soc.* **89**, 729.

Thompson, D. S. (1971a). *J. Chem. Phys.* **54**, 1411.

Thompson, D. S. (1971b). *J. Phys. Chem.* **75**, 789.

Timasheff, S. N., and Townend, R. (1970). *In* "Physical Principles and Techniques of Protein Chemistry" (Sidney J. Leach, ed.), Part B. Academic Press, New York.

Uzgiris, E. E. (1972). *Opt. Commun.* **6**, 55.

Uzgiris, E. E. (1974). *Rev. Sci. Instrum.* **45**, 74.

Uzgiris, E. E., and Costaschuk, F. M. (1973). *Nature Phys. Sci.* **242**, 77.

Uzgiris, E. E., and Kaplan, J. H. (1974). *Rev. Sci. Instrum.* **45**, 120.

Van Hove, L. (1954). *Phys. Rev.* **95**, 249.

Volterra, V. (1969). *Phys. Rev.* **180**, 156.

Wada, A. (1974). *Biopolymers* **13**, 237.

Wada, A., Suda, N., Tsuda, T., and Soda, K. (1969). *J. Chem. Phys.* **50**, 31.

Wada, A., Soda, K., Tanaka, T., and Suda, N. (1970). *Rev. Sci. Instrum.* **41**, 845.

Wada, A., Ford, Jr., N. C., and Karasz, F. E. (1971). *J. Chem. Phys.* **55**, 1798.

Ware, B. R., and Flygare, W. H. (1971). *Chem. Phys. Lett.* **12**, 81.

Ware, B. R., and Flygare, W. H. (1972). *J. Coll. Interface Sci.* **39**, 670.

Welch, J., and Bloomfield, V. A. (1973). *J. Polym. Sci. Part A2* **11**, 1855.

Yeh, Y. (1970). *J. Chem. Phys.* **52**, 6218.

Yeh, Y., and Cummins, H. Z. (1964). *Appl. Phys. Lett.* **4**, 176.

Yeh, Y., and Keeler, R. N. (1969). *Quart. Rev. Biophys.* **2**, 315.

Zimm, B. H. (1956). *J. Chem. Phys.* **24**, 269.

Zimm, B. H., and Kilb, R. W. (1959). *J. Polymer Sci.* **37**, 19.

Zipper, P., Kratky, O., Herrman, R., and Hohn, T. (1971). *Eur. J. Biochem.* **18**, 1.

Zwanzig, R. W. (1965). *Annu. Rev. Phys. Chem.* **16**, 67.

Chapter IX

REACTION KINETICS—CONCENTRATION CORRELATION SPECTROSCOPY

9.1. Introduction

Local concentration fluctuations of a solution can be related not only to diffusion but also to polarizability changes of the species because of chemical reaction. Quasielastic light scattering of chemically reacting systems has been shown theoretically, and in only a few cases experimentally, to be one of the most appealing techniques for the determination of equilibrium and kinetic parameters for fast reactions whenever the conditions are appropriate. The small time-dependent spontaneous local fluctuations of the refractive index are produced by thermal motions of the molecules and require no external perturbations. Furthermore, such small fluctuations permit linearization of the kinetic rate equations. Thus, in many ways, quasielastic light scattering may provide a complementary approach to the rapid perturbation techniques of Eigen and his co-workers (1963). In practice, equilibrium properties of the association reactions of myosin (Herbert and Carlson, 1971) and of F-actin (Fujime and Ishiwata, 1971) have been reported. Experimental studies of chemical kinetics by light scattering are on a much less solid footing. While Yeh and Keeler (1969a) and Yeh (1970) have, respectively, measured the hydration relaxation times of

$$(Me^{2+}(H_2O)SO_4^{2-})_{aq} \rightleftharpoons (Me^{2+}SO_4^{2-})_{aq}$$

where Me^{2+} represents Zn^{2+} or Mn^{2+} and the rates of "melting" of the $[d(A, T)]$ copolymer, definitive experiments have been lacking. Perhaps,

254

the difficulties lie with the fact that reaction rates become detectable only
if there are sufficient differences in either the diffusion coefficients or $\partial n/\partial C$
between the reactants and the products. Furthermore, complex reactions
with multireaction rate constants are simply beyond the simple beating
technique which invariably superimposes all the lines around zero frequency.
Yet, there seem to be ways which one can develop that will eventually make
the application of quasielastic light scattering to the study of reaction rates
more practical. In particular, the imposition of an external electric field
(Berne and Giniger, 1973) or the utilization of fluorescence radiation in
concentration correlation spectroscopy (Magde *et al.*, 1972; Elson and
Magde, 1974; Magde *et al.*, 1974) have made the future of this approach
sufficiently promising that we put reactions kinetics in a separate chapter.

9.2. Simple Reaction Processes

9.2.1. The Reactions $A \rightleftharpoons B$ and $mA \rightleftharpoons nB$

For a nonreacting mixture of species A and B, the dissipative mechanisms
of each component are independent. For example the diffusion equation
for the translational motions of center of mass of A and B are separate so
that

$$\frac{\partial}{\partial t} \delta C_{\mathrm{A}}(\mathbf{K}, t) = -D_{\mathrm{A}} K^2 \, \delta C_{\mathrm{A}}(\mathbf{K}, t) \qquad (9.2.1\mathrm{a})$$

and

$$\frac{\partial}{\partial t} \delta C_{\mathrm{B}}(\mathbf{K}, t) = -D_{\mathrm{B}} K^2 \, \delta C_{\mathrm{B}}(\mathbf{K}, t) \qquad (9.2.1\mathrm{b})$$

Here, C_i and D_i are, respectively, the concentration and the diffusion
coefficient of component i. δC_i represents the local concentration fluctuations of component i. The time correlation function for such a nonreacting
mixture of species A and B is

$$R(K, \tau) \propto (C_{\mathrm{A}}/C) P_{\mathrm{A}}(\theta) \exp(-D_{\mathrm{A}} K^2 \tau)$$
$$+ (C_{\mathrm{B}}/C) P_{\mathrm{B}}(\theta) \exp(-D_{\mathrm{B}} K^2 \tau) \quad (9.2.2)$$

where C $(= C_{\mathrm{A}} + C_{\mathrm{B}})$ is the total molar concentration and $P_i(\theta)$ is the
particle scattering factor of component i. Equation (9.2.2) is a special
case of Eq. (8.2.17) for a system with two species.

Now suppose A and B react. We then have

$$A \underset{k_b}{\overset{k_f}{\rightleftharpoons}} B \qquad (9.2.3)$$

which represents a reversible unimolecular interconversion of A to B with forward and backward rate constants k_f and k_b. We should note that k_f here denotes the rate constant for the forward reaction not the propagation vector for the scattered wave. For the reversible reaction $A \rightleftharpoons B$, the equilibrium constant K_c is

$$K_c = \bar{C}_B/\bar{C}_A = k_f/k_b \qquad (9.2.4)$$

where $\bar{C}_i$ is the equilibrium concentration of component i and Eqs. (9.2.1a) and (9.2.1b) are no longer independent, but are coupled through the chemical rate mechanisms. In other words, local concentration fluctuations will take place due to diffusion as well as reaction. Equations (9.2.1) then have the form

$$d\,\delta C_i(\mathbf{K}, t)/dt = -K^2 D_i\,\delta C_i(\mathbf{K}, t) + \sum_{j=1}^{2} T_{ij}\,\delta C_j(\mathbf{K}, t) \qquad (9.2.5)$$

where $i, j = A, B$. T_{ij} is a reaction matrix commonly encountered in relaxation kinetics (Schwarz, 1968) and contains rate constants and equilibrium concentrations of reactants and products. Equation (9.2.5) takes into account diffusion and reaction as the only important dissipative processes. Fortunately, viscous relaxation and heat conduction are usually not important in macromolecular solutions. Alternatively we may write (Bloomfield and Benbasat, 1971)

$$d\,\delta C(\mathbf{K}, t)/dt = M \cdot \delta C(\mathbf{K}, t) \qquad (9.2.6)$$

where δC is the concentration fluctuation vector $(\delta C_1, \delta C_2, \ldots, \delta C_r)$ and the elements of the matrix M are

$$M_{ij} = -D_i K^2\,\delta_{ij} + T_{ij} \qquad (9.2.7)$$

with δ_{ij} being the Kronecker δ. The rate of change of C_A due to the reversible reaction Eq. (9.2.3) is

$$(\partial C_A/\partial t)_{\text{reac}} = -k_f C_A + k_b C_B \qquad (9.2.8)$$

Since $C_A = \bar{C}_A + \delta C_A$ and $C_B = \bar{C}_B + \delta C_B$, we get

$$(\partial\,\delta C_A/\partial t)_{\text{reac}} = -k_f\,\delta C_A + k_b\,\delta C_B \qquad (9.2.9a)$$

and

$$(\partial\,\delta C_B/\partial t)_{\text{reac}} = k_f\,\delta C_A - k_b\,\delta C_B \qquad (9.2.9b)$$

Thus, the reaction matrix T_{ij} for the reaction $A \rightleftharpoons B$ has the form

$$T_{ij} = \begin{bmatrix} -k_f & k_b \\ k_f & -k_b \end{bmatrix} \tag{9.2.10}$$

and the corresponding matrix M is

$$M = \begin{bmatrix} -D_A K^2 - k_f & k_b \\ k_f & -D_B K^2 - k_b \end{bmatrix} \tag{9.2.11}$$

The solution to Eq. (9.2.6) for the reaction $A \rightleftharpoons B$ is obtained by substituting $\delta C(\mathbf{K}, t) = \delta C(\mathbf{K}, 0) e^{+\lambda t}$ into Eq. (9.2.6) which is an eigenvalue problem with

$$[M - \lambda I] \cdot \delta C(\mathbf{K}, t) = 0 \tag{9.2.12}$$

where

$$[M - \lambda I] = \begin{bmatrix} -D_A K^2 - k_f - \lambda & k_b \\ k_f & -D_B K^2 - k_b - \lambda \end{bmatrix} \tag{9.2.13}$$

The normal modes which obey the expression $|M - \lambda I| = 0$ are

$$\lambda_\pm = \frac{1}{2} \left\{ -K^2 (D_A + D_B) - \tau_r^{-1} \right.$$

$$\left. \pm \tau_r^{-1} \left[1 + 2 \left(\frac{K_c - 1}{K_c + 1} \right) \frac{K^2 \Delta}{\tau_r^{-1}} + \left(\frac{\Delta K^2}{\tau_r^{-1}} \right)^2 \right]^{1/2} \right\} \tag{9.2.14}$$

where $\Delta = D_A - D_B$ and τ_r^{-1} $(= k_f + k_b)$ is the inverse relaxation time of the reversible unimolecular reaction $A \rightleftharpoons B$. Equation (9.2.14) may be simplified to give

$$\lambda_\pm = \tfrac{1}{2} \{ -K^2 (D_A + D_B) - \tau_r^{-1}$$

$$\pm [(\Delta K^2 + \tau_r^{-1})^2 - 4k_b \Delta K^2]^{1/2} \} \tag{9.2.15}$$

The generalization of the above reaction to more complex kinetic problems has been discussed under several approximations by many investigators (Berne and Frisch, 1967; Blum and Salsburg, 1968, 1969; Berne and Pecora, 1969; Blum, 1969; Yeh and Keeler, 1969b; Weinberg and Kapral, 1970; Knirk and Salsburg, 1971; Bloomfield and Benbasat, 1971; Fujime, 1973, 1974). The same problem becomes more difficult when the shape of the macromolecule is taken into account (Fujime et al., 1972; Fujime and Maruyama, 1973). For the reaction $A \rightleftharpoons B$,

$$g^{(1)}(\tau) = (1 - A^*) \exp(\lambda_+ \tau) + A^* \exp(\lambda_- \tau) \tag{9.2.16}$$

where

$$A^* = x(R + \xi)^2/(R^2 + x)(\xi^2 + x)$$

with

$$R = -\tfrac{1}{2}\tau_A\{\Delta K^2 + (k_f - k_b) + [(\Delta K^2 + \tau_r^{-1})^2 - 4k_b\Delta K^2]^{1/2}\}$$

$$\xi = \frac{(\partial n/\partial C)_B f_B(K)}{(\partial n/\partial C)_A f_A(K)} \quad \text{and} \quad x = \frac{M_A \bar{C}_A}{M_B \bar{C}_B}$$

Equation (9.2.16) can be resolved if λ_+ and λ_- are comparable in magnitude and $A^* \sim \tfrac{1}{2}$.

Case I. If $D_A = D_B = D$, $\Delta = D_A - D_B = 0$. Equation (9.2.15) is reduced to

$$\lambda_+ = -DK^2, \quad \lambda_- = -(DK^2 + 1/\tau_r) \qquad (9.2.17)$$

As $DK^2 \to 0$ with decreasing scattering angles, we can make $DK^2 + 1/\tau_r \gg DK^2$ by selecting a scattering angle such that $1/\tau_r \gg DK^2$. However, the second condition $A^* \sim \tfrac{1}{2}$ is not easy to achieve for many protein systems. For example, if $D_A = D_B$, $R = -1$, and for small protein molecules, $(\partial n/\partial C)_A \approx (\partial n/\partial C)_B$ so that $\xi = 1$. Then $A^* = 0$ and the reaction is not detectable. In general, the reaction kinetics is measurable only when $A^* \neq 0$ which implies $D_A \neq D_B$ or $\xi \neq 1$.

Case II. If $\xi = 1$ but $D_A \neq D_B$, and $\tau_r^{-1} \gg \Delta K^2$, then Eq. (9.2.15) has the approximate form

$$\lambda_\pm \approx \tfrac{1}{2}[-K^2(D_A + D_B) \pm (D_A - D_B)K^2] \qquad (9.2.18)$$

so that the terms of Eq. (9.2.18) are separable. However, the rate constants are absent from Eq. (9.2.18). Thus, quasielastic light scattering is not suitable for slow reactions even though, in principle, we can always let $(D_A + D_B)K^2 \to 0$ and $\Delta K^2 \to 0$ by making measurements at increasingly smaller angles. In practice, there is always an experimental limit because of dust or uncertainties in the momentum transfer vector.

For the reaction

$$m\mathrm{A} \underset{k_b}{\overset{k_f}{\rightleftharpoons}} n\mathrm{B} \qquad (9.2.19)$$

the modified diffusion equation due to local concentration fluctuations as well as the reversible reaction, but with negligible temperature and pressure fluctuations is

$$\partial \, \delta C_A / \partial t = D_A \nabla^2 \, \delta C_A - m k_f (\bar{C}_A)^{m-1} \, \delta C_A$$
$$+ n k_b (\bar{C}_B)^{n-1} \, \delta C_B$$
$$= D_A \nabla^2 \, \delta C_A - (1/\tau_A) \, \delta C_A + (1/\tau_B) \, \delta C_B \quad (9.2.20)$$

Similarly,

$$\partial \, \delta C_B / \partial t = D_B \nabla^2 \, \delta C_B + (1/\tau_A) \, \delta C_A - (1/\tau_B) \, \delta C_B \quad (9.2.21)$$

where

$$1/\tau_A = m k_f (\bar{C}_A)^{m-1}$$

$$\quad (9.2.22)$$

$$1/\tau_B = n k_b (\bar{C}_B)^{n-1}$$

Equations (9.2.15) and (9.2.16) hold if we replace k_f and k_b by $1/\tau_A$ and $1/\tau$ of Eq. (9.2.22), respectively. We recall that, for the reaction $A \rightleftharpoons B$, $\tau_A^{-1} = k_f$ and $\tau_B^{-1} = k_b$.

9.2.2. The Reaction $A + B \rightleftharpoons C$

For the reversible reaction

$$A + B \underset{k_b}{\overset{k_f}{\rightleftharpoons}} C \quad (9.2.23)$$

where k_f and k_b are the forward and backward rate constants, the rate of change of C_A due to the reversible reaction of Eq. (9.2.23) is

$$(\partial C_A / \partial t)_{\text{reac}} = -k_f C_A C_B + k_B C_C \quad (9.2.24)$$

and the corresponding equilibrium constant is

$$K_c = k_f / k_b = \bar{C}_C / \bar{C}_A \bar{C}_B \quad (9.2.25)$$

By neglecting terms containing $\delta C_A \, \delta C_B$ as well as temperature and pressure fluctuations, we have

$$\partial \, \delta C_A / \partial t = D_A \nabla^2 \, \delta C_A - k_f (\bar{C}_B \, \delta C_A + \bar{C}_A \, \delta C_B) + k_b \, \delta C_C \quad (9.2.26)$$

Similarly,

$$\partial \, \delta C_B / \partial t = D_B \nabla^2 \, \delta C_B - k_f (\bar{C}_A \, \delta C_B + \bar{C}_B \, \delta C_A) + k_b \, \delta C_C \quad (9.2.27)$$

and

$$\partial \, \delta C_C / \partial t = D_C \nabla^2 \, \delta C_C + k_f (\bar{C}_A \, \delta C_B + \bar{C}_B \, \delta C_A) - k_b \, \delta C_C \quad (9.2.28)$$

The M matrix of Eq. (9.2.11) is modified to give

$$
M = \begin{bmatrix}
-D_A K^2 - k_f \bar{C}_B & -k_f \bar{C}_A & +k_b \\
-k_f \bar{C}_B & -D_B K^2 - k_f \bar{C}_A & +k_b \\
-k_f \bar{C}_B & -k_f \bar{C}_A & -D_C K^2 - k_b
\end{bmatrix} \quad (9.2.29)
$$

and the inverse chemical relaxation time for the reaction $A + B \rightleftharpoons C$ is

$$
\tau_r^{-1} = k_f(\bar{C}_A + \bar{C}_B) + k_b \quad (9.2.30)
$$

The eigenvalue equation $|M - \lambda I| = 0$ yields a cubic equation in λ with three eigenvalues λ_1, λ_2, and λ_3.

For slow reactions, we again have

$$
\lambda_1 = -D_A K^2, \qquad \lambda_2 = -D_B K^2, \qquad \lambda_3 = -D_C K^2 \quad (9.2.31)
$$

when $D_i K^2 \gg \tau_r^{-1}$. The system behaves like a nonreacting mixture.

For very rapid reactions, with $D_i K^2 \ll \tau_r^{-1}$,

$$
\lambda_1 \rightarrow \tau_r^{-1}, \qquad \lambda_2, \lambda_3 \rightarrow 0 \quad (9.2.32)
$$

Unfortunately, the scattering amplitude becomes very low so that the single broad Lorentzian with a half-width of τ_r^{-1} cannot be easily detected.

9.3. Feasibility Considerations for Quasielastic Light Scattering†

Benbasat and Bloomfield have made estimates on the feasibility of determining macromolecular association kinetics by quasielastic light scattering. Such considerations are very important since biomacromolecular systems are weak scatterers where small changes in the linewidths are always difficult to measure. So, if the computed changes are less than, say, 5 % quasielastic light scattering does not provide sufficient return for the amount of work needed to get the answer. Benbasat and Bloomfield introduced reduced variables in terms of ratios of diffusion to reaction rates, and of diffusion coefficients of A, B, and C to one another. Their results are summarized as follows. Figures 9.3.1a–d show contours in log–log plots of D_B/D_A vs D_C/D_A. The shaded areas represent the half-width of the spectrum of the reacting system which differs by less than 5 % from the expected half-width for a nonreacting system ($\tau_r^{-1} = 0$) of the same equilib-

† Benbasat and Bloomfield (1973).

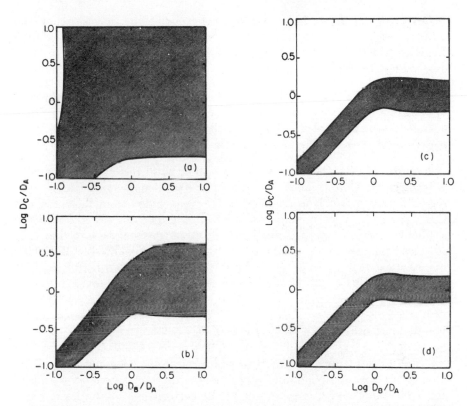

Fig. 9.3.1. Nonshaded regions correspond to values of the diffusion coefficient ratios D_B/D_A for which the spectrum of a reacting mixture has a half-width differing by more than 5 % from the expected half-width of the nonreacting system. Calculations assume $\beta = M_B/M_A = (D_A/D_B)^3$ and $f = 1$. (a) $k_b/K^2 D_A = 10^{-2}$, (b) $= 10^{-1}$, (c) $= 1$, (d) $= 10$ (Benbasat and Bloomfield, 1973, reproduced by permission of American Chemical Society).

rium composition. Calculations were done for the greatest sensitivity in detecting the reaction by assuming $f = K_c C_A^0 = K_c C_B^0 = 1$, which implies that A, B, and C are present in comparable amounts. The superscript zero denotes initial concentration. Benbasat and Bloomfield also took $\beta = M_B/M_A = (D_A/D_B)^3$ and varied $r = k_b/D_A K^2$ from (a) 10^{-2}, (b) 10^{-1}, (c) 1, to (d) 10. Plots with $r > 10$ are virtually indistinguishable from that for $r = 10$.

Benbasat and Bloomfield observed from their computations, as shown in Fig. 9.3.1, that there are three regions (I, II, and III) which are not easily accessible for kinetic studies by means of quasielastic light scattering even if the reactions proceed very fast.

Region I. $D_B/D_A \approx 1$, $D_C/D_A \approx 1$. The conditions indicate that the diffusion coefficients of the reactants and of the product are all comparable. Reaction kinetics can be detected only if the reactants and the product have markedly different polarizabilities.

Region II. $D_B/D_A > 1$, $D_C/D_A \approx 1$. The second region includes the binding of a receptor protein (B) which is rather small to DNA (A) which is large to form a complex (C) which is large, or the addition of a detergent molecule (B) to a micelle (A) to form a slightly larger micelle (C).

Region III. $D_A/D_B > 1$, $D_C/D_B \approx 1$. The third region corresponds to A being small while B and C are of similar size. Region III is the same as region I with A and B interchanged. They concluded from their analysis that a particularly interesting system which would be well suited for kinetic studies by means of quasielastic light scattering consists of a large reactant A which combines with a small reactant B to form a small product C. Such a hypothetical reaction representing the upper left quadrant of Fig. 9.3.1 was indeed proposed by Benbasat and Bloomfield for the reversible combination of the enzyme polynucleotide phosphorylase [$M = 200,000$, $D = 4.8 \times 10^{-7}$ cm²/sec (Godefroy *et al.*, 1970)] and a single-stranded polyribonucleotide chain [$M = 165,000$, $D = 1.6 \times 10^{-7}$ cm²/sec (Bloomfield, 1963)] to give a complex with $M = 365,000$ and $D = 3.9 \times 10^{-7}$ cm²/sec, corresponding to a partial wrapping of the polynucleotide chain around the enzyme (Valentine *et al.*, 1969). Another system consisting of small reactants and a large product that corresponds to the lower right quadrant of Fig. 9.3.1 has been proposed by Benbasat and Bloomfield. They used a small denaturing molecule with a compact globular protein to form a swollen denatured protein chain as an example.

The outcome of such analysis clearly shows that although reaction kinetics can be studied by means of quasielastic light scattering, there are severe limitations to this technique. A feasibility calculation is essential if the reader is not familiar with the difficulties. For example, at the 5 % discrimination level, a reaction between two spherical monomers of equal size ($D_A/D_B = 1$) to form a dumb-bell shaped dimer ($D_C/D_A \approx \frac{3}{4}$) is just at the limit of detectability for $k_b/D_A K^2 > 1$ (Bloomfield *et al.*, 1967). McQueen and Hermans (1972) computed that the effect of fluctuations in the monomer-micelle equilibrium is very small because the integrated intensity of the broader of the two Lorentzians which is determined by both the diffusion coefficient of the monomer and the reaction rate is small compared to that of the purely diffusion broadened line due to micelles. Thus, we come back to the original assertion that although quasielastic light scattering appears to be very attractive for reaction kinetics, the technique is applicable only under some *very restrictive conditions*. In particular, the reaction rates are measurable only if there are substantial changes in $(\partial n/\partial C)$ and/or D.

9.4. Concentration Correlation Spectroscopy

9.4.1. Fluorescence Correlation Spectroscopy

Recently, Magde *et al.* (1972) measured the temporal correlations of thermodynamic concentration fluctuations in a chemical reactive system at equilibrium by observing fluctuations of the fluorescence of a reaction product. Their method requires that either the reactants or the product must be fluorescent. As an illustration, they took the principal chemical reaction between DNA (A) and ethidium bromide (B) to form a fluorescent complex (C) as a single-step biomolecular process with forward and backward rate constants k_f and k_b:

$$A + B \underset{k_b}{\overset{k_f}{\rightleftharpoons}} C \qquad (9.2.23)$$

The autocorrelation function of the photocurrent fluctuation is

$$R_{\delta i}(\tau) = \langle \delta i(t + \tau)\, \delta i(t) \rangle \qquad (9.4.1)$$

where

$$\delta i(t) = i(t) - \langle i(t) \rangle \qquad (9.4.2)$$

The photocurrent due to fluorescence induced by the exciting radiation $I(\mathbf{r})$ is

$$i(t) = g\epsilon Q \int_{-\infty}^{\infty} I(\mathbf{r}) C_C(\mathbf{r}, t)\, d\mathbf{r} \qquad (9.4.3)$$

where g accounts for quantum efficiency, photomultiplier gain, and geometrical and filtering losses and represents the fraction of emitted fluorescent photons actually detected; Q and ϵ are, respectively, the fluorescence quantum yield and the extinction coefficient for the EtBr–DNA complex; and C_C denotes the concentration of complex at position $\mathbf{r}$ and time t. The fluorescent emission delay of 10^{-9} sec uncouples the fluorescence from the coherent exciting radiation. Thus,

$$R_{\delta i}(\tau) = (g\epsilon Q)^2 \int I(\mathbf{r}) I(\mathbf{r}') \langle \delta C_C(\mathbf{r}, t)\, \delta C_C(\mathbf{r}, t + \tau) \rangle\, d\mathbf{r}\, d\mathbf{r}' \quad (9.4.4)$$

$R_i(\tau)$ can be evaluated in terms of solutions of Eq. (9.2.29). The characteristic diffusion time obtained from a convolution of the spatial concentration function with the Gaussian profile of the cylindrical laser beam is

$$\tau_j = a^2/4D_j \tag{9.4.5}$$

where $j = $ A, B, and a is the beam radius at $I(a)/I_{\max} = e^{-2}$ with $\bar{C}_B \sim \bar{C}_C \ll \bar{C}_A \sim K_c^{-1}$, and $D_A = D_C \ll D_B$. Magde *et al.* (1972) obtained

$$R_{\delta i}(\tau) = \frac{(g\epsilon Q)^2 P^2 l \bar{C}_C}{\pi a^2} \left[A_0(\tau) + A_+(\tau) + A_-(\tau) \right] \tag{9.4.6}$$

where P_∞ is the total incident power, l is the length of the illuminated (cylindrical) scattering volume, and

$$A_0(\tau) = K_c \bar{C}_B \left(1 + \frac{\tau}{\tau_A} \right)^{-1}$$

$$A_+(\tau) = \frac{K_c \bar{C}_A}{1 + K_c \bar{C}_A} \frac{1}{1 + \tau/\tau_+} \left(1 + \frac{2}{\tau_B \tau_r^{-1}} \frac{1}{1 + K_c \bar{C}_A} \frac{1}{1 + \tau/\tau_+} \right)$$

$$A_-(\tau) = \frac{1}{1 + K_c \bar{C}_A} \frac{\exp(-\tau_r^{-1}\tau)}{1 + \tau/\tau_-} \left(1 - \frac{2}{\tau_B \tau_r^{-1}} \frac{K_c \bar{C}_A}{1 + K_c \bar{C}_A} \frac{1}{1 + \tau/\tau_-} \right)$$

with characteristic times

$$\tau_+ = \tau_B (1 + K_c \bar{C}_A)$$

and

$$\tau_- = \tau_B (1 + K_c \bar{C}_A)/K \bar{C}_A$$

Since the mean photocurrent $\langle i(\tau) \rangle = g\epsilon Q l P_\infty \bar{C}_C$,

$$\beta^{1/2} = \frac{\delta i_{\mathrm{rms}}}{\langle i(t) \rangle} = \frac{[R_{\delta i}(0)]^{1/2}}{\langle i(t) \rangle} = (\pi a^2 l \bar{C}_C)^{-1/2} \tag{9.4.7}$$

In their experiment, $a \approx 5.5$ μm, $l = 150$ μm, $\pi a^2 l \sim 10^{-8}$ cm^3, and $\bar{C}_C \sim 10^{-7}$ mole or 10^{14} molecules/cm^3 so that $\delta i_{\mathrm{rms}}/\langle i(t) \rangle \sim 10^{-3}$. At 514.5 nm, $\epsilon = 3.8$ (mM cm)$^{-1}$, and $Q = 14$ % for the DNA–EtBr complex while $Q \sim 0.7$ % for the free dye. Magde *et al.* verified Eq. (9.4.7) by measuring $R_{\delta i}(\tau)$ for two pure dyes, rhodamine 6G and EtBr. They observed $R_{\delta i}(\tau) \propto (1 + \tau/\tau_D)^{-1}$ where $\tau_D = a^2/4D_D$ with $D_D \approx 1.5 \times 10^{-6}$ cm^2/sec for both dyes. For the binding of ethidium bromide to DNA, they obtained $k_f = (1.8 \pm 0.8) \times 10^7$ sec^{-1} mole^{-1} and $k_b = 20 \pm 7$ sec^{-1} whence $K_c = k_f/k_b$ gives $4 \times 10^5 \le K_c \le 2 \times 10^5$ mole^{-1}. $k_b = 40 \pm 10$ sec^{-1} and $k_f = 2 \times 10^7$ sec^{-1} mole^{-1} by conventional temperature perturbation methods at 32°C have been reported.

9.4.2. Concentration Correlation Spectroscopy

The method of fluorescence correlation spectroscopy around equilibrium in a reactive system has been demonstrated to be a feasible approach. As suggested by Magde *et al.* (1972) the technique may be extendable to other indicators such as optical absorption or Raman scattering. Although the requirement for an extremely small number of reactive molecules ($\sim 10^4$) in the scattering volume implies a different optical arrangement from quasi-elastic light scattering to this technique, the same restriction may be utilized to our advantage for studies in surface physics and biological systems, such as membranes.

In concentration correlation spectroscopy (CCS), we measure the number of molecules of a specified type in a defined (open) volume of solution as a function of time. The average time behavior of spontaneous concentration fluctuations as expressed by Eqs. (9.4.1.) and (9.4.2) utilizes the crucial quantity $\delta i(t) = i(t) - \langle i(t) \rangle$, which differs from $i(t)$ in Eq. (4.3.3) for quasielastic light scattering. Here, the detectability of a measurement depends upon the ratio $\delta i_{rms}/\langle i(t) \rangle$, as illustrated typically by Eq. (9.4.7), but not upon $i(t)$ as in quasielastic light scattering. Thus, it is essential to provide an optical arrangement and concentration of solution in such a way so as to maximize the $\delta i_{rms}/\langle i(t) \rangle$ ratio and to minimize the random statistical errors. For example, the power of coherence (Section 4.1.3) is no longer an important consideration. The optical system (Section 7.3) should be changed so that the local fluctuations in the number of indicator molecules in an effective observed volume vary appreciably from its mean value. Consequently, very small sample volumes must be used. In this respect, the study of membranes and surfaces that automatically limit one dimension of the sample volume and individual cells that limit the effective observed volume become appealing. However, it should be cautioned that the study of surfaces by light scattering is also related to other interface properties, such as surface tension. Quasi-elastic light scattering has been applied to single surfaces (Bouchiat and Meunier, 1972; Bouchiat *et al.*, 1968; Katyl and Ingard, 1967, 1968) and thin free liquid flims (Fijnaut and Vrij, 1973). Thus, the overall effects could be more complex in the presence of chemical reaction, diffusion, and surface waves, even though the technique as well as the method of analysis are available. The local concentration fluctuations in a volume element also require that the solution concentration be sufficiently low in order to produce a favorable $\delta i_{rms}/\langle i(t) \rangle$ ratio. For example, in the experiment on the reaction of macromolecules DNA with the drug ethidium bromide to form a fluorescent complex (Magde *et al.*, 1974), the sample volume went down to about 10^{-8} mliters with concentration of solute in the 10^{-9} molar range. Such small effective open volumes require that we focus the incident beam down to a very small spot, which cannot be achieved without utilizing the spatial coherent property of a laser. Thus, we need to use a relatively short-focal-length condensing lens and a laser in order to provide a sufficiently small beam cross section and high power density for such experiments.

Studies of fluctuations in the number of particles in a defined open volume of solution can be observed by quasielastic light scattering (Schaefer and Berne, 1972; Schaefer and Pusey, 1972). Unfortunately, the refractive index increments that are the measure of reactant concentration fluctuations in quasielastic light scattering are quite insensitive to chemical reactions. A key feature of concentration correlation spectroscopy is its chemical specificity, which will undoubtedly be extremely useful in interpreting complex kinetic measurements and in observing particular reactions in complex systems. Any sensitive and specific index of concentration can be used as a probe. Thus, in addition to fluorescence, other spectral properties, such as optical rotation, absorption, and Raman scattering, can serve as specific indicators of the concentration of particular chemical species. In fact, Feher and Weissman (Feher, 1970; Feher and Weissman, 1973) have used electrical conductivity as an indicator and have investigated the rate of the ionization reaction of beryllium sulfate by observing conductivity fluctuations. The reader is strongly advised to read the two articles by Elson and Magde (1974) and Magde et $al.$ (1974) for the general principles and theoretical basis of CCS as well as the experimental methods and problems related to fluorescence correlation spectroscopy. The highlights are summarized as follows.

9.4.2.A. Experimental procedures

The basic ingredient of the experimental apparatus is to create a small effective observed volume and to provide means to detect $\delta i(t)$ ($= i(t) - \langle i(t) \rangle$) instead of $i(t)$. The same criteria should be observed independent of the form of the specific indicator used, whether it be fluorescence, absorption, or Raman scattering.

Optical. The very small and well-defined reproducible and precisely characterized effective observed sample volume can be achieved fairly readily using a laser, which permits focusing the beam to a very small spot. The laser beam was passed through a spatial fitter [Eq. (7.2.5)] and a beam expander before final focusing. The resulting TEM$_{00}$ Gaussian beam has an intensity profile of the form:

$$I = I_0 \exp(-2r^2/r_0^2) \tag{7.2.1}$$

The depth of focus can be estimated by means of Eq. (7.2.6). Magde *et al.* (1974) used a 9-cm focal length fused-silica aspheric condensing lens, which produced a focal spot size of about 5.5 μm. The sample cells had inside dimensions 20 × 10 × 0.15 or 0.025 mm, so that the effective observed sample volume was about $\pi \times 5.5^2/4 \times 10^{-6} \times (0.15 \text{ or } 0.025) = (35.6 \text{ or } 5.94) \times 10^{-7} \text{ mm}^3$.

It is essential to maximize the collection optics and to reduce all sources of unwanted fluctuations since the total output from local thermodynamic concentration fluctuations by a relatively small number of molecules is small. In fluorescence correlation spectroscopy, parabolic fluorescence-collecting mirrors were used to obtain a better than 50 % efficiency. Only sample cells made of Suprasil fused silica, which exhibited relatively weak fluorescence, were used, and the entire collecting optics should be constructed of materials that do not emit too much extraneous fluorescence.

The ITT FW 130 PM tube is no longer as advantageous because of its very small photocathode. A selected PM tube, such as EMI 9558B or 9556A, with a 5- or 2.5-cm S-20 photocathode should be more appropriate.

Electronic.† The cathode photocurrent after conversion to voltage was compensated for incident laser light fluctuations by comparing the output signal with the reference signal in a differential amplifier so that the correlator measures $R_{\delta i}$ (Eq. 9.4.1). All other electronic components remain the same as in quasielastic light scattering.

Signal-to-noise consideration. The technique has not yet been adapted for digital photon-correlation (Chapter 6) even though such modifications are technically quite feasible and should yield more precise results.

It appears that Koppel has already analyzed the signal-to-noise (S/N) problem based on digital photon correlation. According to Eq. (6.3.6), the measured photocurrent fluctuation autocorrelation function after N sweeps has the form:

$$R_{\delta n}(t_l) = R_{\delta n}(lT) = \langle \delta n(t_r)\delta n(t_{r+l}) \rangle = \frac{1}{N} \sum_{r=1}^{N} \delta n(t_r)\delta n(t_{r+l}) \qquad (9.4.8)$$

where $\delta n(t_r) = n(t_r) - \langle n \rangle$, $n(t_r)$ is the number of photons detected in the rth channel with sample period T, $\langle n \rangle$ is the average number of photocounts per channel with sample period T. He concluded that when the detection rate of photons is sufficiently high, S/N improves as the square root of the observed number of fluctuations, which is simply the ratio of the length of observation time to the characteristic time of the fluctuations. On the other hand, when the photons are detected in only a small

† Magde *et al.* (1974).

fraction of the sampling intervals, S/N is dominated by photon noise and increases by the square root of the number of observations made, as well as light flux. Thus, the criterion is to make $\beta \langle n \rangle \to 1$. Further increases in the light flux and changes in other experimental parameters bring diminishing returns.

With Eqs. (7.2.3), (9.4.7), and

$$\langle n \rangle = \langle i \rangle T = g \epsilon Q \bar{C}_\mathrm{C} P_\infty l T \qquad (9.4.9)$$

for a single fluorescent species, we get

$$\langle n \rangle \beta = g \epsilon Q P_\infty T / \pi a^2 \qquad (9.4.10)$$

where $a \equiv r_0$ in Eq. (7.2.3). Thus, S/N improves as we increase g, ϵ, and Q and the laser power density $P_\infty / \pi a^2$. It is curious to note that other things being equal, S/N improves with the sample time interval. Magde *et al.* (1974) compensated the short time fluctuations ($< T$) of their analog signal by appropriate electronic filtering before signal correlation. S/N is independent of l.

Magde *et al.* (1974) also considered spurious contributions to systematic errors by way of signal processing, fluctuations in the exciting and collection optics, and other extraneous effects, such as correlations due to local density and temperature fluctuation, bleaching, and laser heating. A small value of $\bar{C}_\mathrm{C}$ is desirable to overcome systematic errors.

9.4.2.B. General theory

The photocurrent due to m species that fluoresce changes Eq. (9.4.3.) to a more general form:

$$i(t) = g \sum_{j=1}^{m} \epsilon_j Q_j \int I(\mathbf{r}) C_j(\mathbf{r}, t) \, d\mathbf{r}$$

Correspondingly,

$$\delta i(t) = i(t) - \langle i \rangle = g \sum_{j=1}^{m} \epsilon_j Q_j \int I(\mathbf{r}) \, \delta C_j(\mathbf{r}, t) \, d\mathbf{r} \qquad (9.4.11)$$

Then the autocorrelation function of the photocurrent fluctuation, Eq. (9.4.1), becomes

$$R_{\delta i}(\tau) \equiv \langle \delta i(t + \tau) \, \delta i(t) \rangle = \sum_{j=1}^{m} \sum_{l=1}^{m} R_{jl}(\tau) \qquad (9.4.12)$$

where $R_{jl}(\tau) = g^2 \epsilon_j \epsilon_l Q_j Q_l \int I(\mathbf{r}) I(\mathbf{r}') \langle \delta C_j(\mathbf{r}, t) \, \delta C_l(\mathbf{r}', t + \tau) \rangle \, d\mathbf{r} \, d\mathbf{r}'$, and the shot-noise term has again been omitted. If we assume that fluctuations of concentrations of different species are uncorrelated, the spatial correlation function of local concentration fluctuations has the form:

$$\langle \delta C_j(r, 0) \, \delta C_l(\mathbf{r}', 0) \rangle = \bar{C}_j \, \delta_{jl} \, \delta(\mathbf{r} - \mathbf{r}') \tag{9.4.13}$$

provided that the spatial correlation length of species j is small and the Poisson statistics obeyed. Elson and Magde (1974) first evaluated $R_{\delta i}(0)$ by means of Eqs. (9.4.13) and 7.2.1):

$$R_{\delta i}(0) = \sum_{j=1}^{m} \sum_{l=1}^{m} g^2 \epsilon_j \epsilon_l Q_j Q_l \int I(\mathbf{r}) I(\mathbf{r}') \bar{C}_j \, \delta_{jl} \, \delta(\mathbf{r} - \mathbf{r}') d\mathbf{r} \, d\mathbf{r}'$$

$$= g^2 \sum_{j=1}^{m} (\epsilon_j Q_j)^2 \bar{C}_j \cdot (P_\infty^2 / \pi a^2) l \tag{9.4.14}$$

where their experimental setup using a thin cell of thickness l in the same z-direction as the laser beam having a Gaussian intensity profile required that

$$\delta C(\mathbf{r}, \tau) = 0, \qquad \text{at} \quad x, y = \pm \infty \tag{9.4.15}$$

and

$$\partial \, \delta C(\mathbf{r}, \tau) / \partial z = 0, \qquad \text{at} \quad z = 0, l \tag{9.4.16}$$

The detailed reaction mechanisms vary with the nature of the system. Although we have discussed a few simple processes in Section 9.2, the task of interpreting reaction schemes requires a thorough knowledge in chemical kinetics (Eigen and de Maeyer, 1963).

Deutsch *et al.* (1972) have considered the spectrum of light scattered from systems with chemical oscillations and dissipative structures. They examined isobaric and isothermal fluctuations from a steady state exhibiting oscillatory decay, marginally stable chemical oscillations, or dissipative structures and found new features consisting of splittings in the chemical lines and dispersive (non-Lorentzian) contributions. Thus far, it appears that from reaction kinetics considerations, quasielastic light scattering is *not* suitable for all chemical relaxation time studies. However, under favorable conditions, the technique may provide a novel approach to examine reaction kinetics which cannot be done otherwise. On the other hand, concentration correlation spectroscopy seems to hold a more promising future in chemical relaxation time studies. New attempts are constantly being proposed. For example, Lovett (1972) suggested that the reacting sample be placed inside the resonant cavity of a laser so as to study the frequency modulation produced by fluctuations about equilibrium of chemical reactions.

References

Benbasat, J. A., and Bloomfield, V. A. (1973). *Macromolecules* **6**, 593.
Berne, B. J. and Frisch, H. L. (1967). *J. Chem. Phys.* **47**, 3675.
Berne, B. J. and Giniger, R. (1973). *Biopolymers* **12**, 1161.
Berne, B. J. and Pecora, R. (1969). *J. Chem. Phys.* **50**, 783.
Bloomfield, V. A. (1963). *Biochem. Biophys. Res. Commun.* **34**, 765.
Bloomfield, V. A., and Benbasat, J. A. (1971). *Macromolecules* **4**, 607.
Bloomfield, V. A., Dalton, W. O., and Van Holde, K. E. (1967). *Biopolymers* **5**, 135.
Blum, L. (1969). *J. Chem. Phys.* **51**, 5024.
Blum, L., and Salsburg, Z. W. (1968). *J. Chem. Phys.* **48**, 2292.
Blum, L., and Salsburg, Z. W. (1969). *J. Chem. Phys.* **50**, 1654.
Bouchiat, M. A., and Meunier, J. (1972). J. de Phys. 33, C1-141.
Bouchiat, M. A., Meunier, J., and Brossel, J. (1968). *C. R. Acad. Sci. Paris Ser. B.* **266**, 255.
Deutsch, J. M., Hudson, S., Ortoleva, P. J., and Ross, J. (1972). *J. Chem. Phys.* **57**, 4327.
Eigen, M., and de Maeyer, L. (1963). *Tech. Org. Chem.* **8**, 896.
Elson, E., and Magde, D. (1974). *Biopolymers* **13**, 1.
Feher, G. (1970). *Biophys. Soc. J. Absract* **10**, 118.
Feher, G., and Weissman, M. (1973). *Proc. Nat. Acad. Sci. U.S.A.* **40**, 870.
Fijnaut, H. M., and Vrij, A. (1973). *Nature Phys. Sci.* **246**, 118.
Fujime, S. (1973). *Macromolecules* **6**, 371; (1974). *Macromolecules* **7**,146.
Fujime, S., and Ishiwata, S. (1971). *J. Mol. Biol.* **62**, 251.
Fujime, S., and Maruyama, M. (1973). *Macromolecules* **6**, 237.
Fujime, S., Maruyama, M., and Asakura, S. (1972). *Macromolecules* **5**, 813.
Godefroy, Th., Cohn, M., and Grunberg-Manago, M. (1970). *Eur. J. Biochem.* **12**, 236.
Herbert, T. J., and Carlson, F. D. (1971). *Biopolymers* **10**, 2231.
Katyl, R. H., and Ingard, U. (1967). *Phys. Rev. Lett.* **19**, 64; (1968) *Phys. Rev. Lett.* **20**, 248.
Knirk, D. L., and Salsburg, Z. W. (1971). *J. Chem. Phys.* **54**, 1251.
Lovett, R. (1972). *J. Statist. Phys.* **4**, 43.
Magde, D., Elson, E., and Webb, W. W. (1972). *Phys. Rev. Lett.* **29**, 705.
Magde, D., Elson, E., and Webb, W. W. (1974). *Biopolymers* **13**, 29.
McQueen, D. H., and Hermans, J. J. (1972). *J. Coll. Interface Sci.* **39**, 389.
Schaefer, D. W., and Berne, B. J. (1972). *Phys. Rev. Lett.* **28**, 475.
Schaefer, D. W., and Pusey, P. N. (1972). *Phys. Rev. Lett.* **29**, 843.
Schwartz, G. (1968). *Rev. Mod. Phys.* **40**, 206.
Valentine, R. C., Thang, M. N., and Grunberg-Manago, M. (1969). *J. Mol. Biol.* **39**, 389.
Weinberg, M., and Kapral, R. (1970). *J. Chem. Phys.* **53**, 4409.
Yeh, Y. (1970). *J. Chem. Phys.* **52**, 6218.
Yeh, Y., and Keeler, R. N. (1969a). *J. Chem. Phys.* **51**, 1120.
Yeh, Y., and Keeler, R. N. (1969b). *Quart. Rev. Biophys.* **2**, 315.

Chapter X
ANEMOMETRY

10.1. Introduction

In Chapter VIII, we have briefly discussed the use of an external electric field in order to induce linear motion in the charged macromolecules so that species with different ionic mobilities can be analyzed and identified in terms of their corresponding Doppler shifts. The use of Doppler effects has been widely exploited as a powerful tool for sensing relative motion. In quasielastic light scattering, Yeh and Cummins (1964) first used optical heterodyning to measure the Doppler shift in laser light scattered from a suspension of polystyrene latex spheres which follow the motion of the flow stream. Foreman *et al.* (1965) then developed a laser Doppler velocimeter to measure localized flow velocities in gases using smoke as scattering centers and in ordinary tap water without the addition of external scattering contaminants (Foreman *et al.*, 1966a). The same technique can be applied for studying turbulence (Frisch, 1967) and extended to the observation of atmospheric wind velocity and turbulence. Hughes *et al.* (1970) have made experimental measurements of artificial wind velocities (0.5–3 m/sec) at a 100-ft range using an argon ion laser and digital autocorrelation. Pike (1970) has also mentioned that the CO_2 laser operating at 10.6 μm in combination with a cooled lead–tin telluride detector shows promise for this application. Huffaker *et al.* (1970) have proposed an arrangement for measuring the three-vector components of wind velocity and have successfully measured wind velocity at short range in one channel of such a system. Hughes and Pike (1973) compared a CO_2 laser heterodyne system with a real fringe visible-wavelength system based on an argon ion laser and concluded that the CO_2 system has considerably greater sensitivity at ranges greater than a few meters. The use of laser Doppler velocimetry in clear-air turbulence studies has been proposed. However, earlier results were marginal at best. Although digital photon correlation improves the prospects for such applications as has been demonstrated by Pike (1972), it is known that propagation of laser beams through the atmosphere over long ranges tends to degrade the efficiency of optical heterodyning because of wavefront distortion (Hodara, 1966). Thus, more fruitful results are likely to come from studies dealing with highly localized flow velocities and turbulence in gases (Abbiss *et al.*, 1972; Durrani and Greated, 1973a), liquids, and especially solutions under controlled conditions. The use of lasers for local measurement of velocity components, species densities, and temperatures has been reviewed by Penner and Jerskey (1973).

Laser anemometry is being developed at a rapid pace. The purpose of this chapter is subjective from the viewpoint of a chemist rather than an engineer. Several important technical developments related to studies dealing with turbulence have been omitted. The outline tries to point out pertinent relations among laser anemometry, electrophoretic light scattering (Chapter VII), and reaction kinetics in the presence of a pulsed electric field (Chapter IX). At this moment, it appears that the optical arrangements and certain statistical considerations for laser anemometry (Greated and Durrani, 1971; Durrani and Greated, 1973b,c, 1974) have been fairly well developed. Thus, the reader should be able to take advantage of those advances that can be utilized readily in electrophoretic light scattering and other, as yet undeveloped, aspects of Doppler shifted studies, such as measurements under streaming conditions where the flow can orient the macromolecules in solution. In laser anemometry, the digital photon correlator remains the most sensitive instrument. However, like in electrophoretic light scattering, the Doppler shift tends to make the time-correlation function more complex than the power spectrum, and the Fourier transform of the time-correlation function can be difficult. Consequently, the (real-time) spectrum analyzer with its wider frequency range or the fast Fourier transform analyzer remains a more versatile and convenient instrument for this type of application. Laser anemometry has been applied in many fields. In particular, Tanaka (Tanaka, 1974; Tanaka *et al.*, 1974) inserted a 0.5-mm diam optical monofiber catheter into the femoral vein of a healthy rabbit and measured a mean velocity of blood flow of 1.3 cm/sec. The heterodyne beat notes were obtained between the local oscillator originating at the end of the fiber and the light scattered from the moving erythrocytes. Further applications and refinements of the Doppler technique will undoubtedly come forth even though the fundamentals will remain the same.

10.2. The Doppler Model

The Doppler frequency is measured by mixing the scattered signal, which has been shifted owing to the velocity of the target, with a portion of the incident reference beam and observing the beats between them.

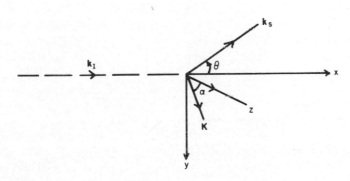

Fig. 10.2.1. Scattering geometry for a particle moving with velocity v; incident light ($\mathbf{k}_I$, ω_I), and Rayleigh scattered light ($\mathbf{k}_s$). $\mathbf{K} = \mathbf{k}_s - \mathbf{k}_I$; $|v|\cos\alpha$ is the component of v in the direction of $\mathbf{K}$; $\mathbf{v} = v_x\hat{\mathbf{x}} + v_y\hat{\mathbf{y}}$ with $\hat{\mathbf{x}}$ and $\hat{\mathbf{y}}$ being the unit vectors in the direction of x ($\parallel \mathbf{k}_I$) and y ($\perp \mathbf{k}_I$): $(\mathbf{K}/|K|)\cdot v_x\hat{\mathbf{x}} = v_x\sin(\tfrac{1}{2}\theta)$, $(\mathbf{K}/|K|)\cdot v_y\hat{\mathbf{y}} = v_y\cos(\pi - \tfrac{1}{2}\theta) = v_y\cos(\tfrac{1}{2}\theta)$.

Figure 10.2.1 shows the scattering geometry for a particle traveling with velocity **v**. The Doppler frequency shift ν_D is given by

$$2\pi\nu_D = \mathbf{K}\cdot\mathbf{v} \qquad (10.2.1)$$

where $\mathbf{K} = \mathbf{k}_s - \mathbf{k}_I$ with $K = (4\pi/\lambda)\sin(\tfrac{1}{2}\theta)$. Equation (10.2.1) has the form

$$\nu_D = (2/\lambda)\,|v|\cos\alpha\sin(\tfrac{1}{2}\theta) \qquad (10.2.2)$$

where λ is the wavelength of light in the medium and $|v|\cos\alpha$ represents the component of **v** in the direction of **K**. As a numerical example, if we take $\lambda = 632.8$ nm and $n = 1.33$, then Eq. (10.2.2) gives

$$\nu_D(\text{kHz}) = 3.66\,|v|\cos\alpha\ (\text{cm/sec}) \qquad (10.2.3)$$

for a typical scattering angle $\theta = 10°$ (Foreman, Jr. *et al.*, 1966b).

If we take **v** to be in the direction of $\mathbf{k}_I$, $\alpha = \tfrac{1}{2}(\pi - \theta)$ so that $\cos\alpha = \cos(\tfrac{1}{2}\pi - \tfrac{1}{2}\theta) = \sin\tfrac{1}{2}\theta$, and

$$\nu_D = (2v_x/\lambda)\sin^2\tfrac{1}{2}\theta \qquad (10.2.4)$$

The laser Doppler velocimeter (LDV) can measure the velocity of the target over a wide range of speed. Using polystyrene spheres of 0.557-μm diam, Yeh and Cummins (1964) considered that they could detect velocities as low as 0.004 cm/sec at $\theta = 30°$, while Foreman *et al.* (1966b) estimated that their LDV should be capable of measuring gas flow velocities as high as $\sim$1800 m/sec corresponding to a $\nu_D \approx 200$ MHz with $\theta = 4°$. Goldstein and Kried (1967) claimed optimistically that the laser Doppler technique can measure velocity within an accuracy of about 0.1 % in a fully developed laminar-flow region of a square duct. Figure 10.2.2 shows a schematic

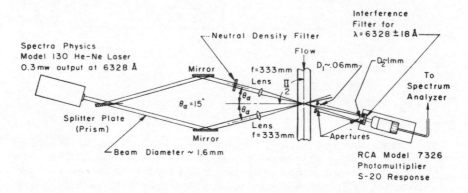

Fig. 10.2.2. Optical system (Goldstein and Kried, 1967). Test fluid is water with 1:50,000 concentration of 0.554-μm polystyrene particles.

diagram of the optical system used by Goldstein and Kried, where $2\theta_\alpha = \theta$ and the scattering volume has dimensions in the 10–100-μm region. The total linewidth of the Doppler-shifted spectrum is the sum of broadening due to the bandwidths of the laser and the spectrum analyzer; Brownian motion of the particles, velocity gradients, and fluctuations; angular uncertainties due to the divergence of the incident beam and detector angular aperture; and the finite time of passage of the scattering particles through the laser beam. Furthermore, additional broadening could be present because of the presence of reactive species. The study of fluid flow is closely related to electrophoretic light scattering and reaction kinetics. Edwards *et al.* (1971) have made a detailed analysis of the spectrum observed with steady flows. The effects of diffusive motion of scattering centers, spatially varying velocities, finite transit time of the particles through the scattering volume, and uncertainties in scattering vector caused by the focusing and collecting optics have been analyzed. For a very large sample volume with no spatial variation of velocity,

$$S(K, \omega) = \text{const}\{DK^2/[DK^2 + (\omega - \mathbf{K}\cdot\mathbf{v})^2]\} \qquad (10.2.5)$$

Equation (10.2.5) shows that the spectrum $S(K, \omega)$ is shifted from the zero beat frequency by an amount $\Omega = \mathbf{K} \cdot \mathbf{v}$, the Doppler shift, and has a half-width of DK^2 which depends only on the translational diffusion coefficient D of the scattering centers and the magnitude of the momentum transfer vector $\mathbf{K}$. Other contributions to the width of the Doppler spectrum have been neglected. In order to resolve the Doppler signal we must satisfy the condition

$$\mathbf{K} \cdot \mathbf{v} > DK^2 \tag{10.2.6}$$

For $\theta = 45°$, $\lambda_{air} = 632.8$ nm, and $D = 10^{-8}$ cm^2/sec, $|v| > 0.001$ cm/sec. The condition imposed by Eq. (10.2.6) is more difficult to satisfy than it appears, since both the translational diffusion coefficient and the flow velocity are inversely proportional to particle size. The reader is advised to read the article by Edwards et al. (1971) for detailed results covering finite sample volume with no spatial variation of velocity and flows with spatial velocity variation.

10.3. Turbulent Velocities

In turbulent flow the rates of transfer of mass, heat, and momentum are substantially increased above the rates of transfer by molecular processes. Thus, measurements of flow-velocity fluctuations using the laser Doppler technique are of considerable technological interest. The only other method capable of measuring turbulence is hot-wire anemometry which has poor spatial resolution, is fragile, requires calibration, and needs introduction of the probe into the turbulence being studied; the laser Doppler technique has none of the above disadvantages. Measurements of turbulent velocities from the Doppler shift in the scattered laser light by means of power spectral analysis have been reported by Goldstein and Hagen (1967), by Lewis et al. (1968), and by Pike et al. (1968).

According to Fig. 10.2.1 and Eqs. (10.2.2) and (10.2.4), we may separate the velocity of the scattering particle into x and y components, parallel and perpendicular to the incident beam, and get

$$\nu_D = (2/\lambda) \sin(\tfrac{1}{2}\theta) [v_x \sin(\tfrac{1}{2}\theta) + v_y \cos(\tfrac{1}{2}\theta)]$$
$$= (2/\lambda) [v_x \sin^2(\tfrac{1}{2}\theta) + v_y \sin(\tfrac{1}{2}\theta) \cos(\tfrac{1}{2}\theta)]$$
$$= (1/\lambda) [v_x (1 - \cos \theta) + v_y \sin \theta] \tag{10.3.1}$$

which is equivalent to Eq. (1) of Pike et al. (1968). If the fluid is in a steady turbulent flow,

$$v = \bar{v} + v' \tag{10.3.2}$$

where v, $\bar{v}$, and v' are the instantaneous, mean, and instantaneous deviation from the mean velocities, respectively. Then,

$$\bar{\nu}_D = (1/\lambda)[\bar{v}_x(1 - \cos\theta) + \bar{v}_y \sin\theta] \qquad (10.3.3)$$

and

$$(\overline{\Delta\nu_D{}^2})^{1/2} = (2/\lambda)\,\sin(\tfrac{1}{2}\theta)[\overline{v_x'^2}\sin^2(\tfrac{1}{2}\theta)$$
$$+ \overline{v_x'v_y'}\sin(\tfrac{1}{2}\theta)\cos(\tfrac{1}{2}\theta) + \overline{v_y'^2}\cos(\tfrac{1}{2}\theta)]^{1/2} \qquad (10.3.4)$$

If turbulence is isotropic,

$$\overline{v_x'^2} = \overline{v_y'^2}$$

and

$$\overline{v_x'v_y'} = 0 \qquad (10.3.5)$$

then,

$$(\overline{\Delta\nu_D{}^2})^{1/2} = (2/\lambda)\,\sin(\tfrac{1}{2}\theta)\,(\overline{v_x'^2})^{1/2} \qquad (10.3.6)$$

Experimentally, Pike *et al.* (1968) found that the best signal-to-noise ratio could be obtained by adjusting the intensity of the reference beam to about five times that of the scattered light. Owing to the rapid passage of particles through the small scattering volume, there is a broadening of the observed Doppler-shifted spectra, analogous to the Doppler radar ambiguity. We can estimate the Doppler ambiguity as follows.

The average time τ of passage of particles through a focused laser beam of cross section d [$= (4/\pi)\lambda f/D_f$ according to Eq. (7.2.4)] is given by

$$\tau \sim d/\bar{v}\cos(\tfrac{1}{2}\theta) \qquad (10.3.7)$$

where we have taken the scattering geometry as shown in Fig. 10.2.2 with $\theta_\alpha = \tfrac{1}{2}\theta$ and the component of $\bar{v}$ perpendicular to the incident beam being $\bar{v}\cos(\tfrac{1}{2}\pi + \tfrac{1}{2}\pi - \tfrac{1}{2}\theta) = \bar{v}\cos(\tfrac{1}{2}\theta)$. Following the same geometry with $\mathbf{v} \parallel \mathbf{K}$, we get from Eq. (10.3.3)

$$\bar{\nu}_D = (2/\lambda)(\sin\tfrac{1}{2}\theta)\bar{v} \qquad (10.3.8)$$

By substituting Eq. (10.3.8) into Eq. (10.3.7), we get for $\Delta\nu_{\mathrm{ambig}}$ ($\propto 1/\tau$):

$$\Delta\nu_{\mathrm{ambig}}/\bar{\nu}_D \sim (\lambda/2d)\cot(\tfrac{1}{2}\theta) \qquad (10.3.9)$$

where the subscript ambig stands for ambiguity. Further shortening of the lifetimes of the Doppler signals was avoided by using a diameter for the cone of coherence (100 μm) which was somewhat larger than the largest signal-beam diameter (80 μm) used (Pike *et al.*, 1968).

In turbulent flow the variances of the observed spectra can be assumed to be equal to the sums of the variances of the spectra produced mainly by instrumental effect and by both the velocity fluctuations and the

Doppler ambiguity. This assumption is not strictly correct since the combinations involve a convolution integral rather than simple additions. Nevertheless, we can experimentally eliminate all other effects, such as the bandwidths of the laser and the spectrometer, and the broadening due to velocity gradients, so that the variances of the spectra are due to velocity fluctuations and Doppler ambiguity. Then

$$(\overline{\Delta\nu_D{}^2})_{vf}{}^{1/2} = (\overline{\Delta\nu_D{}^2})_{tf}{}^{1/2} - (\overline{\Delta\nu_D{}^2})_{lf}{}^{1/2} \qquad (10.3.10)$$

where the subscripts are defined as vf, velocity flow; tf, turbulent flow; and lf, laminar flow; and where $(\overline{\Delta\nu_D{}^2})_{lf}{}^{1/2}$ is the broadening due to the Doppler ambiguity obtained with laminar flow but adjusted to the appropriate turbulent flow velocity.

Wang (1973) has shown that the effect of finite transit times of scatterers crossing the scattering region in a laser Doppler velocimeter is equivalent to a white noise with an amplitude inversely proportional to the average transit time or the beam diameter, and directly proportional to the wavelength of the incident light. Hence, the transit noise can be lowered by increasing the beam diameter. Unfortunately, the spatial resolution of the velocimeter is also dependent upon the beam diameter. The tradeoff is to choose a beam diameter such that the amplitude of the velocity spectrum is equal to the amplitude of the transit-noise spectrum at the maximum measurable frequency.

Information regarding the spatial extent of velocity correlations is obtained by observing the variation of the power spectrum of the intensity fluctuations with the scattering volume provided that the cone of coherence is greater than the signal-beam diameter and that the scattering volume is not so small that the velocity differences through it are negligible. The spectrum of light scattered by particles suspended in a turbulent fluid has been investigated theoretically (Bertolotti *et al.*, 1969). A detailed study of the spatial structure of turbulent flow by intensity fluctuation spectroscopy has been reported (Bourke *et al.*, 1969, 1970).

The reader should consult the articles by Bourke *et al.* (1970) and by Edwards *et al.* (1971) for the complete theoretical analysis. It suffices to say that there is a Doppler spectrum (DS) and an intensity fluctuation spectrum (ifs). In the Doppler spectrum, all terms not containing the reference beam may be neglected, and it is assumed that $a_0{}^2 \gg \langle N \rangle a_p{}^2$ where a_0, a_p, and $\langle N \rangle$ are the amplitude of the reference beam, the amplitude of the scattered beam per particle, and the number of particles in the scattering volume, respectively. In intensity fluctuation spectroscopy, light scattered from pairs of particles at different points within the fluid is optically mixed so that for this case $a_0{}^2 = 0$. Bourke *et al.* (1970) obtained the following relations:

$$S_{DS}(\Omega) = 2\pi a_0{}^2(a_0{}^2 + 2\langle N \rangle a_p{}^2)\,\delta(\Omega) + (2\pi/K)a_0{}^2\overline{a_p{}^2}\langle N \rangle$$
$$\times [p(u) + p(-u)] \quad (10.3.11)$$

and

$$S_{ifs}(\Omega) = 2\pi[(\overline{a_p{}^2})^2\langle N^2 \rangle + \{a_p{}^4 - (\overline{a_p{}^2})^2\}\langle N \rangle\,\delta(\Omega)$$

$$+ (2\pi/K)(\overline{a_p{}^2})^2\langle N^2 \rangle\frac{1}{V}\int_V d\mathbf{r}\int_{-\infty}^{\infty} dv\,p(v, v + u; r) \quad (10.3.12)$$

in which Ω is a particular frequency selected with a wave analyzer of response time T_A whereby

$$S(\Omega) = \left\langle \frac{1}{T_A}\left|\int_{\tau}^{\tau+T_A} |E(t)|^2 \exp(i\Omega t)\,dt\right|^2 \right\rangle \quad (10.3.13)$$

$p(u)$ is the probability of having velocity u ($\equiv \Omega/K$) and $p(v, v + u; r)$ is the joint distribution of simultaneously having velocities v and $v + u$ at a distance r apart. The application of photon correlation spectroscopy to the measurement of turbulent flows has been examined further by Birch *et al.* (1973).

10.4. Filter Model of Doppler Velocimeter†

In the filter model, light from a single laser source is split by a mask M containing two parallel slits of equal width in plane 1. The two beams are then brought to a focus F in plane 2. As the scattering target travels through the focus F, the output frequency of the photodetector measures the rate at which the particle crosses the fringes at F. Figure 10.4.1 shows a generalized filter model of a Doppler meter in one dimension. The transmitted light after plane 2 fluctuates because of blockage of varying amounts of light by the scattering centers at the focus F. Rudd (1969a) introduces a blocking function at plane 2 where the particle crosses a set of fringes at the focus F as $G[(-l)/a]$ with x, a, and l being the coordinate in plane 2, the effective diameter of a scattering center, and its displacement, respectively. The light next passes through a filter $h(\beta)$ in plane 3 and is finally focused on a photodetector in plane 4. The following is a derivation by Rudd (1969a).

† Rudd, 1969a.

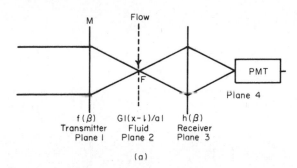

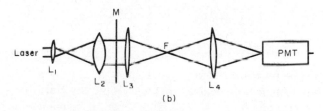

(b)

Fig. 10.4.1. (a) Filter model of a Doppler meter in one dimension. (b) Optical system as used by Greated (1970a). Focal length of lenses used: $L_1 = 21$ mm, $L_2 = L_3 = 15$ cm, $L_4 = 5$ cm; $S =$ slit spacing/slit width $= 10$; slit width ~ 0.6 mm.

The complex amplitude of light has the following forms when it is:

transmitted by plane 1: $A_1 = f(\beta)$ (10.4.1)

incident on plane 2: $A_2 = F(x/\lambda)$ (10.4.2)

transmitted by plane 2: $A_3 = F(x/\lambda)\{1 - G[(x - l)/a]\}$ (10.4.3)

incident on plane 3: $A_4 = f(\beta) - f(\beta) * g(\beta)e^{2\pi i l/a}$ (10.4.4)

[where a factor of a/λ is taken in with $g(\beta)$];

transmitted by plane 3:

$$A_5 = f(\beta)h(\beta) - [f(\beta) * g(\beta)e^{2\pi i l/a}]h(\beta)$$ (10.4.5)

and incident on plane 4:

$$A_6 = F(x/\lambda) * H(x/\lambda) - \{F(x/\lambda)G[(x - l)/a]\} * H(x/\lambda)$$ (10.4.6)

where the functions represented by capital and lower case letters are Fourier transforms of each other and $*$ stands for a convolution. Now, the photodetector measures the intensity which is

$$I = \int |A_6|^2 \, dx$$

$$= \int \left| F\left(\frac{x}{\lambda}\right) * H\left(\frac{x}{\lambda}\right) \right|^2 dx + \int \left[\left\{ F\left(\frac{x}{\lambda}\right) G\left(\frac{x-l}{a}\right) \right\} * H\left(\frac{x}{\lambda}\right) \right]$$

$$\times \overline{\left\{ F\left(\frac{x}{\lambda}\right) * H\left(\frac{x}{\lambda}\right) \right\}} \, dx + \int \overline{\left[F\left(\frac{x}{\lambda}\right) G\left(\frac{x-l}{a}\right) * H\left(\frac{x}{\lambda}\right) \right]}$$

$$\times \left[F\left(\frac{x}{\lambda}\right) * H\left(\frac{x}{\lambda}\right) \right] dx + \int \left| \left\{ F\left(\frac{x}{\lambda}\right) G\left(\frac{x-l}{a}\right) \right\} * H\left(\frac{x}{\lambda}\right) \right|^2 dx$$

$$(10.4.7)$$

The blocking function is small since most of the light is transmitted. Thus the last term can be neglected. The second and third terms are equal for real $F(x/\lambda)$ and $G[(x-l)/a]$. We assign a frequency ν_D which corresponds to the variation of the intensity at the photodetector due to the particles crossing a set of fringes formed by the two beams at F, or

$$2\pi\nu_D = \frac{1}{I} \frac{\partial I}{\partial t} = \frac{v_l}{I} \frac{\partial I}{\partial l} \tag{10.4.8}$$

where v_l ($\equiv \partial l/\partial t$) is the velocity across the beam. Substituting Eq. (10.4.7) into Eq. (10.4.8), we finally obtain

$$2\pi\nu_D = v_l \left(\int \frac{\partial}{\partial l} \left\{ \left[F\left(\frac{x}{\lambda}\right) G\left(\frac{x-l}{a}\right) \right] * H\left(\frac{x}{\lambda}\right) \right\} \overline{\left[F\left(\frac{x}{\lambda}\right) * H\left(\frac{x}{\lambda}\right) \right]} \, dx \right)$$

$$\times \left(\int \left\{ \left[F\left(\frac{x}{\lambda}\right) G\left(\frac{x-l}{a}\right) \right] * H\left(\frac{x}{\lambda}\right) \right\} \overline{\left[F\left(\frac{x}{\lambda}\right) * H\left(\frac{x}{\lambda}\right) \right]} \, dx \right)^{-1} \quad (10.4.9)$$

The first term of Eq. (10.4.7) drops out because it does not contain the parameter l. Rudd (1969a) then proceeds to consider the two specific optical systems which we have already discussed.

In the Goldstein–Kried system (Fig. 10.2.2), there are two transmitting beams and thus filter 1 has the form

$$A_1 = f[\beta - \sin(\tfrac{1}{2}\theta)] + f[\beta + \sin(\tfrac{1}{2}\theta)] \tag{10.4.10}$$

and $h(\beta) = 1$ since there is no further filter in plane 3. Thus,

$$A_2 = F(\beta) \cos[(2\pi x/\lambda) \sin \tfrac{1}{2}\theta] \tag{10.4.11}$$

and

$$2\pi\nu_{\mathrm{D}} = v_l \left(\int \frac{\partial}{\partial l} \left| F\left(\frac{x}{\lambda}\right) \right|^2 \cos^2\left[\left(\frac{2\pi x}{\lambda}\right) \sin \tfrac{1}{2}\theta \right] G\left(\frac{x - l}{a}\right) dx \right)$$

$$\times \left(\int \left| F\left(\frac{r}{\lambda}\right) \right|^2 \cos^2\left[\left(\frac{2\pi x}{\lambda}\right) \sin \tfrac{1}{2}\theta \right] G\left(\frac{x - l}{a}\right) dx \right)^{-1}$$

$$\simeq \frac{4\pi v_l}{\lambda} \sin \tfrac{1}{2}\theta \qquad \text{(for small } a\text{)} \qquad\qquad (10.4.12)$$

which is equivalent to Eq. (10.2.2) with $v_l = |v| \cos \alpha$.

The Yeh–Cummins system can also be deduced from Eq. (10.4.9). In the Goldstein–Kried system, the particles travel across a set of real fringes formed by two beams in the fluid while in the Yeh–Cummins system only virtual fringes are formed outside the fluid.

Figure 10.4.1b shows an actual optical arrangement as used by Greated (1970a) for the measurement of turbulent statistics with a laser velocimeter. Rudd has also considered the coherence requirement for his fringe model. The *chromatic* coherence requires that

$$\Delta\lambda/\lambda \leq \Delta\nu_{\mathrm{D}}/\nu_{\mathrm{D}} \qquad\qquad (10.4.13)$$

where $\Delta\lambda$ is the final spectral width of the light source, and $\Delta\nu_{\mathrm{D}}$ is the expected width of the Dopper-shifted spectrum. The more stringent *spatial* coherence requires that

$$d < \lambda/2 \sin(\tfrac{1}{2}\theta) \qquad\qquad (10.4.14)$$

where d is the effective source diameter. In the Goldstein–Kried and Yeh–Cummins optical systems, the spatial coherence criterion is given by

$$d < (\lambda/2 \sin(\tfrac{1}{2}\theta))(\nu_{\mathrm{D}}/\Delta\nu_{\mathrm{D}}) \qquad\qquad (10.4.15)$$

since there are $\nu_{\mathrm{D}}/\Delta\nu_{\mathrm{D}}$ fringes of size $\tfrac{1}{2}\lambda \sin(\tfrac{1}{2}\theta)$. Finally, *temporal* coherence relates the path difference involved between two interfering beams from the same source. The net amplitude of the wavefront scattered by all the particles is proportional to $\sqrt{N}$.

Rudd (1969b) and Greated (1969) have studied the effects of polymer additive on grid turbulence using just such an improved Doppler meter which gives particularly good results when used in conjunction with a frequency demodulator (Greated, 1970a,b). However, Greated questioned whether direct frequency spectra of the photodetector signal can give accurate predictions of rms turbulent intensities because the length of the fringes formed at the focus is of the same order as the individual fringe spacings. Furthermore, the Rudd system does not permit measurements of other components of the Reynolds stress tensor. Wang (1972a) has proposed a frequency-modulation (FM) demodulation scheme for measuring the instantaneous velocity of turbulent flow.

In a modified Rudd optical system, L_1 and L_2 of Fig. 10.4.1b are changed to cylindrical lenses and the mask M has two square apertures. The pattern of light intensity on the mask is shown in Fig. 10.4.2 with L_1, L_2, L_3, and L_4

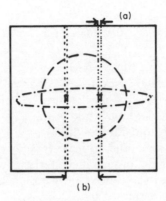

Fig. 10.4.2. Pattern of light intensity on the mask. Dashed line: spherical lenses L_1 and L_2; dot-dash line: cylindrical lenses L_3 and L_4; mask M with square aperture (Greated, 1970, reproduced by permission of Journal of Physics).

having focal lengths of 2, 15, 7.5, and 7.5 cm, respectively, and mask aperture spacings of 6 mm. With the fringes perpendicular to the mean flow, the direct spectra of the photodetector signal can be used with confidence to determine turbulent intensities in the longitudinal direction. By rotating the fringes through $\alpha = \pm 45°$, the cross correlation of the longitudinal and transverse velocity fluctuations can be evaluated (Greated, 1970). Figure 10.4.3 shows the alignment positions of the fringes with respect to the mean flow for the modified Rudd optical system. At position 1, the instantaneous frequency observed at the output of the photodetector

Fig. 10.4.3. Alignment positions of the fringes. Mean flow is in the x direction. The optical axis is in the z direction.

is

$$F_1 = K_R(\bar{v} + v_x')$$ (10.4.16)

where $\bar{v}$ is the mean velocity which is in the x direction, v_x' is the longitudinal component of the turbulent fluctuations in velocity, and K_R is a constant depending upon the fringe spacing. At position 2, the component velocities perpendicular to the fringes are $(\bar{v} + v_x') \cos(\frac{1}{4}\pi)$ and $-v_y' \cos(\frac{1}{4}\pi)$ so that

$$F_2 = (K_R/\sqrt{2})(\bar{v} + v_x' - v_y')$$ (10.4.17)

Similarly, at position 3,

$$F_3 = (K_R/\sqrt{2})(\bar{v} + v_x' + v_y')$$ (10.4.18)

where v_y' and v_z' are the turbulent components in the transverse direction with $\bar{v}_y = \bar{v}_z = 0$. If

$$F_i = \bar{F}_i + F_i'$$ (10.4.19)

and

$$\bar{F}_1 = \sqrt{2}\bar{F}_2 = \sqrt{2}\bar{F}_3$$ (10.4.20)

where $\bar{F}_i$ and F_i' are, respectively, the mean and the fluctuating velocity when the fringes are at position i, then

$$F_1'^2 = K_R^2 v_x'^2$$
$$F_2'^2 = \tfrac{1}{2}K_R^2(v_x'^2 + v_y'^2 - 2v_x'v_y') \qquad (10.4.21)$$
$$F_3'^2 = \tfrac{1}{2}K_R^2(v_x'^2 + v_y'^2 + 2v_x'v_y')$$

By rearranging Eq. (10.4.21), we can get the components of the fluctuating velocity:

$$\overline{v_x'^2} = (1/K_R^2)(\overline{F_1'^2})$$
$$\overline{v_y'^2} = (1/K_R^2)(\overline{F_2'^2} + \overline{F_3'^2} - \overline{F_1'^2}) \qquad (10.4.22)$$
$$\overline{v_x'v_y'} = (1/2K_R^2)(\overline{F_3'^2} - \overline{F_2'^2})$$

where ambiguous broadening of the Doppler spectra has been neglected.

10.5. A Unified Analysis on Laser Doppler Velocimeters

Wang (1972b) has made a unified analysis on various optical arrangements of laser Doppler velocimeters. In order to retain the phase information, it is necessary to use the heterodyne technique where a reference signal is mixed with the scattered light. This reference signal can be obtained using the following three different schemes.

(i)   The local-oscillator heterodyne arrangement, as we have discussed in Section 10.2 in terms of the Doppler effect, uses a local oscillator or a reference beam directly as the reference signal (see Figs. 10.2.2 and 10.5.1).

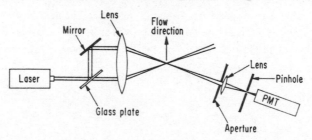

Fig. 10.5.1.   Local-oscillator heterodyne arrangement (Wang, 1972b).

(ii)   The differential heterodyne arrangement, (Rudd, 1969a,b; Penney 1970; Wang, 1971) as we have discussed in Section 10.4 in terms of fringe crossings, uses the light scattered from the same scattering region, but by another coherent light beam incident from a different direction, as the reference signal [see Figs. 10.4.1b and 10.5.2. Note: the omission of an aperture before $L4$ in Fig. 10.4.1b changes the scheme essentially to a combination of (i) and (ii)].

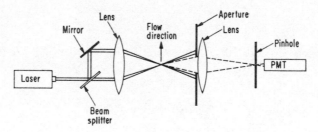

Fig. 10.5.2.   Differential heterodyne arrangement (Wang, 1972b).

(iii)   The symmetric heterodyne arrangement (Mazumder and Wankam, 1970; Wang, 1971), as has been suggested by Rudd (1969a,b) in terms of fringe crossings, uses the light scattered from the same scattering region, but collected in a different direction, as the reference signal (see Fig. 10.5.3).

10.5.1. Local-Oscillator Heterodyne

For a monochromatic incident laser beam of frequency ω_I and wave vector $\mathbf{k}_I$, the scattered electric field at the photodetector due to N par-

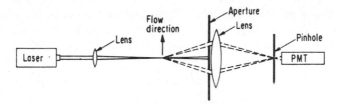

Fig. 10.5.3. Symmetric heterodyne arrangement (Wang, 1972b).

ticles in scattering volume v is given by

$$E_s(t) = \sum_{p=1}^{N} a_p \exp[-i\omega_I t + i\mathbf{K}\cdot\mathbf{v}_p t + i\phi_p] \qquad (10.5.1)$$

where a_p is the amplitude of the scattered beam per particle, ϕ_p is the phase factor depending on the location of the particle, $\mathbf{v}_p$ is the particle velocity, and $\mathbf{K} = \mathbf{k}_s - \mathbf{k}_I$ with $\mathbf{k}_s$ being the scattered wave vector in the direction of the photodetector. The electric field of the reference beam is

$$E_{\mathrm{LO}}(t) = a_0 \exp(-i\omega_I t + i\phi_0) \qquad (10.5.2)$$

where a_0 and ϕ_0 are the amplitude and the phase of the reference electric field, respectively. Mixing of the local oscillator with the scattered field at a point on the photodetector gives by means of Eqs. (4.3.4), (4.3.5), and (4.3.29):

$$S_j(\omega) = \frac{e^2}{2\pi}\, \alpha(a_0{}^2 + \sum_{p=1}^{N} a_p{}^2) + e^2\alpha^2(a_0{}^2 + \sum_{p=1}^{N} a_p{}^2)^2\, \delta(\omega)$$

$$+\ e^2\alpha^2 a_0{}^2 \sum_{p=1}^{N} a_p{}^2\, \delta(\omega \pm \mathbf{K}\cdot\mathbf{v}_p)$$

$$+\ e^2\alpha^2 \sum_{p=1}^{N}\sum_{q=1,\,q\neq p}^{N} a_p{}^2 a_q{}^2\, \delta[\omega + \mathbf{K}\cdot(\mathbf{v}_p - \mathbf{v}_q)] \qquad (10.5.3)$$

In comparison with Eq. (10.2.5), we note that the linewidths have been neglected. If the local-oscillator strength is much greater than the scattered light, i.e.,

$$a_0{}^2 \gg \sum_{p=1}^{N} a_p{}^2 \qquad (10.5.4)$$

then we have

$$S_j(\omega) = \frac{e^2\alpha}{2\pi}\, a_0{}^2 + e^2\alpha^2 a_0{}^4\, \delta(\omega) + e^2\alpha^2 a_0{}^2 \sum_{p=1}^{N} a_p{}^2\, \delta(\omega \pm \mathbf{K}\cdot\mathbf{v}_p) \qquad (10.5.5)$$

Here the first term is the shot noise. The second term is the dc component and the last signal term displays only the Doppler shift. $\mathbf{K} \cdot \mathbf{v}_p$, as shown in Fig. 10.2.1, is $|v|\cos\alpha$ which represents the component of $\mathbf{v}$ in the direction of $\mathbf{K}$.

10.5.2. Differential Heterodyne

In the differential heterodyne scheme, two incident laser beams of the same frequency ω_I but with different wave vectors $\mathbf{k}_{I1}$ and $\mathbf{k}_{I2}$ intersect in a small scattering region. The scattered light is then collected in a large solid angle, as shown in Fig. 10.5.2, and has the form

$$E_s(t) = \sum_{p=1}^{N} a_p \exp(-i\omega_I t)\{\exp[i(\mathbf{k}_s - \mathbf{k}_{I1}) \cdot \mathbf{v}_p t + i\phi_{p1}]$$

$$+ \exp[i(\mathbf{k}_s - \mathbf{k}_{I2}) \cdot \mathbf{v}_p t + i\phi_{p2}]\} \quad (10.5.6)$$

The corresponding power spectral density at one point of the photodetector is

$$S_j(\omega) = \frac{e^2\alpha}{\pi} \sum_{p=1}^{N} a_p{}^2 + 4e^2\alpha^2 (\sum_{p=1}^{N} a_p{}^2)^2 \, \delta(\omega)$$

$$+ e^2\alpha^2 \sum_{p=1}^{N} a_p{}^4 \, \delta(\omega \pm (\mathbf{k}_{I2} - \mathbf{k}_{I1}) \cdot \mathbf{v}_p)$$

$$+ e^2\alpha^2 \sum_{p=1}^{N} \sum_{q=1,q\neq p}^{N} a_p{}^2 a_q{}^2 \{\delta[\omega \pm (\mathbf{k}_s - \mathbf{k}_{I1}) \cdot (\mathbf{v}_p - \mathbf{v}_q)]$$

$$+ \delta[\omega \pm (\mathbf{k}_s - \mathbf{k}_{I2}) \cdot (\mathbf{v}_p - \mathbf{v}_q)] + \delta[\omega \pm (\mathbf{k}_{I2} - \mathbf{k}_{I1}) \cdot \mathbf{v}_p$$

$$\pm (\mathbf{k}_s - \mathbf{k}_{I1}) \cdot (\mathbf{v}_p - \mathbf{v}_q)] + \delta[\omega \pm (\mathbf{k}_{I2} - \mathbf{k}_{I1}) \cdot \mathbf{v}_p$$

$$\pm (\mathbf{k}_s - \mathbf{k}_{I2}) \cdot (\mathbf{v}_p - \mathbf{v}_q)]\} \quad (10.5.7)$$

If all the particles move with the same velocity, Eq. (10.5.7) is reduced to

$$S_j(\omega) = \frac{e^2\alpha^2}{\pi} \sum_{p=1}^{N} a_p{}^2 + 4e^2\alpha^2 [(\sum_{p=1}^{N} a_p{}^2)^2 + \sum_{p=1}^{N} \sum_{q=1,q\neq p}^{N} a_p{}^2 a_q{}^2] \, \delta(\omega)$$

$$+ e^2\alpha^2 (\sum_{p=1}^{N} a_p{}^4 + 2 \sum_{p=1}^{N} \sum_{q=1,q\neq p}^{N} a_p{}^2 a_q{}^2) \, \delta[\omega \pm (\mathbf{k}_{I2} - \mathbf{k}_{I1}) \cdot \mathbf{v}_p] \quad (10.5.8)$$

Equation (10.5.8) shows that the measured Doppler frequency shift depends only on $(\mathbf{k}_{I2} - \mathbf{k}_{I1})$ and is independent of $\mathbf{k}_s$. Thus, light scattered from the scattering region may be collected through a *larger* solid angle with this optical arrangement.

10.5.3. Symmetric Heterodyne

In symmetric hyterodyne, as shown in Fig. 10.5.3, the scattered electric field is given by

$$E_s(t) = \sum_{p=1}^{N} a_p \exp(-i\omega_I t)\{\exp[i(\mathbf{k}_{s1} - \mathbf{k}_I)\cdot\mathbf{v}_p t + i\phi_{p1}]$$
$$+ \exp[i(\mathbf{k}_{s2} - \mathbf{k}_I)\cdot\mathbf{v}_p t + i\phi_{p2}]\} \quad (10.5.9)$$

If we again assume that all particles have the same velocity, Eq. (10.5.8) is retrieved by replacing $(\mathbf{k}_{I2} - \mathbf{k}_{I1})$ with $(\mathbf{k}_{s2} - \mathbf{k}_{s1})$. The differential heterodyne technique is considered superior to all other arrangements for particles with uniform velocity. The largest light-collecting solid angle for the above optical arrangement is limited by the average particle size l_p, i.e.,

$$\Omega_{max} \leq \lambda^2/l_p^2$$

which is $(l_s/l_p)^2$ times larger than the corresponding maximum solid angle of the local-oscillator heterodyne arrangement with l_s being the linear dimension of the scattering region. For nonuniform particle velocities, the relative merit depends on the particular application. Statistical properties of laser Doppler velocimeter signals have been discussed by Adrian (1972); Wilmshurst (1972) has devised a signal simulator for testing laser Doppler fluid-flow velocimeter systems.

10.5.4. Signal–to–Noise Ratio

Wang and Snyder (1974) made an experimental study on the general characteristics and considered S/N, stability, optimum particle concentration, and optimum receiving optics of the three differential optical arrangements (Sections 10.5.1–10.5.3). Aside from an fm demodulator used to obtain the instantaneous velocity, Wang and Snyder used the same Krohn–Hite electronic filter (Model 3322) in screening out the unwanted noise, as we have mentioned in concentration correlation spectroscopy (Section ⸢.4.2.A).

For real-time data analysis, the EMI 9558B photomultiplier tube was fed, via a wide-band operational amplifier (Tektronix Type-0 plug-in unit) and a band-pass filter (Krohn–Hite Model 3322), to a spectrum analyzer (Tektronix 1L5 spectrum analyzer). Such a setup could vastly be improved by replacing the Tektronix 1L5 spectrum analyzer with a real-time spectrum analyzer. Furthermore, the use of a preamplifier between the PM tube and the operational amplifier is advisable. Alternatively, Wang and Snyder recorded the PM output signal on a 7-channel fm magnetic tape recorder (Honeywell Model 7610), which was then played back at reduced speed and digitized by an A/D converter (Scientific Data Systems Model AD35). Power spectral analysis by fast Fourier transform using a digital computer is similar to that mentioned in Section 7.5.

For the three optical arrangements, Wang and Snyder obtained experimental agreement with the following two equations (Wang, 1972b):

$$(S/N)_{loh} \sim n_p \sigma_p (\lambda^2 / l_s^2) \qquad \text{(local oscillator heterodyne)}$$

$$(10.5.10)$$

$$(S/N)_{dh} \sim (1/n_p^{5/3}) \sigma_p (\lambda^2 / 1_p^2) \qquad \text{(differential or symmetric heterodyne)}$$

$$(10.5.11)$$

where n_p is the particle number density and σ_p the Mie scattering cross section of the particle. For local-oscillator heterodyne, high particle concentration and small focal volume are generally needed. It is insensitive to particle size and has a broad frequency spreading unless very small collecting apertures are used. The optical alignment is complex. Thus the local-oscillator heterodyne technique is inferior to the other two optical arrangements. Differential and asymmetric heterodyne techniques are similar in many ways. Symmetric heterodyne has the simplest optical components with a small loss of S/N when compared with differential heterodyne. Both require relatively low particle concentration and can use either small or large focal volume. Both are sensitive to particle size and have low frequency spreading.

10.5.5. Other Developments

Velocimeters operating in the back scattering mode (Greated, 1971) that measures two velocity components have been developed. Orloff and Logan (1973) used two incident beams polarized normally to each other and incorporated a differencing technique (Bossel et al., 1972) to enhance the dual-scatter Doppler signal corresponding to the transverse velocity. Three laser beams with a 0, 45, and 90° polarization plane relationship (Blake, 1972) have been used in a two-component dual-scatter laser Doppler velocimeter for measuring wind tunnel flow velocity (Brayton *et al.*, 1973). The same approach has been extended to make a two-component LDV system that uses two of the colors (488 and 514 nm) emitted from an argon-ion laser for the simultaneous measurement of orthogonal velocities (Grant and Orloff, 1973).

New optical arrangements will be forthcoming. In the differential Doppler laser technique, modulation frequency produced by particles crossing interference fringes determines the flow velocity. The fringe image technique uses localized fringes formed by the optical image of a grating (e.g., a Ronchi grating) illuminated with a nonlaser source (Ballik and Chan, 1973). Thus, the grating system can be incorporated to improve the performance of Doppler velocimeters (Wang, 1974). Foord *et al.* (1974) have devised a solid-state electro-optic phase modulator for laser Doppler anemometry. The simple sawtooth phase modulator can be used to shift the frequency of a laser Doppler signal, permitting determination of velocity sense and assisting interpretation of turbulent distributions.

The unique features of the laser Doppler velocimeter will undoubtedly find increasing uses in many applications. For example, velocity distributions in two-phase suspension flows (Einav and Lee, 1973) and in electrophoretic light scattering (Section 8.7) are similar in theory and practice, while the dual-scatter LDV systems should provide interesting possibilities for studies related to chemotactic response and motile microorganisms (Section 8.9). (For the latest developments, see *Note*, p. xii.)

References

Abbiss, J. B., Chubb, T. W., Mundell, A. R. G., Oliver, C. J., and Pike, E. R. (1972). *J. Phys. D* **5**, L100.

Adrian, R. J. (1972). *J. Phys. E* **5**, 91.

Ballik, E. A., and Chan. J. H. C. (1973). *Appl. Opt.* **12**, 2607.

Bertolotti, M., Crosignani, B., DiPorto, P., and Sette, D. (1969). *J. Phys. A* **2**, 126.

Birch, A. D., Brown, D. R., Thomas, J. R., and Pike, E. R. (1973). *J. Phys. D* **6**, L71.

Blake, K. A. (1972). *J. Phys. E* **5**, 623.

Bossel, H. H., Hiller, W. J., and Meier, G. E. A. (1972). *J. Phys. E* **5**, 893, 897.

Bourke, P. J., Butterworth, J., Drain, L. E., Egelstaff, P. A., Hutchinson, P., Moss, B., Schofield, P., Hughes, A. J., O'Shaughnessey, J. J. B., Pike, E. R., Jakeman, E., and Jackson, D. A. (1969). *Phys. Lett. A* **28**, 692.

Bourke, P. J., Butterworth, J., Drain, L. E., Egelstaff, P. A., Hughes, A. J., Hutchinson, P., Jackson, D. A., Jakeman, E., Moss, B., O'Shaughnessy, J., Pike, E. R., and Schofield, P. (1970). *J. Phys. A* **3**, 216.

Brayton, D. B., Kalb, H. T., and Crosswy, F. L. (1973). *Appl. Opt.* **6**, 1145.

Durrani, T. S., and Greated, C. (1973a). *Proc. IEEE Congr. Instrumentation in Aerospace Simulation Facilties*, ICIASF 73 Record, p. 210.

Durrani, T. S., and Greated, C. (1973b). *IEEE Trans. Instr. Meas.* **IM-22**, 23.

Durrani, T. S., and Greated, C. (1973c). *Proc. IEEE* **120,** 913.

Durrani, T. S., and Greated, C. (1974). *IEEE Trans. Aerospace Electronic Systems* **10.**

Edwards, R. V., Angus, J. C., French, M. J., and Dunning, Jr., J. W. (1971). *J. Appl. Phys.* **42,** 837.

Einav, S., and Lee, S L. (1973). *Rev. Sci. Instr.* **44,** 1478.

Foord, R., Harvey, A. F., Jones, R., Pike, E. R., Vaughan, J. M. (1974). *J. Phys. D* **7,** L36.

Foreman, Jr., J. W., George, E. W., and Lewis, R. D. (1965). *Appl. Phys. Lett.* **7,** 77.

Foreman, Jr., J. W., Lewis, R. D., Thornton, J. R., and Watson, H. J. (1966a). *Proc. IEEE* **54,** 424.

Foreman, Jr., J. W., George, E. W., Jetton, J. L., Lewis, R. D., Thornton, J. R., and Watson, H. J. (1966b). *J. IEEE* **QE-2,** 260.

Frisch, H. L. (1967). *Phys. Rev. Lett.* **19,** 1278.

Goldstein, R. J., and Hagen, W. F. (1967). *Phys. Fluids* **10,** 1349.

Goldstein, R. J., and Kried, D. K. (1967). *J. Appl. Mech.* **34,** 813.

Grant, G. R., and Orloff, K. L. (1973). *Appl. Opt.* **12,** 2913.

Greated, C. A. (1969). *Nature* **224,** 1196.

Greated, C. (1970a). *J. Phys. E* **3,** 158.

Greated, C. (1970b). *J. Phys. E* **3,** 753.

Greated, C. (1971). *J. Phys. E* **4,** 585.

Greated, C., and Durrani, T. S. (1971). *J. Phys. E* **4,** 24.

Hodara, H. (1966). *Proc. IEEE* **54,** 368.

Huffaker, R. M., Jelalian, A. V., and Thomson, J. A. L. (1970). *Proc. IEEE* **58,** 322.

Hughes, A. J., and Pike E. R. (1973). *Appl. Opt.* **12,** 597.

Hughes, A. J., Oliver, C. J., Pike, E. R., and O'Shaughnessy, J. J. B. (1970). *J. Phys. D* **3,** 751.

Lewis, R. D., Foreman, Jr., J. W., Watson, H. J., and Thornton, J. R. (1968). *Phys. Fluids* **11,** 433.

Mazumder, M. K., and Wankum, D. L. (1970). *Appl. Opt.* **9,** 633.

Orloff, K. L., and Logan, S. E. (1973). *Appl. Opt.* **12,** 2477.

Penner, S. S., and Jerskey, T. (1973). *Annu. Rev. Fluid Mech.* **5,** 9.

Penney, C. M. (1970). *Appl. Phys. Lett.* **16,** 167.

Pike, E. R. (1970). International Quantum Electronic Conference, Kyoto, Japan.

Pike, E. R. (1972). *J. Phys. D* **5,** L23.

Pike, E. R., Jackson, D. A., Bourke, P. J., and Page, D. I. (1968). *J. Phys. E* **1,** 727.

Rudd, M. J. (1969a). *J. Phys. E* **2,** 55.

Rudd, M. J. (1969b). *Nature* **224,** 587.

Tanaka, T. (1974). *Bull. Amer. Phys. Soc.* **19,** 244.

Tanaka, T., Yacoby, Y., and Benedek, G. B. (1974). *Bull. Amer. Phys. Soc.* **19,** 481.

Wang, C. P. (1971). *Appl. Phys. Lett.* **18,** 522.

Wang, C. P. (1972a). *Appl. Phys. Lett.* **20,** 339.

Wang, C. P. (1972b). *J. Phys. E* **5,** 763.

Wang, C. P. (1973). *Appl. Phys. Lett.* **22,** 154.

Wang, C. P. (1974). *Appl. Opt.* **13,** 1193.

Wang, C. P., and Snyder, O. (1974). *Appl. Opt.* **13,** 98.

Wilmshurst, T. H. (1972). *J. Phys. E* **5,** 1208.

Yeh, Y., and Cummins, H. Z. (1964). *Appl. Phys. Lett.* **4,** 176.

Chapter XI
‖ CRITICAL OPALESCENCE†

11.1. Introduction

In the neighborhood of the *critical* point, large local density fluctuations of a fluid produce corresponding fluctuations in the index of refraction and the electron density. Such an optically inhomogeneous system scatters light very strongly and looks *opalescent*. This phenomenon is generally known as *"critical opalescence."*

The gas–liquid critical point of a one-component system is the most familiar. However, a variety of other seemingly unrelated systems, such as binary metallic alloys, ferromagnetic crystals, and binary liquid mixtures, have shown similar behaviors. Theoretical insight suggests that the long-range critical fluctuations are remarkably insensitive to the details of the intermolecular potentials. Thus, all such systems can be studied from the same viewpoint. A dominant characteristic of all critical systems is the large increase of the microscopic fluctuations which can reach effectively macroscopic magnitudes. Many equilibrium and transport thermodynamic properties exhibit striking anomalies as the critical point is approached. Consequently, the determination of asymptotic laws governing the approach to a critical point is an important problem for both experimentalists and theorists who are interested in studying the nature of phase transitions. The intensity and the spectral width of scattered light can be related to the magnitude and the dynamics of critical fluctuations.

Fisher (1967) reviewed the theory of equilibrium critical phenomena while Heller (1967) presented a critique of pertinent experimental data and

† Chu, 1972.

technique in a companion article. The studies on critical opalescence have been extensive. Earlier reviews and proceedings (Green and Sengers, 1966), together with the reviews by Cummins (1971) and Chu (1972), are sufficiently detailed that a complete listing of literature references on critical opalescence becomes redundant. The purpose of this chapter is to try to point out the pertinent features of quasielastic light scattering which may be useful for testing the dynamical theory of critical phenomena. It is written on a more advanced level when compared with the discussions of other applications. A novice should read the earlier reviews before he tries to understand the more subtle points of this chapter.

11.2. Fluid Systems[†]

Near the critical point the Rayleigh ratio becomes increasingly dependent upon the momentum-transfer vector $\mathbf{K}$ with magnitude $K = ks = (2\pi n/\lambda_0)[2\sin(\tfrac{1}{2}\theta)]$, n being the index of refraction of the scattering medium. Ornstein and Zernike (1914, 1915, 1916a,b, 1926) were the first to devise a scheme to account for the long-range correlation. The K-dependent Rayleigh ratio has the form

$$\mathcal{R}(K) = (k_0^4/16\pi^2)\sin^2\phi\rho^2(\partial\epsilon/\partial\rho)_T^2 k_B T K_T (1 + \xi^2 K^2)^{-1} \quad (11.2.1)$$

where $k_0 = 2\pi/\lambda_0$ with λ_0 being the incident wavelength in vacuum and θ is the angle between the direction of polarization of the incident plane-polarized light and the direction of observation $\mathbf{R}$. ρ, ϵ, k_B, T, and K_T are the density, the dielectric constant, the Boltzmann constant, the absolute temperature, and the isothermal compressibility $[= (1/\rho)(\partial\rho/\partial P)_T]$, respectively. ξ is the long-range correlation length and is related to K_T by the equation

$$\xi^2 = (K_T/K_T^{\text{id}})R_{oz}^2 \quad (11.2.1a)$$

The direct correlation range R_{oz} is presumed to vary slowly near the critical point, and $K_T^{\text{id}} \; [= (\rho k_B T)^{-1}]$ is the isothermal compressibility of an ideal gas. In deriving Eq. (11.2.1) the net correlation $G(r)$ in the structure factor has the theoretical expression

$$G(r) = (4\pi\rho R_{oz}^2)^{-1}e^{-r/\xi}/r \quad (11.2.2)$$

The Ornstein–Zernike theory has been remarkably successful in representing many experimental data and is often used as a starting point in discussions. However, Eq. (11.2.2) is only correct asymptotically as

† Chu, 1972.

$r \rightarrow \infty$. In the very immediate neighborhood of the critical point, Fisher (1964, 1967) proposed a modified form of the Ornstein–Zernike correlation function:

$$G(r) \propto e^{-r/\xi}/r^{1+\eta} \qquad (11.2.3)$$

whereby the scattering formula predicted a *very slight* downward curvature in a reciprocal scattered intensity versus K^2 plot. There we have

$$\Re(K) = (k_0^4/16\pi^2) \sin^2 \phi \rho^2 (\partial\epsilon/\partial\rho)_T^2 k_B T K_T (1 + \xi^2 K^2)^{(\eta/2)-1} \qquad (11.2.4)$$

with the critical exponent η being a small positive number. According to the three-dimensional Ising model $\eta = 1/18 \pm 0.008$. Equation (11.2.4) has never been verified by direct experiments in one-component systems.

Landau and Placzek (1934) first explained the linewidth of quasielastically scattered light for a simple fluid in terms of entropy fluctuations at constant pressure. Debye (1965) extended the idea to concentration fluctuations in a binary liquid mixture by considering the diffusion broadening as a reflection from standing concentration waves which obey the Bragg relation $K = ks$. For nonpropagating critical fluctuations, the power spectrum is a Lorentzian shaped line with a half-width Γ which is related to the exponential time-correlation function $e^{-\Gamma t}$ by a Fourier transform.

In the hydrodynamic region ($K\xi \ll 1$), the Landau Placzek–Debye equation predicts a Lorentzian shaped Rayleigh line of half-width Γ:

$$\Gamma = \chi K^2 \qquad \text{(simple fluid)} \qquad (11.2.5a)$$

$$\Gamma = D K^2 \qquad \text{(fluid mixture)} \qquad (11.2.5b)$$

where χ and D are the thermal diffusivity and the binary diffusion coefficient, respectively. A more detailed definition of D has been presented by Ahn et al. (1972).

In the nonlocal hydrodynamic region ($\xi K \leq 1$) Fixman (1966), Botch (1963), and Felderhof (1966) extended the Landau–Placzek–Debye theory to include the effect of long-range correlation. The "Fixman-Botch" equation

$$\Gamma = \chi K^2 (1 + \xi_r^2 K^2) \qquad \text{(simple fluid)} \qquad (11.2.6a)$$

$$\Gamma = D K^2 (1 + \xi_r^2 K^2) \qquad \text{(fluid mixture)} \qquad (11.2.6b)$$

assumed that the long-range correlation length ξ has the same magnitude between dynamic and static measurements.

Following a concept introduced by Fixman (1960), Kadanoff and Swift (1968) developed the mode–mode coupling theory which was further extended by Kawasaki (1969, 1970a,b) to include the critical region

($\xi K > 1$). The Kawasaki equation is applicable to all values of $K\xi$:

$$\Gamma_K = (8A/3\pi)\xi^{-3}H_0(X) \qquad (11.2.7)$$

where $A = (\frac{3}{8}\pi)D\xi = k_B T/16\eta_{hf}{}^*$ with $\eta_{hf}{}^*$ being the high-frequency shear viscosity and the function $H_0(X)$ is given by

$$H_0(X) = \tfrac{3}{4}[1 + X^2 + (X^3 - X^{-1}) \arctan X] \qquad (11.2.8)$$

with $X = (K\xi)$.

According to Kawasaki (1970) the value of $\eta_{hf}{}^*$ should lie in the interval $\eta_r{}^* < \eta_{hf}{}^* < \eta_r{}^* + \eta_s{}^* = \eta^*$. $\eta_r{}^*$ is the value of the shear viscosity if there is no critical anomaly while $\eta_s{}^*$ is the singular part of the shear viscosity exhibiting the asymptotic critical behavior. Kawasaki has also taken $\eta_{hf}{}^*$ to be a constant and $\eta = 0$. Ferrell (1970) has obtained similar results in a somewhat simpler way.

The limiting forms of the Kawasaki $H_0(X)$ are

$$\Gamma_K \xrightarrow[X>1]{} AK^3 \qquad (11.2.9a)$$

and

$$\Gamma_K \xrightarrow[X\ll1]{} DK^2 \qquad (11.2.9b)$$

Then, the Rayleigh linewidth in the nonlocal hydrodynamic region ($K\xi < 1$) has the form

$$\Gamma_K = (8A/3\pi\xi)K^2(1 + \tfrac{3}{5}K^2\xi^2) \qquad (11.2.10)$$

which in the hydrodynamic limit ($K\xi < 1$) recaptures the Landau–Placzek–Debye formula. Equation (11.2.10) differs from the "Fixman–Botch" equation by a multiplicative factor of $\frac{3}{5}$. It should be noted that, in writing $D = k_B T/6\pi\eta_{hf}{}^*\xi$, we might visualize "droplets" of radius equivalent to the long-range correlation length ξ moving in a fluid of shear viscosity $\eta_{hf}{}^*$.

Decay rates of order parameter fluctuations near the critical point of fluids have been extensively investigated. It has been shown that Eq. (11.2.7) is applicable to only the singular part of thermodynamic properties (Chu et al., 1972; Chang et al., 1971) and that nondivergent background contributions, especially those related to $\eta_{hf}{}^*$ must be taken into account in comparing theory with experiment. Furthermore, Eq. (11.2.7) can be modified to take into account (a) deviations from the Ornstein–Zernike form of the correlation function (Swinney et al., 1972), (b) vertex corrections (Lo and Kawasaki, 1972), and (c) the nonlocality of the high-frequency shear viscosity $\eta_{hf}{}^*(K\xi)$ (Kawasaki and Lo, 1972).

The spectral width and intensity of light scattered by concentration fluctuations near the critical mixing point of isobutyric acid in water using the technique of time-dependent photocurrent signal correlation (Chu et al., 1968; Lee et al., 1972; Chu et al., 1973) and viscosity (Woermann and Sarholz, 1965; Allegra et al., 1971) results of the same system are compared with Eq. (11.2.7) and its modifications. The conclusions can be summarized as follows.

(1)   In the critical region ($\xi K > 1$) Halperin and Hohenberg (1969) proposed that $\Gamma = K^Z H_0(K\xi)$, where Z is the degree of homogeneity and a specific form of $H_0(K\xi)$ was represented by Eq. (11.2.8). A least-squares fit of thirty-seven linewidths at $T - T_c = 0.003°C$ and of thirty linewidths at $T - T_c = 0.006°C$ give $\Gamma = (1.075 \pm 3.4 \%) \times 10^{-13}K^{[2.976\pm1.5 \%]}$ rad/sec and $(1.028 \pm 2.3 \%) \times 10^{-13}K^{[3.046\pm1.0 \%]}$ rad/sec, respectively. Thus, we find that, at $\xi K > 1$ but not $\gg 1$, Z is indeed equal to 3, and that background contributions must be negligibly small in the critical region since the Kawasaki equation represents only the singular part of the linewidth exhibiting the asymptotic critical behavior. We have intentionally made linewidth measurements at various scattering angles, but at *fixed* temperature distances satisfying the condition $\xi K > 2$. With $A = k_B T/16\eta_{hf}^*$ and $Z = 3$, we have computed the so-called high-frequency shear viscosity which is assumed to be independent of $K\xi$. It should be noted that if η_{hf}^* depends upon $K\xi$, then $\Gamma = AK^3$ cannot be strictly correct over large ranges of $K\xi$. Implicitly, this could mean that the $K\xi$ dependence of η_{hf}^* is not very strong. We find $\bar{\eta}_{hf}^* > \eta^*$ over the entire $K\xi$ range. The superscript bar is used to emphasize the fact that our $\bar{\eta}_{hf}^*$ is averaged over ranges of $K\xi$ since η_{hf}^* depends upon $K\xi$.

(2) $\bar{\eta}_{hf}^*$ depends upon temperature, and in the hydrodynamic limit, it exhibits a similar temperature behavior as the hydrodynamic shear viscosity $\eta^*(T)$. However a cusp behavior in the critical viscosity anomaly remains uncertain.

(3)   Equation (11.2.7) assumes that η_{hf}^* is a constant, independent of $K\xi$ and T. If we force a three-parameter fit using only the linewidth data and $\xi = \xi_0\epsilon^{-\nu}$ with $\epsilon = (T - T_c)/T_c$, we obtain a set of values of ξ_0, ν, and A (or η_{hf}^*) which is not consistent over different ranges of $K\xi$ and with angular dissymmetry and viscosity studies. Thus, it is incorrect to analyze experimental data using this approach and to proclaim a good agreement between experiment and theory.

(4) $D \neq k_B T/6\pi\eta^*\xi$ since we have shown that $\eta_{hf}^* \neq \eta^*$.

(5)   It is invalid to obtain the long-range correlation length by means by Eq. (11.2.10) because η_{hf}^* depends upon $K\xi$. The ratio of slope to intercept in a Γ/K^2 vs K^2 plot will be slightly distorted. As a result, temperature dependence of the long-range correlation length is incorrect if we use Eq. (11.2.10) in the nonlocal hydrodynamic region.

(6) $D \neq D_0\epsilon^{\gamma*}$. The critical exponent $\gamma*$ is obviously an apparent one. The viscosity term has a complex temperature dependence. With $D = k_B T/6\pi\eta_{hf}*\xi$, a single critical exponent $\gamma*$ cannot represent the temperature dependence of the diffusion coefficient over large temperature distances.

(7)   Kawasaki and Lo have removed the ambiguity associated with the so-called "high-frequency" shear viscosity in Eq. (11.2.7) by considering the nonlocal shear viscosity which depends upon $K\xi$ as well as temperature. The so-called high-frequency viscosity $\eta_{hf}*$ is related to the macroscopic shear viscosity $\eta*(T)$ by

$$\eta_{hf}* = [H_0(K\xi)/H(K\xi)]\eta*(T) \qquad (11.2.11)$$

The correction is quite important amounting to about 30 % for $K\xi = 20$ and remains finite ($\sim$5.5 %) even in the hydrodynamic region. In the hydrodynamic limit, both the correlation function and nonlocal viscosity corrections contribute an approximate 5 % change in the computed linewidth. With the vertex correction, either correlation function or nonlocal viscosity is sufficient to account for the discrepancy between experiment and theory, however, in the critical region, $\eta*/\bar{\eta}_{hf}* \simeq 1.25$. Thus, the main correction terms must be contributions due to nonlocal viscosity. We note that the agreement between the modified Kawasaki theory and experiments is within a few percent. The implication could be that deviation from the approximate Ornstein–Zernike correlation function must be small and the critical exponent η is a small number. Figure 11.2.1 (Chu et al., 1973) shows a comparison of the modified linewidth function:

$$\Gamma_K = (k_B T/6\pi\eta*\xi^3) H(K\xi) \qquad (11.2.12)$$

with our experimental data. Note that no adjustable parameters enter the theoretical curve. The measured linewidths are compared with Eq. (11.2.12) which can be computed using hydrodynamic shear viscosity by the capillary method and correlation length by the angular dissymmetry method. Higher-order effects appear to be unimportant since we have already achieved good agreement between experiments and theory. The background contribution (if any), the correlation function modification, and the vertex correction, play only secondary roles, or there could be effects canceling one another. The agreement among the two experiments and the modified Kawasaki theory is remarkable. However, in the nonlocal hydrodynamic region, we note that the measured data are higher than the computed curve which contains no adjustable parameters. Thus, it becomes necessary to consider a breakdown of the Ornstein–Zernike form of the correlation function. Since the vertex correction provides a decrease in the computed linewidth in the hydrodynamic limit, we estimate $\eta < 0.1$ in order to account for the discrepancy. In the critical region, the values for the 3-methylpentane-

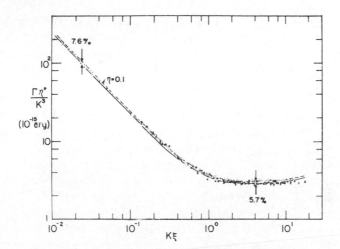

Fig. 11.2.1. A plot of $(\Gamma/K^3)\eta^*$ vs $K\xi$. Solid circles represent experimental data for the isobutyric acid–water system. The parameters used are $A = 1.06 \times 10^{-13}$ cm³/sec, $\nu = 0.613$, and $\xi_0 = 0.357 \times 10^{-7}$ cm. The solid curve represents Eq. (11.2.12) which includes the nonlocal viscosity correction but not the correlation function and vertex corrections. The dashed line represents Eq. (11.2.12) $\times C(K\xi)$ where $C(K\xi)$ accounts for the deviation of the Ornstein–Zernike correlation function but not the vertex correction. The solid triangles represent typical experimental data for the 3-methylpentane-nitroethane system from Fig. 3 of Chang *et al.*, 1971 (Chu, *et al.*, 1973).

nitroethane appear a bit too low. There is a possibility that the capillary method becomes less reliable in the critical region because of gravitational effects at small temperature distances from the critical mixing point. It should be noted that the viscosity exponent depends strongly upon the mathematical representation of the power law used. However, we may safely conclude that the viscosity anomaly is weak and the possibility of a cusp remains even though the precision of present-day experimental data is not able to rule out a very weak power law or logarithmic divergence (Tsai and McIntyre, 1974).

Lyons *et al.* (1973) have measured the diffusion coefficient of Brownian particles (Teflon microspheres of 0.31-μm mean diameter) in a binary critical mixture. Their data support a logarithmic divergence in the shear viscosity. The technique, which has also been suggested by Polonski and Chen (1970), provides an interesting and promising approach to investigating the wave-vector and frequency dependence of the shear viscosity near the critical mixing point. The main difficulty is to be able to characterize the microspheres sufficiently carefully so that the effects of polydispersity do not come into play. The discrepancy between the isobutyric acid–water system and the modified Kawasaki theory can be reduced if we utilize the correlation function modification, as shown by the dotted line in Figure 11.2.1. This dotted line represents $H(K\xi)C(K\xi)k_BT/(6\pi\xi^3K^3)$ where $C(K\xi)$ is the correction factor that takes into account the correlation function modification with

$$\widehat{G}_2(K) \propto (K^2 + \xi^{-2})^{-(1-\eta/2)} \qquad (11.2.13)$$

and $\eta = 0.1$. There are two remarks worthwhile mentioning. First, we are considering discrepancies of only a few percent, thus, the conclusions from those comparisons must necessarily be on a less solid footing. Second, with precise experimental data, we see a new method of determining the form of the correlation function by comparing data with theory over the entire $K\xi$ range. Equation (11.2.13) is one of the forms of $\widehat{G}_2(K)$. In fact, better forms for $\widehat{G}_2(K)$ exist even though we are not yet prepared to state which is the best proposed form at the present time. Such a new approach cannot yet be utilized until the modified Kawasaki theory, which already includes vertex, correlation functions, and nonlocal viscosity corrections, and the viscosity measurements are further improved. In Fig. 11.2.1, the measured data at $K\xi > 1$ appear to level off faster than the computed curve even though the discrepancy can hardly be detected in such an insensitive log–log plot. Experimentally, it is not likely that any appreciable error exists in our Rayleigh linewidth measurements. The magnitude of ξ should not change the qualitative behavior. There could be possible errors in the hydrodynamic shear viscosity studies. Nevertheless, we believe that we have alleviated part of the difficulties by utilizing the computed viscosity values near the critical point, thus, further improvements of the modified Kawasaki–Lo theory and viscosity measurements should be worthwhile.

Investigation of critical opalescence by means of quasielastic light scattering has reached such a refined stage that very precise measurements are required in order to test the finer points of the theory of critical phenomena. A detailed review has been presented by Swinney and Henry (1973). Aside from the spectrum of light scattered by the bulk material, measurements of the spectrum of light scattered inelastically from thermal excitations on the liquid–vapor interface can be related to the surface tension (Katyl and Ingard, 1968). Bouchiat and her co-workers (1969) have done extensive work on such surface tension studies. Zollweg et al. (1971) have measured the spectrum of light scattered inelastically from thermal excitations on the liquid–vapor interface of xenon near its critical point using the approximate theoretical expression of Cruchon et al. (1969a,b). A more detailed discussion of the spectrum of light scattered from surface waves thermally excited on a liquid interface has been reported by Bouchiat and Meunier (1972). In fact, recent developments on critical phenomena have been summarized by two published proceedings—*Ber Bunsenges. Physik. Chem.* **76,** 1972 and *J. de Physique* **33,** 1972.

In *J. de Physique*, topics such as Rayleigh and Brillouin scattering in liquid and gases, liquid crystals, and depolarized Rayleigh scattering, as well as collision induced scattering, have been included. The reader is advised to consult the proceedings directly—in particular, the techniques of Pike and Stoicheff as related to photon correlation and interferometry deserve special attention. Books on phase transitions and critical phenomena (Stanley, 1971; Domb and Green, 1972) for general discussions and reviews of specific related topics are available. A bibliography and selected articles on cooperative phenomena near phase transitions have been edited by Stanley (to be published).

Further studies on critical opalescence can be arbitrarily grouped into three directions:

1. With refined experimental techniques and a reasonable theoretical understanding of simple critical systems, we can now proceed to examine higher-order critical points first pointed out by Kohnstamm (1926), then discovered by Krichevskii *et al.* (1963) and Efremova and Shvarts (1966) in three- (or four-) component fluid systems, known as tricritical points. The Russian workers have made several initial thermodynamic phase determinations on a few tricritical systems, such as methanol–water–carbon dioxide (Efremova and Shvarts, 1966, 1969), ethanol–water–carbon dioxide (Shavarts and Efremova, 1970, ethane–n-eicosane–n-hexadecane (Efremova and Shavarts, 1970), methanol–ethane–carbon dioxide (Efremova and Shavarts, 1972); while four-component systems in which tricritical points are known are $(NH_4)_2SO_4$–water–ethanol–benzene (Radyshevaskaya *et al.*, 1962), water–phenol–pyridine–n-hexane (Myasnikova *et al.*, 1969; Nikurashina *et al.*, 1971), and methanol–ethanol–water–carbon dioxide (Efremova and Shvarts, 1969). Widom (1973) was able to determine the critical composition of the $(NH_4)_2SO_4$–water–ethanol–benzene system. Theoretical developments on tricritical point behaviors have been pursued actively by Griffith (1973, 1974), Griffith and Widom (1973), and by Wegner and Riedel (1973). Angular distribution of scattered intensity and its power spectrum should again provide crucial tests to current theories of critical phenomena.

2. Critical opalescence studies have been along either the critical isochore or the coexistence curve. Further studies are likely to examine the solution behavior, in general, away from the critical point, or very near the critical point at large ranges of $K\xi$. Light scattering from nonideal solutions, especially depolarized light scattering, which can examine angular correlations (Alms *et al.*, 1973, 1974), is now feasible with stabilized lasers, photon correlation and servo-controlled Fabry–Perot interferometers. The

large ranges of $K\xi$ become accessible by utilizing the critical point exponent renormalization (Widom, 1967; Fisher and Scesney, 1970).

3. More exotic systems are being examined. Hawkins and Benedek (1974) have experimentally determined the equation of state of a two-dimensional "gas" of pentadecyclic-acid molecules moving on the surface of water, while Keyes *et al.* (1973) observed the tricritical behavior in a liquid–crystal system. Other considerations involve He^3–He^4 mixtures (Leung and Griffiths, 1973), surfaces and films (Fisher, 1973), and divergence of chlorestic pitch near a smectic-A transition (Pindak *et al.*, 1974). Thus, the immediate trends in liquid studies clearly point toward tricritical-point behavior of more complex systems and solutions and liquids in general.

References

Ahn, M. K., Jensen, S. J. K., and Kivelson, D. (1972). *J. Chem. Phys.* **57**, 2940.

Allegra, J. C., Stein, A., and Allen, G. F. (1971). *J. Chem. Phys.* **55**, 1716.

Alms, G. R., Bauer, D. R., Brauman, J. I., and Pecora, R. (1973). *J Chem. Phys* **58**, 5570.

Alms, G R , Bauer, D. R., Brauman, J. I., and Pecora, R. (1974). *J. Chem. Phys.* **59**, 5310, 5321.

Botch, W. D. (1963). Ph.D. thesis, University of Oregon, Eugene, Oregon, p. 63.

Bouchiat, M. A., and Meunier, J. (1969). *Phys. Rev. Lett.* **23**, 752.

Bouchiat, M. A., and Meunier, J. (1972). *J. Phys. (Paris)* **33**, C1-141.

Chang, R. F., Keyes, P. H., Sengers, J. V., and Alley, C. O. (1971). *Phys. Rev. Lett.* **27**, 1706.

Cruchon, D., Meunier, J., and Bouchiat, M. A. (1969a). *C. R. H. Acad. Sci. Ser. B* **268**, 92.

Crucion, D., Meunier, J., and Bouchiat, M. A. (1969b). *C. R. H. Acad. Sci. Ser. B* **268**, 422.

Chu, B. (1972). *Ber. Bunseng. Ges. Phys. Chem.* **76**, 202.

Chu, B., Schoenes, F. J., and Kao, W. P. (1968). *J. Amer. Chem. Soc.* **90**, 3042.

Chu, B., Thiel, D., Tscharnuter, W., and Fenby, D. V. (1972). *J. Phys. (Paris)* **33**, C1-111.

Chu, B., Lee, S. P., and Tscharnuter, W. (1973). *Phys. Rev. A* **7**, 353.

Cummins, H. Z. (1971). *In* "International School of Physics Enrico Fermi, Course LI on Critical Phenomena, Varenna, Italy, 1970," p. 380. Academic Press, New York.

Debye, P. (1965). *Phys. Rev. Lett.* **14**, 783.

Domb, C., and Green, M. S. (1972). "Phase Transitions and Critical Phenomena" Vols. 1 and 2. Academic Press, New York.

Efremova, G. D., and Shvarts, A. V. (1966a). *Russ. J. Phys. Chem.* (English translation) **40**, 486.

Efremova, G. D., and Shvarts, A. V. (1969b). *Doklady Chem. Technology* (English translation) **188**, 201.

Efremova, G. D., and Shvarts, A. V. (1969). *Russ. J. Phys. Chem.* (English translation) **43**, 968.

Efremova, G. D., and Shvarts, A. V. (1970). *Russ. J. Phys. Chem.* (English translation) **44**, 470.

Efremova, G. D., and Shvarts, A. V. (1972). *Russ. J. Phys. Chem.* (English translation) **46**, 237.

Felderhof, B. U. (1966). *J. Chem. Phys.* **33**, 1357.

Ferrell, R. A. (1970). *Phys. Rev. Lett.* **24**, 1169.

Fisher, M. E. (1964). *J. Math. Phys.* **5**, 944.

Fisher, M. E. (1967). *Rep. Progr. Phys.* **30**, 615.

Fisher, M. E. (1973). *J. Vac. Sci. Technol.* **10**, 665.

Fisher, M. E., and Scesney, P. E. (1970). *Phys. Rev. A* **2**, 825.

Fixman, M. (1960). *J. Chem. Phys.* **33**, 1357.

Fixman, M. (1966). *In* "Pontifica Academica Scientiarum Scripta Varia 31 on Molecular Forces," p. 329. Pontifical Academy of Science, Vatican City.

Green, M. S., and Sengers, J. V. (eds.) (1966). "Critical Phenomena, Proceedings of a Conference, Washington, D.C., 1965," NBS Misc. Publ. No. 273. U.S. GPO, Washington, D.C.

Griffiths, R. B. (1973). *Phys. Rev. B.* **7**, 545.

Griffiths, R. B. (1974). *J. Chem. Phys.* **60**, 195.

Griffiths, R. B., and Widom, B. (1973). *Phys. Rev. A* **8**, 2173.

Halperin, B. I., and Hohenberg, P. C. (1969). *Phys. Rev.* **177**, 952.

Hawkins, G. A., and Benedek, G. B. (1974). *Phys. Rev. Lett.* **32**, 524.

Heller, P. (1967). *Rep. Progr. Phys.* **30**, 731.

Kadanoff, L. P., and Swift, J. (1968). *Phys. Rev.* **166**, 89.

Katyl, R. H., and Ingard, U., (1968). *Phys. Rev. Lett.* **20**, 248.

Kawasaki, K. (1969). *Phys. Lett. A* **30**, 325.

Kawasaki, K. (1970a). *Ann. Phys.* (N.Y.) **61**, 1.

Kawasaki, K. (1970b). *Phys. Rev. A* **1**, 1750.

Kawasaki, K., and Lo, S. M. (1972). *Phys. Rev. Lett.* **29**, 48.

Keyes, P. H., Weston, H. T., and Daniels, W. B. (1973). *Phys. Rev. Lett.*, **31**, 628.

Kohnstamm, P. (1926). *Handbuch der Physik* **10**, 271.

Krichevskii, I. R., Efremova, G. D., Pyranikova, R. O., and Serebryakova, A. V. (1963). *Russ. J. Phys. Chem.* (English translation), **37**, 1046.

Landau, L., and Placzek, G. (1934). *Physik. Z. Sowjetunion* **5**, 172.

Lee, S. P., Tscharnuter, W., and Chu, B. (1972). *Phys. Rev. Lett.* **28**, 1509.

Leung, S. S., and Griffiths, R. B. (1973). *Phys. Rev. A* **8**, 2670.

Lo, S. M., and Kawasaki, K. (1972). *Phys. Rev. A* **5**, 421.

Lyons, K. B., Mockler, R. C., and O'Sullivan, W. J. (1973). *Phys. Rev. Lett.* **30**, 42.

Myashikova, K. P., Nikurashina, N. I., and Mertslin, R. V. (1969). *Russ. J. Phys. Chem.* (English translation) **43**, 223.

Nikurashina, N. I., Kharitonova, G. I., and Pichugina, L. M. (1972). *Russ. J. Phys. Chem.* (English translation) **45**, 444.

Ornstein, L. S., and Zernike, F. (1914). *Proc. Acad. Sci.* (*Amsterdam*) **17**, 793.

Ornstein, L. S., and Zernike, F. (1915). *Proc. Acad. Sci.* (*Amsterdam*) **18**, 1520.

Ornstein, L. S., and Zernike, F. (1916a). *Proc. Acad. Sci.* (*Amsterdam*) **19**, 1312.

Ornstein, L. S., and Lernike, F. (1916b). *Proc. Acad. Sci.* (*Amsterdam*) **19**, 1321.

Ornstein, L. S., and Zernike, F. (1926). *Physik. Z.* **27**, 761.

Pindak, R. S., Huang, C. C., and Ho, J. T. (1974). *Phys. Rev. Lett.* **32**, 43.

Polonski, N. (1970). Ph.D. dissertation, University of Paris.

Radyshevskaya, G. S., Nikurashina, N. I., and Mertslin, R. V. (1962). *Russ. J. Gen. Chem.* (English translation) **32**, 673.

Shvarts, A V., and Efremova, G. D. (1970). *Russ. J. Phys. Chem.* (English translation) **44**, 614.

Stanley, H. E. (1971). "Introduction to Phase Transitions and Critical Phenomena." Oxford Univ. Press, London and New York.

Stanley, H. E. (ed.). "Cooperative Phenomena Near Phase Transitions: A Bibliography and Selected Readings." MIT Press, Cambridge, Massachusetts (to be published).

Swift, J. (1968). *Phys. Rev.* **173**, 257.

Swinney, H. L., Henry, D. L., and Cummins, H. Z. (1972). *J. Phys. (Paris)* **33**, C1-81.

Swinney, H. L., and Henry, D. L. (1973). *Phys. Rev.* **8**, 2586.

Tsai, B. C., and McIntyre, D. (1974). *J. Chem. Phys.* **60**, 937.

Wegner, F. T., and Riedel, E. K. (1973). *Phys. Rev. B* **7**, 248.

Widom, B. (1967). *J. Chem. Phys.* **46**, 3324.

Widom, B. (1973). *J. Phys. Chem.* **77**, 2196.

Woermann, D., and Sarholz, W. (1965). *Ber. Bunsen. Phys. Chem.* **69**, 319.

Zollweg, J., Hawkins, G., and Benedek, G. (1971). *Phys. Rev. Lett.* **27**, 1182.

AUTHOR INDEX

Numbers in italics refer to the pages on which the complete reference is listed.

A

Abbiss, J. B., 272, *289*
Adam, M., 163, *198*, 202, *250*
Adler, J., 245, *249*
Adrian, R. J., 138, 287, *150*, *289*
Ahn, M. K., 293, *300*
Ailawadi, N. K., 203, *249*
Akins, D. L., 175, *198*
Alfano, R. R., 185, *198*
Alkemade, C. T. J., 89, *104*
Allegra, J. C., 295, *300*
Allen, G. F., 295, *300*
Alley, C. O., 294, 297, *300*
Alms, G. R., 299, *300*
Alon, Y., 185, *199*
Anderson, H. C., 203, *249*
Anderson, K. A., 176, *198*
Angus, J. C., 98, *105*, 202, 207, *250*, 274, 275, 277, *289*
Arecchi, F. T., 89, 97, 98, 124, *104*, *150*, 207, *249*
Aref'ev, I. M., 197, *198*
Asakura, S., 228, *251*, 257, *270*
Asch, R., 148, 149, 150, *150*
Avidor, J. M., *xii*

B

Ballik, E. A., 289, *289*
Bancroft, F. C., 207, 216, *250*
Barakat, R., 147, *147*, *150*, 188, *198*
Bargeron, C. B., 216, 229, 242, *250*
Bates, B., 195, *198*
Bauer, D. R., 299, *300*
Bearman, R. J., 62, *63*
Bedard, G., 98, 124, 125, *104*, *150*
Benbasat, J. A., 256, 257, 260, 261, *270*
Bendjaballah, C., 140, 147, *147*, *150*
Benedek, G. B., 3, 5, *6*, *7*, *15*, 38, 42, 54, 60, *63*, *64*, 91, 99, 103, *104*, *132*, *150*, 162, 163, 164, 171, 172, 173, 195, *198*, *199*, 202, 207, 208, 209, 216, 220, 224, 225, 226, 232, *250*, *251*, *252*, 243, *253*, 272, *290*, 298, 300, *301*, *302*
Bennett, W. R., Jr., 92, *105*, 190, *198*
Ben-Reuven, A., 5, *7*, 202, *250*
Ben-Yosef, N., 243, *250*
Berg, H. C., 249, *250*
Berge, P., 98, *104*, 162, 163, *198*, 202, 206, 243, *250*
Berne, A., 98, *104*, 124, *150*

303

SUBJECT INDEX

A

Adiabatic pressure disturbances, 33
Amplifiers, in photon-counting technique, 183–185
Anemometry, 271–289
  Doppler model in, 273–275
  filter model of Doppler meter in, 278–283
  signal-to-noise ratio in, 287–288
  turbulent velocities in, 275–278
  unified analysis on laser Doppler velocities, 283–289
Anistropy scattering, 222–224
Anti-Stokes component, of scattered radiation, 59
Argon laser, 158–159
Autocorrelation, photocount, *see* Photocount autocorrelation
Autocorrelation function, *see* Photocount autocorrelation function

B

Bacteria, chemotactic response and scattering from, 248–249
Bose–Einstein distribution, 88–89
Brewster's angle, 166–168, 172–173
Brewster's law 169

Brillouin

Brillouin scattering, 4, 106
  detection techniques and applications of, 5
  energy changes and, 6
  as function of angle, 172
  optical interferometers and, 6
  optical superheterodyning and, 173
Brillouin shifts, asymmetry and, 60
Brillouin–Mendel'shtam lines, 3
Brownian particles, 244
Browning motion, 243
  diffusion coefficient and, 297

C

Chemotactic response, in bacteria, 248–249
Clausius–Messotti relation, 28
Clipped digital correlator, sampling scheme of, 128–132
Clipped photocount autocorrelation function, 140
Clipping, in photon-counting fluctuations, 146–147
Coherence, second-order, 66–70
Coherence angle, scattering volume and, 73–74
Coherence properties, of scattered electric field, 65–78